STUDENT
WORKBOOK

to accompany

How to Design and Evaluate
Research in Education
Fifth Edition

STUDENT
WORKBOOK

to accompany

How to Design and Evaluate Research in Education
Fifth Edition

Jack R. Fraenkel
San Francisco State University

Norman E. Wallen
San Francisco State University

There's some good stuff in here!

Boston   Burr Ridge, IL   Dubuque, IA   Madison, WI   New York   San Francisco   St. Louis
Bangkok   Bogotá   Caracas   Kuala Lumpur   Lisbon   London   Madrid   Mexico City
Milan   Montreal   New Delhi   Santiago   Seoul   Singapore   Sydney   Taipei   Toronto

McGraw-Hill Higher Education

A Division of The **McGraw-Hill** *Companies*

Student Workbook to accompany
HOW TO DESIGN AND EVALUATE RESEARCH IN EDUCATION
Jack R. Fraenkel, Norman E. Wallen

1 2 3 4 5 6 7 8 9 0 CUS/CUS 0 9 8 7 6 5 4 3 2

ISBN 0-07-253184-3

www.mhhe.com

Contents

The Nature of Educational Research

CHAPTER 1

Activity 1.1:
Empirical vs. Nonempirical Research

Empirical research is research that involves the collection of firsthand information. Nonempirical research does not involve the collection of information at first hand. Thus, research that consists of locating and comparing references on a particular topic—the customary term paper—is not an example of empirical research. In *How to Design and Evaluate Research in Education,* we are concerned primarily with empirical research.

In the list of research topics that follows below, place an X in front of those that are examples of empirical research.

1. _____ A study of the effectiveness of a social learning program on the employability of severely disabled adults.

2. _____ The relationship between television watching and school achievement: a review of the literature.

3. _____ A reanalysis of the evidence on school effectiveness.

4. _____ The relationship between self-esteem and age at school entrance of fourth-grade students in the San Francisco Unified School District.

5. _____ Logical inconsistencies in writings of Sigmund Freud.

6. _____ A comparison of the effectiveness of behavior therapy as compared with client-centered therapy in homes for adolescent runaways.

Activity 1.2:
Basic vs. Applied Research

Listed below are a number of research projects that you can use to review your understanding of the distinction between basic and applied research. Place a "B" in front of those that you think are examples of basic research and an "A" in front of those that you think are examples of applied research.

1. _____ A comparison of the attitudes of different student ethnic groups toward the general education requirements at the City University of New York.

2. _____ The effectiveness of counselors who are recovering alcoholics as compared with other counselors at the Rosewood Recovery Center.

3. _____ A comparison of the effects of phonics versus look-say teaching on the achievement of Latino children in reading as based on the Amalo theory.

4. _____ Employer perceptions of changes in essential secretarial skills of his employees between 1945 and 1995.

5. _____ The relationship between adolescent self-esteem and alcoholism in parents.

6. _____ The effectiveness of using manipulative materials in teaching first-grade mathematics.

Activity 1.3:
Types of Research

What would be the most appropriate type of research to investigate each of the topics listed below? Match the letter of the appropriate research methodology from Column B with its topic in Column A.

COLUMN A: TOPIC	COLUMN B: TYPE OF RESEARCH
1. _____ Diplomatic relationships between Japan and the United States between 1918 and 1941.	a. A group-comparison experiment
	b. A survey
2. _____ Images of women in U.S. history text-books.	c. A correlational study
	d. A content analysis
3. _____ Relationship between student atten-dance and achievement in chemistry classes.	e. A case study
4. _____ Number of single mothers on welfare in the city of Chicago.	f. An ethnography
	g. A historical study
5. _____ Daily activities of an operating room nurse in a big-city hospital.	h. A single-subject experiment
6. _____ A comparison of the inquiry method and the lecture method in teaching high school biology.	
7. _____ Changing impulsive behavior through the use of praise.	

Activity 1.4:
Assumptions

What assumptions underlie each of the following statements?

1. "Spare the rod and spoil the child!"

    _____

    _____

    _____

2. "We couldn't beat McAteer High last season and we probably won't be able to beat them this year either."

    _____

    _____

    _____

3. "A stitch in time saves nine."

    _____

    _____

    _____

4. "Oh, brother, I have another one of the Johnson kids in my class next semester!"

    _____

    _____

    _____

5. "Boy, I dread the thought of taking algebra from Mrs. West next semester!"

    _____

    _____

    _____

Activity 1.5:
General Research Types

Each of the following represents an example of one of the general research types we discussed on pages 14-16 in the text. Identify each as being either *descriptive*, *associational*, or *intervention* research.

1. A study of the possible relationship that may exist between class size and learning in remedial mathematics courses _____

2. A survey of the attitudes of parents in a large urban school district toward the advanced placement courses offered by the district _____

3. A study designed to compare the effectiveness of two methods of teaching spelling to first graders _____

4. An investigation by a researcher in an attempt to confirm that abstract concepts can be taught to six year olds _____

5. A historical study of high school graduation requirements _____

6. A detailed ethnographic study of the daily activities of a teacher in an inner-city high school _____

7. A comparison of inquiry and lecture methods of teaching 11th grade history _____

8. A study designed to compare the attitudes of male and female students toward chemistry _____

The Research Problem

CHAPTER 2

Activity 2.1:
Research Questions and Related Designs

Select the appropriate research design for each question listed below.

Case Study   Experimental
Causal-Comparative   Historical
Content Analysis   Survey
Correlational   Ethnography

1. What do elementary school teachers in the San Francisco Unified School District think about full inclusion as practiced in their district?

2. Is there a relationship between students' level of social skills and successful transition into mainstream classes?

3. How do individuals with physical disabilities perceive themselves in comparison to their able-bodied peers in terms of work-related activities?

4. Does a whole-language curriculum lead to higher student achievement than a phonics curriculum does?

5. How are teachers implementing the whole-language approach to reading in their curricula at Harding Elementary School?

6. What were the key events that led to the demise of affirmative action in state hiring and college admissions in California?

7. How do magazines targeted at teenagers present information on safe-sex practices?

8. Are the reasons Native American Indian students give for dropping out of school different from those given by non-Native American Indian students?

Activity 2.2:
Changing General Topics into Research Questions

Change the following topics into researchable questions.

1. Class size and student achievement

2. Multicultural education at Thurgood Marshall Middle School

3. Testing anxiety

4. Women college professors and tenure

5. Alcohol consumption on New Year's Eve and Super Bowl Sunday

6. Single parents and affordable child care

7. Counseling style

8. Asian-American students and positive stereotypes

9. The charter school movement in the twentieth century

10. Diet and exercise

Activity 2.3:
Operational Definitions

Which of the following are operational definitions for the phrase "motivated to learn in a research methods class" and why?

1. Smiles a lot in class.

2. Is observed by the teacher to ask questions about past and present reading assignments.

3. Tells the instructor she would rather conduct a literature review than interview students.

4. States he likes the instructor.

5. Is described by the instructor as a student who hands in all assignments on time.

6. Has a record of checking out books on research design at the library.

7. Enjoys reading journal articles on quasi-experimental studies.

8. Scored 100 percent on the midterm exam.

9. Asks the instructor if s/he can prepare an extra-credit assignment on recent trends in the field of educational research.

10. Voluntarily creates an interactive Web site for the class so that students can discuss course material online.

Activity 2.4:
Justification

A researcher wished to study the following question: "Are 'open' classrooms more effective (do children learn more) than structured, non-open classrooms?"

Here are two different justifications that were written. Which do you think would be most likely to attain support to convince skeptics as to the importance of the study?

(1) The general purpose of this research is to add knowledge to the field of education at this time when classroom freedom is a cornerstone of today's educational revolution. Various authorities (Leonard, Holt, Kozel, etc.) have suggested that the strictly structured, teacher-directed classroom may impede the learning process of students. They argue that less-structured, "open" environments may help students to learn more, faster, and in greater depth. It is this controversial thesis (since many "structuralists" disagree strongly) that has provoked many teachers to modify their classrooms in hopes of achieving greater educational gains for their students. While the reformers have written convincingly from an inspirational point of view, scant "hard data" exist to provide support. If educators are to jump on this bandwagon, and if money is to be diverted from the more traditional type of arrangement to support open classrooms, they should have information of the type that answers to this research question will provide. It is one thing to think something has potential for improving the learning of the young; it is quite another to have evidence that illustrates that this is so. Hopefully, this study will provide some information in this regard.

(2) Education of children in elementary schools has always been a controversial issue among parents and teachers. There are various ideas regarding the type of setting that would be (or provides) a constructive learning situation for children. One such setting might be the open classroom type. That is what this research will set out to determine.

Variables and Hypotheses

CHAPTER 3

Activity 3.1:
Directional vs. Non-Directional Hypotheses

For each of the hypotheses listed below, indicate in the space provided whether it is directional (D) or non-directional (ND).

1. _____ Students being taught by a team of three teachers will like the subject more than will students taught by one teacher.

2. _____ Male and female elementary school teachers will differ in the amount of satisfaction they receive from teaching.

3. _____ Students who engage in higher levels of gross physical activity will have lower achievement levels, while students who engage in lower levels of gross physical activity will have higher achievement levels.

4. _____ Patients receiving drug "A" will, on average, have fewer heart attacks than patients receiving drug "B."

5. _____ First-, second-, and third-graders will feel differently toward school.

Activity 3.2:
Testing Hypotheses

Most people have ideas that could be researched if they wished to investigate the ideas more carefully. And these ideas usually come from one or more *observations*; that is, from noticing events and how they are related to other events. Here are some examples.

1. The best professors at the University are really interested in their students.

2. Parents who order their kids not to use drugs are more likely to have kids who try drugs than those who let their kids make their own decisions about whether or not to use drugs.

3. Women don't get appointed to top management positions in industry.

Each of the above statements is an observation about a relationship between two factors. Identify the two factors for which a relationship is implied in each statement and write them in the spaces provided below.

1. _____ is related to _____.

2. _____ is related to _____.

3. _____ is related to _____.

Notice that these are assertions. They are not necessarily true. They are at the very least a person's subjective impressions. Restate each below in such a way that we could test them—that is, check them out to see if the statements are true.

1. _____.

2. _____.

3. _____.

Activity 3.3:
Categorical vs. Quantitative Variables

For each of the variables listed below, indicate whether it is categorical (CV), or quantitative (QV):

1. _____ Counseling style (Rogerian vs. non-Rogerian)

2. _____ Scores on a ten-point biology quiz

3. _____ Grade level (freshman, sophomore, junior, senior)

4. _____ Handedness (left- vs. right-handed)

5. _____ Weight (in pounds)

6. _____ Religion (Buddhist, Catholic, Jewish, Protestant, Other)

7. _____ Grade point average

8. _____ Anxiety level

Activity 3.4:
Independent and Dependent Variables

For each of the situations listed below, name the independent and the dependent variable. Also identify the constant if there is one.

1. Half of a group of third-graders was shown a film on "sharing," while the other half was not shown the film. The attitudes of the students in both groups toward sharing candy was then measured, and their average scores were compared.

   The independent variable is _____

   The dependent variable is _____

   The constant is _____

2. A U.S. history class of eleventh-grade students was randomly divided into three groups. One group was taught a unit on the Civil War using a standard textbook; the second group was taught the same unit using a series of case studies in addition to the textbook; and the third group was taught using the textbook, the case studies, and some audiovisual materials. Student knowledge about the events of the Civil War was compared at the end of the unit.

   The independent variable is _____

   The dependent variable is _____

   The constant is _____

3. Fourteen elementary schools in a large urban school district were selected to participate in a study investigating the effects of computers on learning. Seven of the schools, chosen at random, received new Macintosh computers for every student in their fifth/sixth-grade classes to use, while the other seven did not receive or possess any computers. At the end of the semester, student achievement in the two groups of schools was compared.

   The independent variable is _____

   The dependent variable is _____

   The constant is _____

Ethics and Research

CHAPTER 4

Activity 4.1:
Ethical or Not?

1. A professional sex therapist in a large midwestern city is interested in obtaining more information about the sexual preferences of both heterosexual and homosexual men. He designs a questionnaire that includes a number of highly personal questions and asks a professor at a nearby university to administer it to the students in her introductory psychology class. All of the students in the class are required to complete the questionnaire. Is there an ethical problem here?

2. The spread of AIDS (acquired immune-deficiency syndrome) has brought about a considerable amount of research into the effectiveness of various drugs in controlling the disease. The U.S. Food and Drug Administration restricted the distribution of these drugs until they were clinically tested. During the tests, some AIDS patients would receive these drugs (the experimental group) while others (the control group) would not. Some members of the control group even received a placebo. AIDS patients strongly objected, saying this was unethical. Were they justified in doing so? Why or why not? Is there an ethical dilemma here?

3. In the summer of 1972, newspapers around the country revealed that the U.S. Public Health Service (PHS) for 40 years had been conducting a study to investigate the effects of untreated syphilis on black males in Macon County, Alabama. Public Health Service physicians had administered a variety of blood tests and regular examinations to 399 men who were in various stages of the disease and to 200 others who were in a control group. The study was limited strictly to compiling data on the effects of syphilis and not on ways to treat the disease.

   The participants were never told the purpose of the study or for what they were or were not being treated. No drugs were ever used with these men. A PHS nurse who was monitoring the participants informed local physicians as to who was participating in the study and informed them that they were not to be treated for syphilis. Some of the participants who were offered treatment by other physicians, in fact, were told they would be dropped from the study if they took the treatment.

   The participants were never aware of the danger to which they were exposed by the study. Furthermore, no effort was ever made to explain their situation to them. In fact, they were enticed with a variety of incentives to participate, such as hot meals, free treatment for other ailments, free rides to and from the clinic, even a $50 burial stipend.

   What ethical standards were violated in this study?

Activity 4.2:
Some Ethical Dilemmas

1. A psychologist conducts the following experiment: A team of subjects plays a game of skill against a computer for money rewards. Unknown to the subjects, one team member is a stooge whose stupidity causes the team to lose regularly. The experimenter observes the subjects through one-way glass. Her intent is to study the behavior of the subjects toward the "stupid" team member.

    This experiment involves no risk to the subjects and is intended simply to create the kind of situation that might occur in any pickup basketball game. To create the situation, the subjects are deceived. Is this deception morally objectionable? Explain your position.

2. Almost all clinical trials that have studied the effects of such factors as blood cholesterol, taking aspirin, or exercise on heart attacks have used middle-aged male subjects. Women's groups have complained that this leads to better health information about men than about women. The researchers reply that in order to get clear results in the five years or so that such a study lasts, they must choose their subjects from the groups that are most likely to have heart attacks. That points to middle-aged men. What would you suggest?

3. The information given to potential subjects in a clinical trial before asking them to decide whether or not to participate might include:

    a. The basic statement that an experiment is being conducted; that is, that something beyond simply treating your medical problem will occur in your therapy.
    b. A statement of any potential risks from any of the experimental treatments.
    c. An explanation that a coin will be tossed to decide which treatment you get.
    d. An explanation that one "treatment" is a placebo and a statement of the probability that you will receive the placebo.

    Do you feel that all of this information is ethically required? Discuss.

Activity 4.3:
Violations of Ethical Practice

Listed below in Column A are a number of violations of ethical practice. Match the letter of the violation from Column B with the example listed in Column A to which the violation refers.

COLUMN A: PRACTICE	COLUMN B: ETHICAL VIOLATION
1. _____ Researcher requires a group of high school sophomores to sign a form in which they agree to participate in a research study.	a. Protecting participants from harm.
	b. Ensuring confidentiality of research data.
	c. Deception of subjects.
2. _____ Researcher asks first-graders sensitive questions without obtaining the consent of their parents to question them.	d. Right of an individual to participate or withdraw from a study at any time.
3. _____ Researcher deletes data he collects that does not support his hypothesis.	e. Reporting accurately the results of a research investigation.
4. _____ Researcher gives information to students to see whether it increases their stress when taking an examination.	f. Coercion of subjects.
	g. Parental permission.
5. _____ The teachers in a study of punitive practices are told that it is their students who are being observed.	

Activity 4.4:
Why Would These Research Practices Be Unethical?

Figure 4.2 on page 60 of the text presents a number of individuals describing unethical research practices. In the space provided below, explain why each of the statements suggest something that would be unethical.

1. "We are required to ask you to sign this consent form. You needn't read it; it's just routine."

   _____

   _____

   _____

2. "A few cases seemed quite different from the rest, so we deleted them."

   _____

   _____

   _____

3. "Yes, as a student at this university you are required to participate in this study."

   _____

   _____

   _____

4. "There is no need to tell any of the parents that we are modifying the school lunch diet for this study."

   _____

   _____

   _____

5. "Requiring students to participate in class discussions might be harmful to some, but it is necessary for our research."

   _____

   _____

   _____

Reviewing the Literature

CHAPTER 5

Activity 5.1:
Library Worksheet

LOCATIONS FOR LIBRARY SOURCE MATERIAL

Be sure you can locate each of the following.

1. *Education Index*   Location: _____

2. *Journal of Educational Research*   Location: _____

3. NSSE Yearbooks   Location: _____

4. *Encyclopedia of Educational Research*   Location: _____

5. M.A. theses   Location: _____

6. *Dissertation Abstracts International* (DAI)   Location: _____

7. The research journal in your field   Location: _____

8. *ERIC*   Location: _____

9. The World Wide Web   Location: _____

What is the name of the major journal(s) in your field?

_____

_____

_____

Activity 5.2:
Where Would You Look?

Where might you look to find information about each of the following?

1. A review of recent research on moral education

2. A brief summary of the history of educational programs for the gifted

3. A topic of interest that has not been reviewed during the last two years

4. A summary of a recently published article in the field of psychology

5. A summary of a Ph.D. dissertation on mastery learning

6. An article published within the last month on social studies education

7. Some of the major ideas in educational sociology

8. Some popular articles on education that appeared during the last year in *U.S. News and World Report* and *Newsweek* magazines

Activity 5.3:
Do a Computer Search of the Literature

Use ERIC to do a computer search of the literature on a topic of interest to you.

1. The topic I chose for my search was (describe as precisely as you can below):

   _____

   _____

   _____

2. I reviewed _____ (number) of references.

3. I used the following descriptors.

   _____

   _____

   _____

4. Here are the results of my search.

   Search #1 _____

   Search #2 _____

   Search #3 _____

   Search #4 _____

5. Here are the names of three of the references (abstracts or articles) identified using these descriptors.

   _____

   _____

   _____

   _____

Sampling

Activity 6.1:
Identifying Types of Sampling

For each of the situations described below, identify the type of sampling that is being used.

a. Simple random sampling
b. Stratified random sampling
c. Cluster sampling
d. Two-stage random sampling

e. Convenience sampling
f. Purposive sampling
g. No sampling — entire population is being studied

1. _____ A researcher surveying opinions about a university president first determines the proportion of the total faculty in each college in the university. She then randomly selects the same proportions for her sample.

2. _____ A researcher is interested in interviewing all the members of the New York City police force who do not live in the city. He gets a roster of the names of all officers on the force, randomly selects five police stations, and then conducts interviews of all officers in those stations.

3. _____ A researcher is interested in interviewing alumni of San Simeon College who graduated between the years 1990 and 1996. He gets the roster of the names of these individuals from the alumni office, and mails a questionnaire to everyone on this roster.

4. _____ Another researcher is also interested in interviewing alumni of San Simeon College who graduated between the years 1990 and 1996. She gets the roster of the names of these individuals from the alumni office, selects the names of 100 individuals who graduated during these years using a table of random numbers, and then mails a questionnaire to everyone selected.

5. _____ A researcher is interested in identifying the attitudes of the physicians who work for Keyser Hospital toward the Republican plan for health care. She obtains a list of all the Keyser Medical Centers in southern California and randomly selects ten of these centers. Then she obtains a list of all the physicians at these centers and randomly selects eight physicians from each center to interview.

6. _____ A graduate student enrolled in the Marriage and Family Counseling Program at Daytona University is interested in determining how other graduate students feel about the program. He interviews all of the students he has access to on a given Monday night when he takes one of his counseling courses.

7. _____ A student enrolled in the Hotel and Restaurant Management School at Colorado State is researching the best restaurants in Denver based on the opinions of food critics. She begins by asking her advisor, who refers the student to four food critics who have written extensively on the subject and whom the student then contacts to interview for her study.

8. _____ Fifty black marbles are selected (using a volunteer) from a large jar in which there are 250 marbles, evenly divided between black and white in color.

9. _____ A high school teacher interviews all of the students who are members of the school glee club.

10. _____ A researcher interviews all the students who are assigned to after-school detention the day before a championship football game.

Activity 6.2:
Drawing a Random Sample

In this exercise, you will learn how to use a Table of Random Numbers to draw a random sample, and how the size of a sample affects its representativeness. Use the hypothetical population of 99 students in Table 6.2. Use the Table of Random Numbers located in the back of the textbook to select a sample of 10 students from the hypothetical population. List their numbers in the first column of the chart below, and then fill in the related information from the table for each of the students you have selected.

STUDENT NUMBER	GENDER	SCHOOL	IQ

Now, compute the proportion for Gender and School (divide your totals by 10 to obtain a decimal), and the average IQ (divide by 10 to obtain a whole number) for your sample, and enter these into the appropriate boxes below.

AVERAGES SAMPLE (N = 10)	GENDER M F	SCHOOL A B C	IQ
Average =			

Find three other groups of students in the class, obtain the averages they got from their samples on the three characteristics, and write them in the boxes below.

AVERAGES FROM 3 OTHER GROUPS	GENDER M F	SCHOOL A B C	IQ
Group #1			
Group #2			
Group #3			

Now average the four samples (yours plus the three others), and write the averages in the boxes below.

AVERAGES FOR SAMPLE (N = 40)	GENDER		SCHOOL			IQ
	M	F	A	B	C	
Average =						
Population						

How do the data for the sample of size 10 differ from the data for the sample of size 40? How would you explain this? What conclusion can you draw from this exercise?

_____

_____

_____

_____

_____

_____

_____

_____

_____

Activity 6.3:
When Is It Appropriate to Generalize?

1. On a television talk show, a psychiatrist discussed his study of airplane hijackers at some length and pointed out that their outstanding characteristic (which he discovered through extensive psychiatric interviewing) was a consistent history of failure. His sample consisted of approximately 20 hijackers who were interviewed while in jail. Although not explicitly stated, it seems obvious that the population to whom he intended to generalize was "all hijackers." Would it be appropriate to generalize to this population?

   Yes _____ No _____ If not, why not? _____

   _____

   _____

2. Assume that you wish to study the hypothesis that among career women between the ages of 30 and 50, career satisfaction is related to the adequacy of their relationship with their father during adolescence.

   a. To what target population would you want to generalize? _____

   _____

   b. What population would be sufficiently accessible? _____

   _____

   c. How might you get a random sample from the accessible population? _____

   _____

   d. If you had to use a convenience sample — for example, in just one or two locations — what descriptive information should you try to obtain?

   _____

   _____

   _____

Activity 6.4:
True or False?

Write "T" in front of the statements below that are true; write "F" in front of those that are false.

1. _____ A "population," as used in research, refers to the group to whom the researcher wishes to generalize the results of a study.

2. _____ Systematic sampling would be an example of a random sampling method.

3. _____ A purposive sample is a sample selected because the individuals have special characteristics or qualities of some sort.

4. _____ A representative sample is one that is similar to its population in all characteristics.

5. _____ The target population is usually larger than the accessible population.

6. _____ A simple random sample is usually a convenience sample.

7. _____ When a study is replicated, it is not always repeated under the same conditions.

8. _____ The term "ecological generalizability" refers to the extent to which the results of a study can be generalized to conditions or settings different from those that existed in a particular study.

9. _____ The term "external validity," as used in research, refers to whether the sample has been randomly selected or not.

10. _____ Convenience samples can be randomly selected.

Instrumentation

CHAPTER 7

Activity 7.1:
Major Categories of Instruments and Their Uses

Match the letter of the instrument from Column B with its most likely use listed in Column A.

COLUMN A: PURPOSE   **COLUMN B: INSTRUMENT**

---

1. _____ A researcher wishes to observe and record the behavior of an individual over time.

    a. Questionnaire

2. _____ A researcher wishes to survey a large group of individuals.

    b. Interview schedule

    c. Projective test

3. _____ A researcher wants to find out how much someone knows about the French Revolution.

    d. Achievement test

    e. Attitude scale

4. _____ A researcher wants to evaluate the quality of a new microwave oven.

    f. Rating scale

5. _____ A researcher wishes to get in-depth information from a small group of people.

    g. Anecdotal record

6. _____ A researcher wants to gain some idea of how students in a graduate program in teacher education feel about their student teaching experience.

Activity 7.2:
Which Type of Instrument is Most Appropriate?

For each of the items listed below, indicate whether it would be most likely to be measured by an aptitude test (AT), a questionnaire (Q), an interview (I), a rating scale (RS), a tally sheet (TS), or a performance checklist (PC).

1. _____ a person's self-concept

2. _____ readiness for kindergarten

3. _____ a person's experiences in high school

4. _____ assessing paramedic skills

5. _____ quality of a college application

6. _____ ability to work with others on a research project

7. _____ educational experiences of exceptional teachers

8. _____ potential of high school seniors for college work

9. _____ type of questions asked by students in a chemistry class

10. _____ prevalence of different kinds of errors in baseball

11. _____ student evaluations of instructor competence

12. _____ how a particular student feels about poetry

13. _____ public reactions to a recently announced plan to raise property taxes

14. _____ ability to use a calculator

15. _____ who participates — and how much — in the discussions that occur in an advanced-placement twelfth-grade American government class

Activity 7.3:
Types of Scales

Match the letter of the correct type of measurement scale from Column B with the example listed in Column A to which the scale applies.

COLUMN A: PRACTICE	COLUMN B: MEASUREMENT SCALE

1. _____ Type of scale that possesses a true zero point

   a. Nominal scale

2. _____ Type of scale that possesses all of the characteristics of the other scales

   b. Ordinal scale

3. _____ Type of scale that indicates only relative standing among individuals

   c. Interval scale

4. _____ Type of scale in which a researcher simply assigns numbers to different categories in order to show differences

   d. Ratio scale

5. _____ Type of scale that is rarely encountered in educational research

6. _____ Type of scale that cannot be used to measure quantitative variables

7. _____ Type of scale in which all of the distances between the points on the scale are equal, but does not have a true zero point

8. _____ The type of scale that provides the least information

9. _____ Type of scale that assumes that equal differences between scores really mean equal differences in the variable being measured

Activity 7.4:
Norm-Referenced vs. Criterion-Referenced Instruments

For each of the items listed below, indicate whether a Norm-referenced (N) or a Criterion-referenced (C) instrument is described.

1. _____ Provides a clear-cut goal to work toward

2. _____ Indicates that an individual was able to run a mile in at least 12 minutes

3. _____ Compares an individual's scores with the scores of a group

4. _____ Focuses more directly on instruction than the other type

5. _____ Indicates how an individual did compared with other members in his or her class

6. _____ Is almost always easier than the other type

7. _____ Desired difficulty level is at or about 50 percent

8. _____ Generally is inferior to the other type for research purposes

9. _____ Generally will provide more variability in scores

Activity 7.5:
Design an Instrument

Try to design an instrument (see Chapter 7 in the text) on a topic of interest.

1. Prepare either a rating scale or a questionnaire and describe it on the back of this page.

2. In the spaces below, describe how you checked for:

   instrument validity

   _____

   _____

   instrument reliability

   _____

   _____

3. Administer the instrument to a group (at least five) of your friends. Summarize the results here.

   _____

   _____

   _____

   _____

   _____

4. What problems did you encounter?

   _____

   _____

   _____

   _____

   _____

5. What could you do better next time to avoid such problems?

   _____

   _____

   _____

   _____

   _____

Activity 7.6:
Developing a Rating Scale

In one of our research classes, a student designed a study to investigate the following hypothesis:
"The more open the classroom, the higher the amount of student motivation."

As part of the process, she developed a rating scale to assess both the degree of openness and the level of student motivation within a particular classroom. Only by having some kind of measurement of each of these variables could she determine if a relationship existed between them.

Her first step was to produce a number of items related to the idea of "openness." She began by listing various things that could be taken as indicators of openness. Certain groupings began to emerge from the list of indicators. For example, a number of indicators seemed to concern the physical arrangement of the classroom, so that constituted one grouping. Listed below are some of the indicators and categories she formulated:

Physical environment: Are the desks placed in rows? Are there specific learning centers for subjects? Are classes sometimes held outdoors? Is there a general meeting area for students in the classroom? Are any other types of furniture used besides desks (e.g., sofas, rocking chairs, etc.) used? How many adults (teachers, paraprofessionals, etc.) are there in the classroom?

Curriculum: What amount of time does the teacher spend on planning? On evaluation? Does the teacher have a list of overall objectives she tries to attain? How much time is spent on the academic curriculum? On arts and crafts? On discussions or problem solving? Do the students direct their own planning? Devise their own curriculum? Are affective objectives included in the curriculum? Are students taught to express their feelings? Are grades given?

Teacher-student relationships: How often does the teacher give directions? Help students? How often do students initiate activities? Can students leave the classroom on their own, or must they request permission? Does the teacher work with students individually? Work in small groups? Teach the entire class? Do students and teachers jointly evaluate student work? Are class meetings student or teacher-directed? Can students set their own free time?

Materials: Are students assigned specific materials to use? What kinds of materials are available to students? How much time is spent on workbook assignments? Are there manipulative materials available? Are the materials easily accessible, or must students request them? Is the use of materials directed by teacher or students? Are art materials available? What sorts of books do students use? What other materials exist?

Social environment: Are students encouraged to help one another? To tutor others? Are students free to talk with others in class? How often? Do students work alone, or may they work with others? Do students group themselves, or is this done by the teacher? Do students share in room cleanup? How many times must the teacher ask for quiet? Does physical aggression ever occur between students? If so, how often? Who handles aggression, teacher or students?

Parental participation: Are parents allowed in the classroom? Observers? Others? Are parents and others free to enter the classroom when they wish, or is there a formal procedure they must go through? Is there a volunteer parent-aide program? What kinds of tasks do parents perform? How often are parents present?

Once she felt that she had a sufficient number of items within each of these categories, she worked to refine and clarify the indicators in each of the categories and then to convert them into items for a rating scale. Shown below is her completed rating scale:

RATING SCALE FOR CLASSROOM OPENNESS

1. Students do not move without teacher permission	1 2 3 4 5	1. Students may move in or out of class without permission
2. All students work at the same task at the same time	1 2 3 4 5	2. A great variety of tasks are performed at the same time
3. The teacher is the only resource in the classroom	1 2 3 4 5	3. Several human resources other than the teacher are in the classroom
4. Human resources are only clerical or housekeeper aides to the teacher	1 2 3 4 5	4. Human resources interact with students or with small groups
5. Furniture is permanently arranged	1 2 3 4 5	5. Furniture is spontaneously arranged
6. Everyone works at own desk	1 2 3 4 5	6. There are many floating study centers
7. Desks, tables, and chairs are arranged traditionally	1 2 3 4 5	7. There is a complete variety of furniture in a variety of arrangements
8. Students cannot interact without direct permission of the teacher	1 2 3 4 5	8. Students are free to interact with others in any way they desire
9. The teacher initiates all the activities	1 2 3 4 5	9. Students also initiate activities
10. The teacher teaches the class as a group	1 2 3 4 5	10. The teacher works with small groups or individual students
11. The teacher is addressed formally (e.g., Mrs. X; hands are raised; etc.)	1 2 3 4 5	11. The teacher is addressed informally (first name, etc.)
12. Reprimands are punitive	1 2 3 4 5	12. No reprimands or only friendly reminders are given
13. No feelings are verbally expressed	1 2 3 4 5	13. Feelings are expressed verbally
14. The textbook is closely followed	1 2 3 4 5	14. No formally prepared materials are used in class

What differences do you notice between the original list of indicators and the final rating scale above?

_____

_____

_____

_____

_____

_____

_____

_____

_____

Validity and Reliability

Activity 8.1:
Instrument Validity

A valid instrument is one that measures what it says it measures. If a researcher is interested in measuring how much a student knows about the U.S. Civil War, for example, he or she needs an instrument that will measure exactly that — the student's knowledge — *not* his or her feelings, attitudes, beliefs, or skills. For each of the three objectives listed below, write one example of the kind of question or observation you might engage in to measure, at least to some extent, attainment of the objective.

1. **Objective:** To measure the degree to which a person enjoys modern art

   Instrument question or observation strategy:

2. **Objective**: To measure the level of anxiety that exists among university students during final exam period

   Instrument question or observation strategy:

3. **Objective**: To measure the attitudes of local residents toward the building of a new ballpark in downtown San Francisco

   Instrument question or observation strategy:

Activity 8.2:
Instrument Reliability (1)

A *reliable* instrument is one that is *consistent* in what it measures. If an individual scores highly on the first administration of a test, for example, he or she should, if the test is reliable, score highly on a second administration. In this exercise, we are going to evaluate the reliability of an instrument.

Imagine that you are conducting a study for which you must develop a mastery test in mathematics for ninth-grade students. You develop a 30-point test and distribute it to a class of ninth-graders in a certain school district on the west coast of the United States in May of 2001. You then give the test again one month later to the day in June, 2001. The scores of the students on the two administrations of the test are shown below. What do they suggest to you about the reliability of this test? Explain.

30-POINT MATHEMATICS MASTERY TEST (FIRST ADMINISTRATION)	30-POINT MATHEMATICS MASTERY TEST (SECOND ADMINISTRATION)
17	15
22	18
25	21
12	15
7	14
28	27
27	24
8	5
21	25
24	21

Activity 8.3:
Instrument Reliability (2)

For each of the situations listed below, match the type of reliability with what the researchers involved are evaluating.

COLUMN A: SITUATION	COLUMN B: INSTRUMENT RELIABILITY

COLUMN A: SITUATION

1. _____ A researcher develops two versions of a test meant to measure interests in students prior to their taking an examination. He gives one version of the test to a group of college sophomores on a Monday, and the other version of the test to them the next day.

2. _____ A teacher develops a new test for high school biology. She gives the test twice, once to the students in her morning class and once to the students in her afternoon class. She then compares the scores for the two classes of students.

3. _____ A college professor is interested in evaluating her end-of-semester course evaluations that are completed by her students. The instrument consists of 20 five-point rating scale items. She obtains an average score for each student on the first 10 items, and also an average score for each student on the second 10 items. She then compares the scores.

4. _____ A researcher prepares a 15-item multiple-choice test designed to measure student knowledge of the causes of the Spanish-American War. She asks two of her colleagues, specialists in American history, to identify any items that they think do not measure what she is after.

5. _____ A teacher prepares an algebra test and gives it to her students at the end of the semester and again two months later.

COLUMN B: INSTRUMENT RELIABILITY

a. internal consistency

b. test-retest reliability

c. equivalent forms reliability

d. none of the above

6. Which of the following would be a way of assessing unreliability due to content and time?
   a. Administering a reading test (Form X) on Monday and again one month later
   b. Administering a reading test (Form X) on Monday and calculating a split-half correlation
   c. Administering a reading test (Form X) on Monday and Form Y one month later
   d. Administering a reading test (Form X) on Monday and deleting any questions that more than 50 percent of those taking the test missed

Activity 8.4:
What Kind of Evidence: Content-Related,
Criterion-Related or Construct-Related?

As we mention in the text, *validity* depends on the amount and type of evidence there is to support one's interpretations concerning data that has been collected. On page 159, we describe three kinds of evidence that a researcher might collect: content-related, criterion-related, and construct-related evidence of validity.

Listed below are a number of questions that each represent one of these three types. In the space provided, write *content* if the question refers to content-related evidence, *criterion* if the question relates to criterion-related evidence, and *construct* if the question refers to construct-related evidence of validity.

1. How strong is the relationship between student scores obtained using this instrument and their teacher's rating of their ability? _____

2. How adequately do the questions in the instrument represent that which is being measured? _____

3. Do the items that the instrument contains logically get at that which is being measured? _____

4. Are there a variety of different *types* of evidence (e.g., test scores, teacher ratings, correlations, etc.) that all measure this variable? _____

5. How well do the scores obtained using this instrument predict future performance? _____

6. Is the format of the instrument appropriate? _____

Activity 8.5:
What Constitutes Construct-Related Evidence of Validity?

On page 164 of the text, we provide an example of one piece of evidence that could be used to establish construct validity for a pencil and paper test on honesty.

1. In the space provided below, suggest some *additional* information that a researcher might collect as evidence of honesty in an effort to establish construct validity for the test.

_____

_____

_____

_____

_____

_____

_____

_____

2. *What about interest in the subject of chemistry?* Suppose another researcher wishes to develop a test to measure an individual's interest in chemistry. What sort of information might he or she collect in an attempt to establish construct validity for the test?

_____

_____

_____

_____

_____

_____

_____

_____

Internal Validity

Activity 9.1:
Threats to Internal Validity

Which threat to internal validity exists in each of the situations listed below?

COLUMN A: SITUATION	COLUMN B: THREAT TO INTERNAL VALIDITY

COLUMN A: SITUATION

1. A researcher wishes to compare changes in achievement motivation of males and females during their high school years. During her study, she discovers that more males than females failed to complete high school.

2. Two groups of students are compared with regard to their attitude toward a career in the military. Two different recruiting officers administer the same attitude scale to each group. The recruiter who administers the scale to the first group is in uniform; the second recruiter is in civilian clothes.

3. Those students who score in the top 2 percent on a biology test have, on average, lower scores the second time they take the test.

4. A researcher wants to measure changes in student attitudes toward their graduate programs at a local university. He finds a questionnaire used by another researcher the previous year that asks most of the questions he wants to ask. To improve it, he changes some of the questions and adds a few more.

5. A researcher observes level of attention in a special program during the month of September and again in May.

6. A researcher interviews two groups of individuals. One group is interviewed in his classroom; the other group, although asked the same questions, is interviewed in the student union.

COLUMN B: THREAT TO INTERNAL VALIDITY

a. Maturation

b. Mortality

c. Data collector characteristics

d. Location

e. Instrumentation

f. Regression

Activity 9.2:
What Type of Threat?

Match the letter of the appropriate research methodology from Column B with its topic in Column A.

COLUMN A: EXAMPLES   **COLUMN B: TYPE OF THREAT**

---

1. _____ The scorers of an examination uncon-   a. Subject characteristics
   sciously grade the exam papers for a
   comparison group in such a way that   b. History
   some students receive lower scores than
   they deserve.   c. Maturation

2. _____ The taking of a pretest by students par-   d. Attitude of subjects
   ticipating in a research study allows
   them to figure out the nature of the study.   e. Mortality

3. _____ Two existing groups are compared with   f. Data collector bias
   respect to their scores on an achieve-
   ment test.   g. Testing

4. _____ A fire drill occurs during the taking of a   h. Instrument decay
   final examination by the experimental
   group. Several students complain they
   did not have enough time to complete
   the exam.

5. _____ Change during an intervention is due
   just to the passing of time rather than the
   intervention itself.

6. _____ The way in which students are asked to
   participate in a study affects how they
   perform.

Activity 9.3:
Controlling Threats to Internal Validity

Suggest a way to control each of the following threats to internal validity.

1. Instrument decay _____

   _____

2. Subject characteristics _____

   _____

3. Loss of subjects (mortality) _____

   _____

4. Data collector characteristics _____

   _____

5. Location _____

   _____

6. Regression _____

   _____

7. Implementation _____

   _____

8. Attitude of subjects _____

   _____

Descriptive Statistics

Activity 10.1:
Construct a Frequency Polygon

For the most complete description of a group of scores, construct a **frequency polygon:** a graphic illustration of all the scores in a group. A comparison of frequency polygons is the most meaningful way to evaluate groups of scores. That is what we will do in this exercise.

Suppose that you have obtained the scores for two groups of students on a 30-item test of critical thinking. One group has been taught by the inquiry method, and the other group by the lecture method. On the test, the highest score received by a student in either group was 32, and the lowest score was 3. There are 40 students in each group. The raw scores for each group are listed in Table 10.1 below.

TABLE 10.1A

RAW SCORES FOR GROUP I (TAUGHT BY THE INQUIRY METHOD)	RAW SCORES FOR GROUP II (TAUGHT BY THE LECTURE METHOD)
3, 7, 8, 9,	5, 7, 9, 9, 10, 10, 11,
11, 11, 13, 13, 13, 14,	11, 11, 12, 13, 13, 13,
15, 15, 16, 16, 17, 17,	13, 14, 14, 15, 15, 15,
17, 17, 18, 18, 19, 19,	15, 15, 16, 16, 17,
19, 20, 20, 20, 21,	17, 17, 17, 18, 18, 18, 18,
21, 21, 21, 22, 22,	20, 20, 20, 20, 20, 20,
22, 22, 22, 23, 23,	20, 20, 20, 21, 21,
23, 23, 23, 23, 24	22, 22, 22, 22, 22,
24, 24, 25, 25, 26	23, 23, 23, 24, 25,
26, 26, 26, 26, 27, 27	25, 26, 26, 28, 28,
28, 28, 28, 29, 30,	28, 30, 30
30, 32	

Now, follow these steps.

Step 1. Determine the difference between the highest and the lowest score. This is $32 - 3 = 29$.

Step 2. Divide this difference by 15 and round to the nearest whole number. In this case, $29 / 15 = 1.93$, which rounds to 2. This number is the size of the intervals to be used in the polygon.

Step 3. Beginning with the lowest score, set up intervals as shown in Table 10.2. Make one interval schedule for each group.

TABLE 10.1B

GROUP I: TAUGHT BY THE INQUIRY METHOD		GROUP II: TAUGHT BY THE LECTURE METHOD	
SCORE	**FREQUENCY**	**SCORE**	**FREQUENCY**
31-32	_l_ _ _	31-32	_ _ _
29-30	_l l l_	29-30	_ _ _
27-28	_ _ _	27-28	_ _ _
25-26	_ _ _	25-26	_ _ _
23-24	_ _ _	23-24	_ _ _
21-22	_ _ _	21-22	_ _ _
19-20	_ _ _	19-20	_ _ _
17-18	_ _ _	17-18	_ _ _
15-16	_ _ _	15-16	_ _ _
13-14	_ _ _	13-14	_ _ _
11-12	_ _ _	11-12	_ _ _
9-10	_ _ _	9-10	_ _ _
7-8	_ _ _	7-8	_ _ _
5-6	_ _ _	5-6	_ _ _
3-4	_ _ _	3-4	_ _ _

Step 4. Tally the number of scores in each interval for each group and enter the tally in Table 10.2 under the column entitled "Frequency." We have begun this for the inquiry group, using the data from Table 10.1. As you can see, there is one score of 31 or 32 and three scores of 29 or 30 in the Inquiry group.

Step 5. Draw a pair of axes as shown in Figure 10.1. Mark off points on the X axis to represent the score intervals. The lowest interval is placed near the Y axis. The distance between the points must be the same. Then mark off points on the Y axis to represent frequencies. These must begin with 0. The highest point is the largest frequency in either group. You should have discovered (by looking at your tallies in Table 10.2) that the largest frequency in the inquiry group is nine (for scores of 21 or 22, and for 23 or 24).

Step 6. Plot each frequency for each interval for the inquiry group. Place an open (white) dot directly opposite a frequency of 1 on the Y axis and directly above the 3-4 interval on the axis. Place another white dot directly opposite a frequency of 0 on the Y axis and directly above the 5-6 interval on the X axis, and so forth until you have all of the frequencies for the inquiry group entered on the graph. Now plot the frequency (which is zero) for one interval below and one interval above the actual range of scores. This is called *anchoring* the polygon.

Step 7. Connect the points (the white dots) in sequence, being sure not to skip any interval. Notice that the line must touch the X axis at both ends: that is why we plotted zero frequencies at interval 1-2 and interval 33-34.

Step 8. Repeat the above steps for the lecture group, only use closed (black) dots. When you are finished, you will have two frequency polygons on the same graph, showing the comparative performances of the inquiry and lecture groups on the critical thinking test.

Which group, overall, performed better? Inquiry _____ Lecture _____

How can you tell? _____

_____

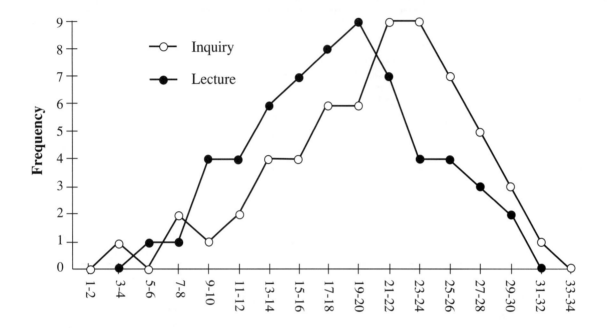

Activity 10.2:
Comparing Frequency Polygons

Often we want to compare two or more groups on some measurement. One way to do this effectively is to use frequency polygons plotted on the same graph. Look at Figure 10.2 below. It illustrates a study in which two fourth-grade classes were compared: one in which a new social studies curriculum was being tried out (E), and a similar comparison group (C). End-of-year scores are being compared, the test being one designed to measure student understanding of social studies concepts.

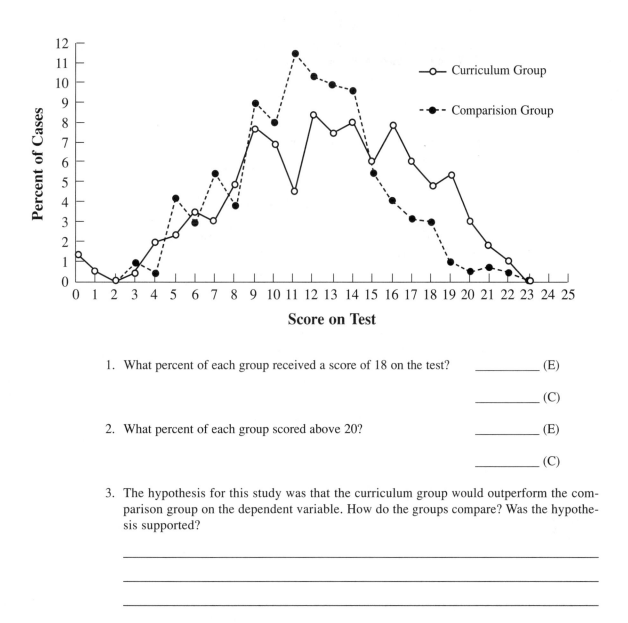

1. What percent of each group received a score of 18 on the test? _____ (E)

   _____ (C)

2. What percent of each group scored above 20? _____ (E)

   _____ (C)

3. The hypothesis for this study was that the curriculum group would outperform the comparison group on the dependent variable. How do the groups compare? Was the hypothesis supported?

   _____

   _____

   _____

Activity 10.3:
Calculating Averages

1. As we discussed in the text, the mean for a group of scores is determined by adding up all of the scores in the group and dividing by the total number of scores in the group. What is the mean for the following group of scores?

10   **12**   **15**   **16**   **20**   **50**

2. The median is the point in a group of scores below and above which 50 percent of the scores fall. What is the median for the group of scores above?

3. Consider the following two sets of scores:

Set A: 44, 48, 50, 54, 59

Set B: 5, 36, 50, 65, 99

How would you describe these two sets of scores? (Hint: Compare their means and medians.) What do these tell you about the two sets?

Activity 10.4:
Calculating the Standard Deviation

Although it takes a bit of time, calculating the standard deviation of a set of scores is actually quite easy. Just follow these steps.

1. List the scores in the first column of a table, as shown in Table 10.3.

2. Calculate the mean of the scores.

3. Subtract the mean from each score to obtain the difference.

4. Square each difference score, as shown in the last column.

5. Sum the scores in the last column.

6. Divide this sum by the total number of scores in the distribution.

7. Take the square root of this number to obtain the standard deviation.

TABLE 10.4

SCORE	SUBTRACT	MEAN	EQUALS	DIFFERENCE	SQUARE THE DIFFERENCE
5	-	20	=	-15	225
10	-	20	=	-10	100
15	-	20	=	-5	25
20	-	20	=	0	0
25	-	20	=	5	25
30	-	20	=	10	100
35	-	20	=	15	225
					Total = 700

Standard Deviation = square root of 700/7 = square root of 100 = 10

Now, here is a new set of scores. What is the standard deviation of this set?

$$2 \quad 3 \quad 10 \quad 20 \quad 35 \quad 35 \quad 35$$

Activity 10.5:
Calculating a Correlation Coefficient

Is there a relationship between the number of pencils and the number of pens a student owns? Use the hypothetical data in Table 10.4 to find out by calculating the Pearson r correlation coefficient:

TABLE 10.5
PENCILS VS. PENS

STUDENT'S NAME	NUMBER OF PENCILS (X)	NUMBER OF PENS (Y)	X^2	Y^2	XY
A	3	2	9	4	6
B	6	6	36	36	36
C	5	7	25	49	35
D	2	5	4	25	10
E	6	7	36	49	42
F	2	3	4	9	6
TOTALS	$\Sigma = 24$	$\Sigma = 30$	$\Sigma = 114$	$\Sigma = 172$	$\Sigma = 135$

1. Multiply ΣXY by n: = _____

2. Multiply ΣX by ΣY = _____

3. Subtract step 2 from step 1: _____

4. Multiply ΣX^2 by n: _____

5. Square ΣX: _____

6. Subtract step 5 from step 4: _____

7. Multiply ΣY^2 by n: _____

8. Square ΣY: _____

9. Subtract step 8 from step 7: _____

10. Multiply step 6 by step 9: _____

11. Take the square root of step 10 _____

12. Divide step 3 by step 11 _____ (You should get **.75**)

Now, what does this correlation (r) of **.75** tell you? Explain briefly

_____

_____

_____

Activity 10.6:
Analyzing Crossbreak Tables

1. Suppose that a researcher wished to study the possible relationship between type of thera-peutic approach used by counselors and the institution where the counselor received his or her training. The researcher obtains the data shown in Table 10.5. What conclusions can you draw from the table?

TABLE 10.6A
COMPARISON OF THERAPEUTIC METHOD AND TRAINING INSTITUTION

	METHOD			
TRAINING INSTITUTION	**ROGERIAN**	**GESTALT**	**BEHAVIOR MODIFICATION**	**FREUDIAN**
Happy Valley State	7	20	10	8
Multiversity II	8	6	25	11
College of the Specific	15	10	5	5

2. Table 10.6 indicates how participants in a research project in an inner-city elementary school rated paraprofessionals working in the project. Table 10.7 indicates how they rated each other's cooperation. What do these tables reveal?

TABLE 10.6B
RATINGS OF PARAPROFESSIONALS

	RATING				
	EXCELLENT	**GOOD**	**FAIR**	**POOR**	**TOTAL**
Teachers	17	7	5	0	29
Paraprofessionals	12	15	1	0	28
Other staff	6	6	2	0	14
Total	35	28	8	0	71

TABLE 10.7C
RATINGS OF PARTICIPANT COOPERATION

	RATING				
	EXCELLENT	**GOOD**	**FAIR**	**POOR**	**TOTAL**
Teachers	5	7	12	6	30
Paraprofessionals	6	12	7	3	28
Other staff	2	3	4	5	14
Total	13	22	23	14	72

Activity 10.7:
Comparing z-Scores

1. Suppose that James received a raw score of **75** on a test where the average (mean) was **73** and the standard deviation was **1,** while Felicia received a score of **82** on a similar test where the mean was **80** and the standard deviation was **2**. Who did better on their test in z-score terms?

2. Assume that a normal distribution of scores has a mean of 50 and a standard deviation of 5. What would be the z-score equivalent for the following raw scores?

   a.   45   z = _____

   b.   50   z = _____

   c.   52.5   z = _____

3. Assume that another normal distribution of scores has a mean of 85 and a standard deviation of 15. What would be the raw score equivalent for the following z-scores?

   a.   z = -2   raw score = _____

   b.   z = +2.33   raw score = _____

   c.   z = -.33   raw score = _____

Inferential Statistics

Activity 11.1:
Probability

1. Take a coin and test the hypothesis that the coin is dishonest, that is, that it comes up heads more times than it comes up tails.

2. Flip the coin four times. Record the number of heads here: _____

3. On the basis of just this amount of data, would you accept or reject the hypothesis?

   Accept _____ Reject _____ Why?_____

4. Suppose that you had gotten four heads (maybe you did). Would you then accept or reject the hypothesis? _____ Why? _____

5. Now flip the same coin four more times and record the number of heads. Do this 16 times. (Note: Each set of four flips can be considered a sample. For each sample, the possible number of heads is 0, 1, 2, 3, or 4.)

FLIP NUMBER	NUMBER OF HEADS	FLIP NUMBER	NUMBER OF HEADS
1		9	
2		10	
3		11	
4		12	
5		13	
6		14	
7		15	
8		16	

6. Next, tally the number of times each possible outcome occurred. Then change each to a percent by dividing by 16.

OUTCOME	NUMBER OF TIMES OUTCOME OCCURRED	PERCENT
0 heads		
1 head		
2 heads		
3 heads		
4 heads		

7. If you were to use several coins and many more samples, you would (almost certainly) arrive at a table that presents the results to be expected with an honest coin. It would be very similar to that shown below.

OUTCOME	PERCENT	PROBABILITY
0 heads	6	.06
1 head	25	.25
2 heads	38	.38
3 heads	25	.25
4 heads	6	.06
Total	100	1.00

8. These percentages are actually probabilities. They tell us how often we would expect each outcome to occur with an honest coin. Now, return to your original sample (the first set of four flips of your coin). Would you now change your interpretation in any way?

Yes _____ No _____. If yes, how so? _____

If not, why not? _____

_____

_____

Activity 11.2:
Learning to Read a *t*-Table

There are certain probabilities that researchers take as indicative of a stable nonchance relationship. If the probability of obtaining a particular result or relationship in a sample is less than **.05** (one chance in **20**), we customarily consider it to be *statistically significant* — that is, as probably not due to chance. If the probability is less than 5 percent (for example, 1 percent), we can be even more confident that we are not simply dealing with chance. These values (1 percent and 5 percent) are frequently referred to as *levels of statistical significance.*

Hence, when a research report states that a particular result (e.g., a difference in means) or relationship (e.g., a correlation coefficient) is significant at the 5 percent level, it means that the chance of the finding being simply a fluke (due to the particular sample that was used) is less than 5 in 100. It means that the relationship or result is worth noting and tentatively acceptable as a reproducible relationship for a specified population. Note that *statistical significance* is not the same thing as *practical significance,* however.

A *t*-test is used to test the statistical significance of a difference between two means. A *t*-table shows the value of *t* required for a particular result to be considered statistically significant at various degrees of freedom (d.f.). Once the appropriate d.f. have been determined and the *t* value has been calculated, the table indicates what a calculated *t* value must be (the critical *t* value) to be considered statistically significant at different levels of significance (e.g., **.05, .01**).

For example, a *t* value calculated for a sample having **10 d.f.** using a one-tailed (i.e., directional) test must be at least **1.812** to be considered statistically significant at the **.05** level, as shown in the normal curve table presented below. What must the *t* value be for such a sample to be statistically at the **.01** level? _____ Now, suppose another sample has **25** degrees of freedom. What must the *t* value be to be considered statistically significant at the **.05** level? _____ At the **.01** level? _____

	PROPORTION IN CRITICAL REGION			
DEGREES OF FREEDOM	**.005**	**.10**	**.05**	**.01**
1	63.657	3.078	6.314	31.821
5	4.032	1.476	2.015	3.365
10	3.169	1.372	1.812	2.764
25	2.787	1.316	1.708	2.485
40	2.704	1.303	1.684	2.423
60	2.660	1.296	1.671	2.390

Activity 11.3:
Calculate a *t*-Test

A researcher wishes to compare the achievement of two groups of students who were taught social studies by two different methods. Group I (n = **26**) was taught by the inquiry method. Group II (n = **26**) was taught by the lecture method. The average (mean) score of each group on a 100-point final examination was **85** for the lecture group (standard deviation = **3** points) and **87** for the inquiry group (standard deviation = **2** points).

Use **Table D.2** in the Appendix in the text to calculate a *t*-test for the difference in means. Follow the steps in Table D.2 to fill in the table below (we have filled in the first two lines).

	INQUIRY GROUP	LECTURE GROUP
Mean	87	85
Standard deviation (SD)	2	3
Standard error of the mean (SEM)		
Standard error of the difference (SED)		

t = _____ Degrees of freedom (d.f.) is obtained by $n_1 + n_2 - 2 = 26 + 26 - 2 = 50$

Consult the table below to determine if the obtained *t*-value is statistically significant at the **.05** level.

	PROPORTION IN CRITICAL REGION			
DEGREES OF FREEDOM	.005	.10	.05	.01
1	63.657	3.078	6.314	31.821
5	4.032	1.476	2.015	3.365
10	3.169	1.372	1.812	2.764
25	2.787	1.316	1.708	2.485
40	2.704	1.303	1.684	2.423
60	2.660	1.296	1.671	2.390

The difference between the inquiry and the lecture groups was _____ or was not _____ statistically significant

*Note: This exercise is designed to illustrate the procedure. When the number of cases in each group, as here, is less than 30, a somewhat different formula should be used. It can be found in any basic statistics text.

Activity 11.4:
Perform a Chi-Square Test

Chi-square is the most commonly used statistic for determining whether a relationship between two categorical variables is statistically significant. The formula for calculating chi-square is:

$$X^2 = \sum \frac{(f_O - f_E)^2}{f_E}$$

Suppose a researcher wishes to determine whether, at selected high schools, there is a relationship between number of students enrolling in physical education courses and participation in intramural sports. The data might look like that shown in Table 11.4.

TABLE 11.4

UNIVERSITY	NUMBER OF STUDENTS ENROLLING IN PHYSICAL EDUCATION COURSES	NUMBER OF STUDENTS PARTICIPATING IN INTRAMURAL SPORTS	TOTALS
Alpha	70 (60)	30 (40)	100
Beta	130	70	
Kappa	160	140	
Totals	360		

The numbers in each of the cells in the table represent the observed frequencies (f_O). To obtain chi-square, go through the following steps:

1. Add up (total) both columns and rows. For example, the total number of students enrolling in physical education courses is **360**. Enter the totals in the table.

2. Calculate the proportion of the total frequency that falls in each row and column. Thus, you should see that Alpha University has **100/600,** or **1/6** of the total number of students.

3. Multiply each row proportion by its column total. These are expected frequencies (f_E). Thus, for Alpha University, the expected frequencies for the number of students enrolling in physical education courses is **1/6(360) = 60**. For the number of students participating in intramural sports, it is **1/6(240) = 40.** Enter these in parentheses, as we did for Alpha University, in each of the other cells.

4. For each cell, subtract the expected frequency (f_E) from the obtained frequency (f_O), square the result, and then divide it by (f_E). Fill in the results below.

$(70 - 60)^2/60 = 10^2/60 = 100/60 = 1.67$

$(30 - 40)^2/40 = -10^2/40 = 100/40 =$ _____

$(130 - 120)^2/120 = 10^2/120 = 100/120 =$ _____

$(70 - 80)^2/80 = -10^2/80 = 100/80 =$ _____

$(160 - 180)^2/180 = -20^2/180 = 400/180 =$ _____

$(140 - 120)^2/120 = 20^2/120 = 400/120 =$ _____

5. Next, total these six values, as symbolized by

$$X^2 = \sum \frac{(f_O - f_E)^2}{f_E}$$

to obtain a chi-square value of _____ (You should get **11.80**)

6. Now, to determine whether this value is statistically significant, compare the calculated value of chi-square to the values in the chi-square table below. To determine the degrees of freedom (d.f.), multiply the number of rows minus one (r – 1) times the number of columns minus one (c – 1). In this case, it would be **(3 – 1) x (2 – 1) = 2.** The chi-square table indicates that, with two d.f., a value of _____ is required for a result to be statistically significant. Is the value you obtained **(11.80)** statistically significant? Yes _____ No _____

DEGREES OF FREEDOM	α LEVELS				
	.10	.05	.02	.01	.001
1	2.71	3.84	5.41	6.64	10.83
2	4.60	5.99	7.82	9.21	13.82
3	6.25	7.82	9.84	11.34	16.27
4	7.78	9.49	11.67	13.28	18.46
5	9.24	11.07	13.39	15.09	20.52
10	15.99	18.31	21.16	23.21	29.59
20	28.41	31.41	35.02	37.57	45.32
25	34.38	37.65	41.57	44.31	52.62
30	40.26	43.77	47.96	50.89	59.70

To be significant, the χ^2 obtained from the data must be equal to or larger than the value shown in the table.

Activity 11.5:
Conduct a *t*-Test

Identify a group of at least 10 people (classmates, friends, neighbors, etc.).

1. Divide the group into two roughly equal sub-groups, based on some characteristic such as gender, age, height, etc.

2. Ask each person independently to pick a number from 1 to 9.

3. Calculate the mean of these numbers for each group.

4. Write the difference between the means of the two groups here. _____

5. Calculate a *t*-test for the difference in means using Table D-2 in the appendix of the text. Use the portion of the *t*-table shown below to determine the statistical significance of the difference in means that you obtained for the two groups.

	PROPORTION IN CRITICAL REGION			
DEGREES OF FREEDOM	**.005**	**.10**	**.05**	**.01**
1	63.657	3.078	6.314	31.821
5	4.032	1.476	2.015	3.365
10	3.169	1.372	1.812	2.764
25	2.787	1.316	1.708	2.485
40	2.704	1.303	1.684	2.423
60	2.660	1.296	1.671	2.390

Were the results statistically significant? Yes _____ No _____

6. What basic assumption must be met to justify using a *t*-test?_____

_____

_____

7. Was it met? Yes _____ No _____ Explain why it was or was not. _____

_____

_____

_____

Statistics in Perspective

Activity 12.1:
Statistical vs. Practical Significance

In each of the following, discuss whether the result or relationship is likely to be practically significant (PS), and then explain your reasoning.

1. A researcher finds that a particular relationship can occur by chance about 20 times in 100.

2. A researcher finds that students who use a new biology textbook recently purchased by the school district scored an average of 20 percent higher on an end-of-the-course examination.

3. A medical researcher finds that the use of a certain drug decreases the incidence of a life-threatening drug among a group of senior citizens by 3 percent

4. A small appliance store owner finds that advertising in the local neighborhood newspaper increases her sales each week by 1 percent.

5. A new method of teaching five-year-olds how to tie their shoes results in their being able to do so three weeks earlier than similar five-year-olds not taught this method.

6. A researcher finds that a correlation of .18 has only a 1 in 1,000 likelihood of occurring by chance.

Activity 12.2:
Appropriate Techniques

Match the technique in Column A with the appropriate description from Column B

COLUMN A	COLUMN B
1. Effect size	a. A graphic way to show all of the information about a group
2. Inferential statistics	b. An unusual score
3. Known groups	c. Takes into account the size of a difference, regardless of whether it is statistically significant.
4. Scatterplot	d. Graphic technique for illustrating a relationship between quantitative variables within a single group
5. Crossbreak table	e. A means of assessing generalizability
6. Test of statistical significance	f. Often a useful frame of reference to use in interpreting the magnitude of a difference between means of two groups
7. Outlier	g. Should be reported in addition to (or instead of) significance levels whenever possible
8. Confidence interval	h. Sometimes may be insignificant in any real or educational sense
	i. A device used to illustrate relationships among categorical data

Activity 12.3:
Interpret the Data

Review Activity 11.5 and then respond to the following.

1. What does the difference in means tell you? _____

    _____

2. What does the *t*-test tell you? _____

3. What other indexes might be useful? _____

4. What would they tell you? _____

    _____

Activity 12.4:
Collect Some Data

Imagine that you and a colleague conducted a study with two large random samples of Swedes and Germans. You find a mean I.Q. difference of six points in favor of the Swedes. Assume that this difference was statistically significant at the .05 level.

1. Give these hypothetical "results" to five friends or acquaintances and ask them what they think this all means. Summarize the responses of each below.

   Person #1 _____

   _____

   Person #2 _____

   _____

   Person #3 _____

   _____

   Person #4 _____

   _____

   Person #5 _____

   _____

2. Summarize similarities and differences between the responses and record what you learned below.

   _____

   _____

   _____

   _____

(Be sure to tell your participants afterward that these results are fake.)

Experimental Research

CHAPTER **13**

Activity 13.1:
Group Experimental Research Questions

Which of the following questions would lend themselves well to group experimental research?

1. What factors influence job success?

2. Which is more effective in reducing the anxiety of clients, client-centered or traditional therapy?

3. Does personal counseling improve student achievement?

4. Why do teachers experience burnout?

5. What is the relationship (if any) between teacher gender and student achievement?

6. How do science textbooks used in the 1940s compare with those used today?

7. Do students like history more if taught by the case study or the inquiry method?

8. What makes a good high school counselor?

9. What sorts of problems do most first-year teachers face?

Activity 13.2:
Designing an Experiment

Fizz Laboratories, a pharmaceutical company, has developed a new pain-relief medication. Sixty patients suffering from arthritis and needing pain relief are available. Each patient will be treated and then asked an hour later, "About what percentage of pain relief did you experience?"

1. Why should Fizz not simply administer the new drug and record the patient's responses?

2. Draw the design below of an experiment to compare the drug's effectiveness with that of aspirin and a placebo.

3. Should patients be told which group they are in? How would this knowledge affect their reactions?

4. If patients are not told which treatment they are receiving, the experiment is single-blind. Should this experiment also be double-blind? Explain.

Activity 13.3:
Characteristics of Experimental Research

Match the concept from Column A with the correct definition from Column B.

COLUMN A	COLUMN B
1. Experimental group	a. Refers to the result(s) or outcome(s) being studied
2. Control group	b. A process wherein every member of a population has an equal chance to be a member of the sample
3. Random selection	
4. Random assignment	c. An unplanned-for variable that may be a cause of a result observed in a study
5. Independent variable	d. The group that does not receive a treatment in an experiment
6. Dependent variable	
7. Extraneous variable	e. A process of pairing two individuals whose scores on a particular measure are similar
8. Matching	f. Sometimes referred to as the treatment variable in a study
	g. Every individual who is participating in an experiment has an equal chance of being assigned to any of the experimental or control conditions being compared
	h. The sample of individuals participating in an experiment
	i. The group that receives a treatment of some sort in an experiment

Activity 13.4:
Random Selection vs. Random Assignment

Described below are four examples of randomization. Write **RS** if random selection is involved; **RA** if random assignment is involved; **B** if both random selection and random assignment are involved; or **O** if no randomization is involved.

1. _____ Using all fifth-grade classes in the campus demonstration school, a researcher divides the students in each class into two groups by drawing their names from a hat.

2. _____ All students with learning handicaps in a school district are identified and the names of 50 are pulled from a hat. The first 25 are given an experimental treatment, and the remainder are taught as usual.

3. _____ All third-grade students in an elementary school district who are being taught to read by the literature method are identified, as are all students who are being taught with basal readers. The names of all students in each group are placed in a hat and then 50 students from each group are selected.

4. _____ Students in three classes with computer assistance are compared with three classes not using computers.

Single-Subject Research

CHAPTER 14

Activity 14.1:
Single-Subject Research Questions

Which of the following questions would lend themselves well to single-subject research?

1. How do students view the president of the University?

2. Which is more effective in helping students to learn a language, individual instruction or language laboratories?

3. What is the daily routine of a high school guidance counselor?

4. How are women portrayed in advertisements in popular magazines?

5. How can Jimmy Thomas be encouraged to speak up more in class?

6. Why do some students have trouble learning to read?

7. What makes a good teacher lose his or her enthusiasm for teaching?

8. Is praise an effective technique to use with disruptive students?

Activity 14.2:
Characteristics of Single-Subject Research

Match the concept from Column A with the correct definition from Column B.

COLUMN A	COLUMN B
1. Baseline	a. Single-subject designs are weak when it comes to this
2. Data points	b. Starting point for a single-subject study
3. Condition line	c. Indicates where the intervention conditions change in a single-subject study
4. Comparison of two or more groups	d. Represent the data collected at various times during a single-subject study
5. Treatment condition	e. The end point of a single-subject study
6. Generalizability	f. Important if single-subject studies are to have external validity
7. Replication	g. The intervention in a single-subject study
8. Single-subject research	h. Does not occur in single-subject research
	i. Used to study changes in behavior of an individual after exposure to a treatment of some sort

Activity 14.3:
Analyze Some Single-Subject Data

Alicia Morales, a sixth-grade teacher in Sarasota, Florida, wishes that Jamie Brown, one of her students, would pay more attention in class (behavior 1). She also would like to see him volunteer to answer questions more frequently (behavior 2), as well as speak directly to other students during class discussions (behavior 3). Consequently, she decides to use a multiple-baseline design to see if she can increase these behaviors by systematically praising Jamie (the "treatment" she plans to use) whenever one of these behaviors occurs. She is fortunate in that she has a teacher's aide who can observe Jamie while class is in session and she is teaching. After three weeks, the results of the intervention are shown below: What do you think? Was the treatment effective?

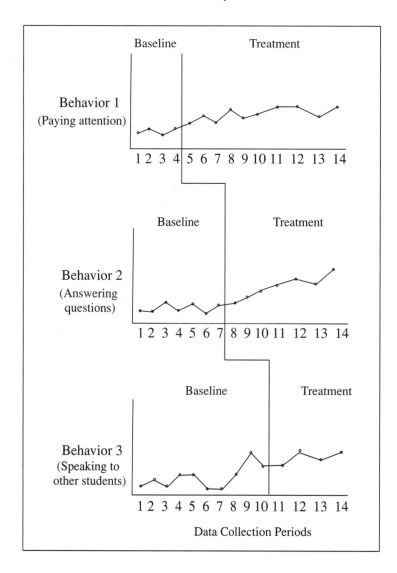

Correlational Research

Activity 15.1:
Correlational Research Questions

Which of the following questions would lend themselves well to correlational research?

1. What are student attitudes toward environmental organizations?

2. Do students like history more if taught by the inquiry method?

3. What does a high school football coach do when he isn't coaching?

4. What sorts of themes appear in the editorials in the *New York Times?*

5. Does early success in school lead to financial success in adulthood?

6. Is teacher praise related to student achievement?

Activity 15.2:
What Kind of Correlation?

Would each of the following be positively, negatively, or not correlated?

1. _____ height and weight of people ages 1-18

2. _____ weight and speed of people ages 20-50

3. _____ health and length of life

4. _____ running speed and liking for mystery novels

5. _____ size and strength of people ages 10-30

6. _____ achievement in school and absenteeism

7. _____ television viewing (in hours) and reading achievement

8. _____ food intake at a meal and stomach comfort

9. _____ height and life expectancy

Activity 15.3:
Think Up an Example

In the space provided, write an example of two things that would have:

1. A strong positive correlation: _____ and _____

2. A strong negative correlation: _____ and _____

3. A weak positive correlation: _____ and _____

4. A weak negative correlation: _____ and _____

5. Little or no correlation: _____ and _____

Activity 15.4:
Match the Correlation Coefficient to Its Scatterplot

Shown below are eight scatterplots. In the space alongside each, write in the appropriate correlation coefficient from the following list:

r = .90; r = .65; r = .35; r = .00; r = -.90; r = -.75; r = -.50; r = -.10

a)
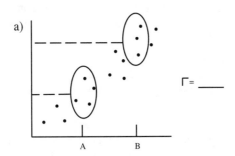
Γ = ____

e)
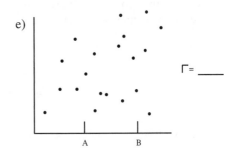
Γ = ____

b)
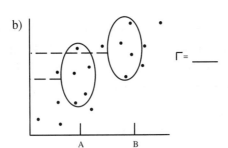
Γ = ____

f)
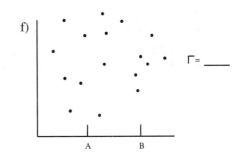
Γ = ____

c)
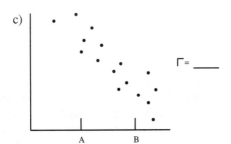
Γ = ____

g)
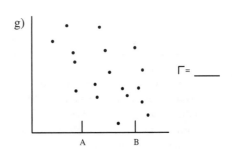
Γ = ____

d)
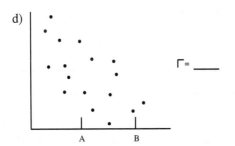
Γ = ____

h)
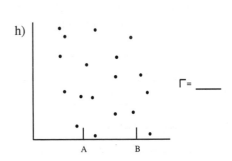
Γ = ____

Activity 15.5:
Calculate a Correlation Coefficient

Actually, there are many different correlation coefficients, each applying to a particular circumstance and each calculated by means of a different computational formula. The one we will use in this exercise is the one most frequently used: the Pearson product-moment coefficient of correlation. It is symbolized by the lowercase letter r. When the data for both variables are expressed in terms of quantitative scores, the Pearson r is the appropriate correlation coefficient to calculate. It is designed for use with interval or ratio data. The formula for calculating the Pearson r coefficient is:

$$r = \frac{n\Sigma XY - (\Sigma X)(\Sigma Y)}{\sqrt{[n\Sigma X^2 - (\Sigma X)^2][n\Sigma Y^2 - (\Sigma Y)^2]}}$$

The Pearson formula looks a lot more complicated than it really is. It does have a lot of steps to follow before you actually get to the end, but each step is easy to calculate. For this exercise, let's imagine we have the following sets of scores for two variables — reading and writing — for five students:

STUDENT NAME	VARIABLE X— READING SCORE	VARIABLE Y— WRITING SCORE
Al	20	20
Beth	18	16
Cathy	18	20
Dave	15	12
Ed	10	10
Total	$\Sigma X = 81$	$\Sigma Y = 78$
$\Sigma XY = 1328$	$\Sigma X^2 = 1373$	$\Sigma Y^2 = 1300$

What we would like to know is whether these two variables are related, and if so, how—positively or negatively. To answer these questions, apply the Pearson formula and calculate the correlation coefficient for the two sets of scores. In other words, plug the appropriate numbers into the formula to calculate the r. Most of the computation has already been done for you and is provided in the bottom two rows of boxes. (See Appendix D at the end of the textbook for a step-by-step example of how to calculate a correlation coefficient using this formula.) Once you have calculated the correlation coefficient, describe below in one sentence the type of relationship that exists between reading and writing scores among this sample of five students:

_____

_____

_____

_____

_____

Activity 15.6:
Correlation in Everyday Life

Below we present a number of everyday sayings that suggest relationships. What correlations do they suggest? Are they positive or negative?

1. A fool and his money are soon parted.

2. As the twig is bent, so grows the tree.

3. You can't grow grass on a busy street.

4. Virtue is its own reward.

5. What fails to destroy me makes me stronger.

6. To get along, go along.

7. You can't make an omelet without breaking some eggs.

8. You can't make a silk purse out of a sow's ear.

9. All that glitters is not gold.

10. If at first you don't succeed, try, try again.

Causal-Comparative Research

CHAPTER 16

Activity 16.1:
Causal-Comparative Research Questions

Which of the following questions would lend themselves well to causal-comparative research?

1. How many students were enrolled in Psych 101 this semester?

2. Which subject do high school students like least?

3. How do elementary school teachers teach phonics?

4. Are two-year-old girls more aggressive than two-year-old boys?

5. Do "C' students do better in athletics than "A" and "B" students?

6. How might Jimmy Thomas be helped to read?

7. Is teacher enthusiasm related to student success in academic classes?

8. What is the best way to teach arithmetic?

Activity 16.2:
Analyze Some Causal-Comparative Data

Just prior to the commencement of the fall semester at a large midwestern university, Professor Judith Brown, an ardent feminist who has a Ph.D in statistics, gets into a discussion with one of her male colleagues about who are better statistics students, males or females. She hypothesizes that the females in her classes, on average, will outperform the males.

Listed in Table 16.2 are the scores on the final examination earned by each of the 24 students (12 females and 12 males) in her introductory class. Calculate the mean (the average) score for both the male and the female students in Dr. Brown's class. Is there a difference? If there is a difference, can Dr. Brown argue that gender is the cause of this apparent difference in ability (indeed, that her hypothesis is correct)? Explain your conclusion in the space provided under the table.

TABLE 16.2:
SCORES ON A FINAL EXAMINATION

FEMALES	MALES
70	90
75	68
93	91
84	80
65	77
87	80
90	91
95	76
88	75
78	62
86	77
84	87
Total =	Total =
Female mean =	Male mean =

_____

_____

_____

_____

_____

_____

Activity 16.3:
Causal-Comparative vs. Experimental Hypotheses

Listed below are a number of hypotheses. Which could be studied best as an *experiment* and which could be carried out best as a *causal-comparative* study?

1. *Hypothesis #1:* Deaf high school students in residential settings who receive instruction in English through a combination of signed English and American Sign Language (ASL) will demonstrate higher levels of written English than those taught using only signed English.

   Experimental study _____ Causal-comparative study _____

2. *Hypothesis #2:* Adult homosexual males have had greater exposure to sexual abuse in childhood than adult heterosexual males.

   Experimental study _____ Causal-comparative study _____

3. *Hypothesis #3:* Male high school students who participate in a four-week simulation of pregnancy will subsequently demonstrate more responsible attitudes toward parenthood than similar students not participating in the simulation.

   Experimental study _____ Causal-comparative study _____

Survey Research

CHAPTER 17

Activity 17.1:
Survey Research Questions

Which of the following questions would lend themselves well to survey research?

1. How do sophomore students feel about the new counseling program?

2. In what ways were delinquent and non-delinquent boys similar and different during the 1930s?

3. Is inquiry teaching more effective than lectures in the teaching of sociology?

4. How much college tuition are parents able and willing to pay?

5. How many single mothers were on welfare in Contra Costa county during the past nine months?

6. Do professors think it is ethical to require graduate students to participate in a professor's research project?

7. What does a high school principal do each day?

Activity 17.2:
Types of Surveys

Match the concept from Column A with the correct statement from Column B

COLUMN A	COLUMN B
1. Longitudinal survey	a. The researcher surveys the same sample of individuals at different times during the course of a study
2. Cross-sectional survey	
3. Trend study	b. An advantage of this type of survey is that it gives the respondents time to think about their answers
4. Cohort study	
5. Panel study	c. Used whenever a researcher has access to all (or most) of the members of a particular group in one place
6. Census	
7. Mail survey	d. Researcher collects information at different points in time in order to study changes over time
8. Personal interview	
	e. Probably the most effective way there is to enlist the cooperation of the respondents in a survey
	f. Researcher obtains different samples of a particular population whose members do not change over the course of the study
	g. Researcher samples a population whose members may change over time
	h. Major purpose is to describe the characteristics of an invited sample
	i. An entire population is surveyed

Activity 17.3:
Open vs. Closed-Ended Questions

In the space below each of the following open-ended questions, see if you can change them to closed-ended questions.

1. What was your favorite subject when you were in elementary school?

2. What makes a good teacher?

3. What factor contributed the most to the election of George W. Bush in 2000?

4. Why is it that many poor people in the United States today cannot improve their status?

Activity 17.4:
Conduct a Survey

How do the grades that students expect to get correspond to the quality of their work in class? In this exercise, you are asked to conduct a survey to find out how other students feel about this question. Contact a sample of at least 25 students in two different courses (a total of 50) and ask them to rate the quality of their work in one of their courses and tell you the grade they expect to get in that course. Use an expanded copy of the form below.

RATING SCALE

A = Distinguished
B = Superior
C = Average
D = Below Average
F - Failure

COURSE #1

FIRST NAME OF STUDENT	RATING OF WORK IN CLASS	EXPECTED GRADE

COURSE #2

FIRST NAME OF STUDENT	RATING OF WORK IN CLASS	EXPECTED GRADE

Use the table below to record the number and percent of the total for each grade. How do the ratings compare? What conclusions can you draw?

COURSE #1

PERFORMANCE	RATING OF WORK IN CLASS	EXPECTED GRADE
A		
B		
C		
D		
F		

COURSE #2

PERFORMANCE	RATING OF WORK IN CLASS	EXPECTED GRADE
A		
B		
C		
D		
F		

The Nature of
Qualitative Research

CHAPTER 18

Activity 18.1:
Qualitative Research Questions

Which of the following questions would lend themselves well to qualitative research?

1. Do students learn more in a language laboratory than they do in a teacher-directed classroom?

2. What sorts of conditioning drills do physical education teachers use?

3. How do elementary school teachers teach children to read?

4. Is client-centered therapy more effective than traditional therapy with teenagers?

5. What kinds of things do history teachers do as they go about their daily routine?

6. How many district administrators took a sabbatical leave this past year?

7. Is the fingerprinting of student teachers legal?

8. How did teachers teach science during the 1920s?

9. What methods do the volunteer tutors use in the after-school tutoring program?

Activity 18.2:
Qualitative vs. Quantitative Research

In the space provided after each of the characteristics listed below, write "Qualitative" if the characteristic refers primarily to one or more qualitative research methodologies. Write "Quantitative" if the characteristic refers primarily to one or more quantitative research methodologies.

1. A preference for hypotheses that emerge as the study progresses _____

2. A preference for precise definitions stated at the outset of the study _____

3. A preference for statistical summary of results _____

4. Data are analyzed inductively _____

5. A preference for random techniques for obtaining meaningful samples _____

6. A lot of attention devoted to assessing and improving the reliability of scores obtained from instruments _____

7. A willingness to manipulate conditions when studying complex phenomena _____

8. The researcher is the key instrument _____

9. Primary reliance is on the researcher to deal with procedural bias _____

10. The natural setting is the direct source of data _____

11. Data are collected primarily in the form of numbers _____

Activity 18.3:
Approaches to Qualitative Research

Match the approach to qualitative research listed in Column B with its description in Column A.

COLUMN A: DESCRIPTION	COLUMN B: APPROACH TO QUALITATIVE RESEARCH
1. _____ Researchers assume that there is some commonality to the perceptions human beings have in how they interpret an experience	a. Biography
2. _____ Description of the cultural behavior of a group or individual	b. Phenomenology
3. _____ Researchers start with an area of study and then allow what is relevant to that area to emerge	c. Grounded theory
4. _____ Interest is in the experiences of a single individual	d. Case study
5. _____ Researcher is interested in studying a particular case only as a means to some larger goal he or she has in mind	e. Ethnography
6. _____ Researcher studies an individual's reactions to a particular experience or set of experiences	
7. _____ Researchers doing this type of study use what is known as the *constant comparative* method	
8. _____ Often involves a study of just one classroom or program	

Observation and Interviewing

Activity 19.1:
Observer Roles

Match the role listed in Column B with its description in Column A.

COLUMN A	COLUMN B
1. _____ Researcher observes the activities of a group without in any way becoming a participant in those activities	a. Complete participant
	b. Participant as observer
2. _____ Individual identifies himself or herself as a researcher, but does not pretend to be a member of the group being observed	c. Observer as participant
	d. Complete observer
3. _____ This role is sometimes suspect on ethical grounds	
4. _____ Researcher participates fully in the activities of the group being observed	
5. _____ Researcher is least likely to affect the actions of the group in this role	
6. _____ Researcher's identity is not known to any of the individuals he or she is observing	

Activity 19.2:
Types of Interviews

Match the type of interview listed in Column B with its description in Column A. (Note: Some descriptions may apply to more than one type of interview.)

COLUMN A: DESCRIPTION	COLUMN B: TYPE OF INTERVIEW
1. _____ Tends to resemble a casual conversation	a. Structured
2. _____ Requires the least training of the interviewer	b. Semi-structured
3. _____ Probably the most difficult of all to conduct	c. Informal
4. _____Can be any one of the other three types	d. Retrospective
5. _____ Offers the most natural type of situation for the collection of data	
6. _____ Most often used for obtaining information to test a specific hypothesis a researcher wished to investigate	
7. _____ Least likely of the four to provide reliable data for the researcher	

Activity 19.3:
Types of Interview Questions

Match the type of interview question listed in Column B with the appropriate example in Column A.

COLUMN A: EXAMPLES	COLUMN B: TYPE OF INTERVIEW QUESTION
1. _____ What sorts of things do you do in drama class?	a. Demographic
	b. Knowledge
2. _____ What is the highest degree you received?	c. Behavior
3. _____ To what extent are you excited about playing in next week's game?	d. Values/opinions
4. _____ What kinds of questions do you think are the most helpful for a teacher to ask during a class discussion?	e. Feelings
	f. Sensory
5. _____ What do you think about the new detention policy?	
6. _____ How old was General Johnson when he died?	
7. _____ How many credits does one need to get a degree?	

Activity 19.4:
Do Some Observational Research

Go to a nearby parking lot where there are a lot of cars going in and out fairly frequently (a shopping mall lot or garage would be ideal). Observe drivers when they back out of their parking spaces. The research question for you to investigate is whether people do or do not take longer to back out of a space when someone is waiting for that space.

You are to obtain data on the time a person takes to back out when another car is waiting and when there is no car waiting. You also will obtain data on the gender of the driver and the number of passengers in the waiting car.

A simple observation sheet for you to use is given below. Use a new line for each driver you observe. You should feel free to modify this sheet if you can think of ways to improve it. Observe as many drivers as you can in a 30-minute period.

NUMBER	START TIME*	END TIME**	WAITING***	GENDER	TYPE OF CAR
			Y/N	M/F	
			Y/N	M/F	
			Y/N	M/F	
			Y/N	M/F	
			Y/N	M/F	
			Y/N	M/F	

*Start timing when the driver opens the driver's side door.

**Stop timing when the front bumper clears the parking space.

***A car is waiting if someone is waiting for the spot and the driver notices (turns toward) the waiting car before opening his or her car door.

After you have collected all of your data, record your results using an expanded copy of the form above.

Average time to back out when car is waiting _____

    When driver is female _____

    When driver is male _____

Average time to back out when car is not waiting _____

    When driver is female _____

    When driver is male _____

What do you conclude with regard to the research question?

_____

_____

_____

_____

Content Analysis

CHAPTER 20

Activity 20.1:
Content Analysis Research Questions

Which of the following questions would lend themselves well to content analysis?

1. Do students like school more if taught by a teacher of the same ethnicity?

2. What sorts of techniques do tennis coaches use to increase the motivation of 12-year-olds to play tennis?

3. Is violence on television different from violence in classical drama?

4. Do boys or girls score higher on SAT examinations?

5. Are women or men portrayed more favorably in 1930 movies?

6. Are after-school detection programs effective?

7. How do the ingredients found in recipes in 1940s cookbooks compare with those found in 1990s cookbooks?

8. To what extent did capitalism develop in nineteenth-century China?

Activity 20.2: Do a Content Analysis

A professor at a large midwestern university is trying to decide what to do in a class entitled "Values of American Society," which she has recently been asked to teach. One of her colleagues suggests that one way to approach the subject is to ask her students to do a content analysis of advertisements taken from various national magazines and newspapers.

Following is a sample of three advertisements that she collects. Read these over carefully. Then ask yourself what societal values are reflected in these advertisements. Decide on a few categories and tally how often each value is represented in this sample of ads. What conclusions can you suggest on the basis of your content analysis of this brief sample?

HAVE YOU SEEN THE NEW ROVER?

What a beauty! Undreamed of power (until now) is provided by the newly designed V-8 engine with extra oomph! Several new safety features enhance your security. And sound! Wow! You have to listen to a symphony on the CD player. A real-life concert never sounded this good. Visit your dealer today for a demonstration!!

HAD YOUR PICTURE TAKEN LATELY?

Our cameras are the best in the business — unmatched for fidelity, ease of use, and reliability. If you want to take exceptional pictures with ease, get one today. You won't be sorry! (P.S. Tell them Jake sent you.)

**WE'VE GOT IT!
NO MATTER WHAT YOU ARE LOOKING FOR ON THE INTERNET, WE'VE GOT IT. CHECK OUR WEBSITE AT WWW.INERNET.COM**

Activity 20.3:
Advantages vs. Disadvantages of Content Analysis

In the space provided in front of each of the statements listed below, write "T" if the statement is true. Write "F" if the statement is false.

1. _____ Content analysis deals mainly with recorded information.

2. _____ Content analysis is unobtrusive.

3. _____ Content analysis is strongly influenced by the researcher's presence.

4. _____ Content analysis cannot be done with songs.

5. _____ Content analysis is extremely difficult to do.

6. _____ Content analysis is relatively economical compared to other research methodologies.

7. _____ Content analysis data are primarily in the form of numbers.

8. _____ The information needed to do a content analysis usually is readily available.

9. _____ It is fairly easy to establish validity in content analysis.

10. _____ Content analysis requires extensive training before one can undertake it.

Activity 20.4:
Content Analysis Categories

What categories could be used by a researcher who wishes to do a content analysis of the following?

1. *Coverage of minority groups in social studies textbooks.*

   Possible categories might include:

   _____

   _____

2. *How characters are portrayed in Saturday morning television cartoon programs.*

   Possible categories might include:

   _____

   _____

3. *Issues discussed in newspaper editorials.*

   Possible categories might include:

   _____

   _____

4. *Themes used in magazine advertisements.*

   Possible categories might include:

   _____

   _____

5. *Emotions presented in popular songs.*

   Possible categories might include:

   _____

   _____

Ethnographic Research

CHAPTER 21

Activity 21.1:
Ethnographic Research Questions

Which of the following questions would lend themselves well to ethnographic research?

1. Which do students like better, filmstrips or movies about the same topic?

2. What is the social structure of children attending nursery school?

3. How do beginning counselors interact with teachers?

4. Is client-centered therapy more effective than traditional therapy with teenagers?

5. How do middle school teachers plan their daily routine?

6. What is the status of social studies supervision in our state?

7. How are women portrayed in popular television shows?

8. In what ways do the questions parents and teachers ask of children differ?

Activity 21.2:
True or False?

Write "T" in the space provided in front of each of the statements listed below that are true. Write "F" in front of each statement that is false.

1. _____ There is no experimental "treatment" in ethnographic research.

2. _____ Participant observation is not used in ethnographic research.

3. _____ Ethnographic researchers usually begin their research with precise hypotheses.

4. _____ A particular strength of ethnographic research is that it can reveal nuances and subtleties that other methodologies may miss.

5. _____ Ethnographic research is particularly suitable for topics that defy simple quantification.

6. _____ Most ethnographic studies are done in laboratory settings.

7. _____ The samples studied by ethnographers are usually quite small.

8. _____ A major advantage of ethnographic research is that it provides the researcher with a much more comprehensive perspective than do other forms of educational research.

9. _____ Ethnographic research is highly dependent on the particular researcher's observations.

10. _____ A major check on the accuracy of an ethnographer's observations lies in the quality of his or her field notes.

11. _____ Ethnographic data are usually collected in the form of numbers.

Activity 21.3:
Do Some Ethnographic Research

Observe a class session or other group meeting of one kind or another. Take careful field notes in which you try to record *everything* important that occurs. Immediately afterwards, write up a field diary of your observations. Describe your conclusions below. What problems, if any, did you encounter?

Conclusions:

_____

_____

_____

_____

_____

_____

_____

_____

_____

_____

_____

Problems:

_____

_____

_____

_____

_____

_____

_____

_____

_____

_____

_____

Historical Research

Activity 22.1:
Historical Research Questions

Which of the following questions would lend themselves well to historical research?

1. What was life like for a woman teacher in the 1920s?

2. What sorts of techniques do speech teachers use to improve an individual's ability to give an extemporaneous speech?

3. How do art teachers teach drawing to primary school children?

4. Is client-centered therapy more effective with teenagers than traditional therapy?

5. What were the beginnings of the modern social studies?

6. Is the deception of research subjects ever seen as appropriate by students?

7. How were women portrayed in 1930s fiction?

8. When should children be enrolled in swimming classes?

9. How did the age of children leaving home change between the years 1920 and 1980?

Activity 22.2:
Primary or Secondary Source?

In the space provided after each of the items listed below, write "P" if the item is a primary historical source or "S" if it is a secondary source.

1. An essay written by an eighth-grader in 1935 _____

2. A 1945 photograph of a high school cheerleading squad _____

3. A magazine article describing a school board meeting in 1920 _____

4. A World War II veteran's description of an air raid _____

5. A history textbook _____

6. A description of a scientific experiment carried out by one of the authors of this textbook _____

7. A complete set of the *Encyclopaedia Britannica* for years 1949-1953 _____

8. Music charts composed for use by the Benny Goodman sextet in the 1930s _____

9. A newspaper editorial commenting on the death of John F. Kennedy _____

Activity 22.3:
What Kind of Historical Source?

Match the historical source listed in Column B with the appropriate example in Column A.

COLUMN A: EXAMPLES

COLUMN B: KIND OF HISTORICAL SOURCE

1. _____ A 1994 high school yearbook

2. _____ A table found in an eighteenth-century colonial home

3. _____ A baseball cap worn by Babe Ruth in the 1930s

4. _____ A copy of the Ph.D. dissertation of one of the authors of this text

5. _____ A letter written by the wife of Henry Kissinger

6. _____ A cartoon from a copy of a 1940s issue of *Time* magazine

7. _____ The diary of a nineteenth-century schoolmarm in rural Kentucky

8. _____ A copy of the year 2000 census report

9. _____ A school budget from a large urban high school district for the year 1984

10. _____ A recorded interview with folksinger Joan Baez

a. document

b. numerical record

c. oral statement

d. relic

Activity 22.4:
True or False?

Write "T" in the space provided in front of each of the statements listed below that are true. Write "F" in front of each statement that is false.

1. _____ A major advantage of historical research is that it permits the study of certain kinds of topics and questions that can be studied in no other way.

2. _____ *Internal criticism* in historical research refers to the genuineness of the documents that the researcher uses.

3. _____ A *primary source* is a document prepared by an individual who was not a direct witness to an event.

4. _____ A disadvantage of historical research is that the measures used to control for internal validity in other kinds of research are not available in a historical study.

5. _____ It would be difficult to draw a representative sample of data when doing a historical study.

6. _____ Many historical studies are done in libraries.

7. _____ It would be unusual to find a hypothesis in a historical study.

8. _____ There is no manipulation of variables in historical research.

9. _____ "How were young women educated in nineteenth-century convent schools?" would be an example of a question investigated through historical research.

10. _____ "Where was that document written?" is one example of a question that involved *external criticism.*

11. _____ The reading and summarization of historical data are rarely a neat, orderly sequence of steps to be followed.

Action Research

Activity 23.1:
Action Research Questions

Which of the following questions might lend themselves well to action research?

1. Do students learn more from older or younger children?

2. Is the content found in the literature anthologies in our district biased, and if so, how?

3. Would filmstrips help our elementary teachers teach multiplication to third-graders?

4. Is phonics more effective than look-say as a method of teaching reading?

5. What kinds of things do music teachers do as they go about their daily routine?

6. How might we improve the quality of our school's social studies program?

7. Is the use of detention successful with our elementary school students?

8. What are the effects of giving the students with serious behavior problems at Adams Elementary School choices about how to behave in class?

9. What has been the effect of federal legislation on school reform at the district level?

Activity 23.2:
True or False?

In the space provided in front of each statement below, write "T" if the statement is true. Write "F" if the statement is false.

1. _____ Action research is research conducted so that a decision can be reached about an issue of concern at the local school level.

2. _____ Administrators would rarely participate in action research.

3. _____ Those involved in action research generally want to solve some day-to-day immediate problem.

4. _____ One advantage of practical action research is that it is not limited in generalizability.

5. _____ Action research requires mastery of at least one of the major types of educational research.

6. _____ An assumption underlying action research is that those who work in schools want to engage, at least to some degree, in some form of systematic research.

7. _____ An important aspect of participatory action research is that the question or problem being investigated is one that is of interest to all the parties involved.

8. _____ It is not unusual in action research to find the use of more than one instrument.

9. _____ The researcher is the key instrument in participatory action research studies.

10. _____ A key characteristic of participatory action research is that the data collection methods are chosen by the stakeholders.

11. _____ Action research can be done by teachers.

12. _____ Unfortunately, action research cannot help teachers to identify problems and issues systematically.

Writing Research Proposals and Reports

CHAPTER 24

ACTIVITY 24.1 Put Them in Order

Activity 24.1:
Put Them in Order

Listed below are many of the major sections of a research report, but they are out of the order we recommend. Rearrange them into the proper order.

1. Description of the sample

2. Suggestions for further research

3. Purpose of the study

4. Table of contents

5. Definition of terms

6. Description of findings

7. Justification of the study

8. Description of the methods of data analysis used

9. Description of the research design

10. Research question

11. Review of related literature

12. Description of the instruments used

13. Discussion of internal validity

14. Detailed explanation of the procedures followed

15. Discussion of findings and conclusions

Authors' Suggested Answers

Chapter 1: The Nature of Educational Research

ACTIVITY 1.1: EMPIRICAL VS. NONEMPIRICAL RESEARCH

Topics 1, 4, and 6 are examples of empirical research. They clearly indicate information to be obtained directly from subjects. The other three represent examples of nonempirical research. Topic 2 deals with a review of previous research that does not involve the collection of data. Topic 3 implies that previously collected data are to be reexamined in a new way. Topic 5 is a logical analysis of written material, but does not involve any raw data.

ACTIVITY 1.2: BASIC VS. APPLIED RESEARCH

Topics 3, 5, and 6 are examples of basic research, as they are intended to have wide applicability. Topic 3 also has clear theoretical implications, whereas 5 and 6 have implied theoretical implications. Topics 1, 2, and 4 are examples of applied research. All focus on specific local groups.

ACTIVITY 1.3: TYPES OF RESEARCH

1. g
2. d
3. c
4. b
5. f
6. a
7. h

ACTIVITY 1.4: ASSUMPTIONS

Many answers are possible. Here are ours.

1. One assumption here is that punishment is necessary to ensure "good" behavior on the part of children.
2. An assumption here is that the two teams are little different this year from last year.
3. An assumption is that a small amount of effort now will save one having to do a large amount later.
4. A possible assumption is that siblings are very similar in the ways they behave.
5. An assumption here is that taking algebra with Mrs. West is going to be unpleasant.

ACTIVITY 1.5: GENERAL RESEARCH TYPES: AUTHORS' SUGGESTED ANSWERS

a. Associational
b. Descriptive
c. Intervention
d. Intervention
e. Descriptive
f. Descriptive
g. Intervention
h. Associational

Chapter 2: The Research Problem

ACTIVITY 2.1: RESEARCH QUESTIONS AND RELATED DESIGNS

1. survey
2. correlational
3. survey
4. experimental
5. case study
6. historical
7. content analysis
8. causal-comparative

ACTIVITY 2.2: CHANGING GENERAL TOPICS INTO RESEARCH QUESTIONS

A variety of possibilities exist. Here are a few.

1. Is class size related to student achievement?
2. What are the main characteristics of multicultural education at Thurgood Marshall Middle School?
3. What factors are related to text anxiety among students?
4. What difficulties do women college professors have in gaining tenure?
5. How does the amount of alcohol consumption on New Year's Eve compare with that consumed on Super Bowl Sunday?
6. What are the main problems single parents face in getting affordable child care?
7. Which style of counseling — client-centered or behavioral therapy — is more effective?
8. What are the effects of the positive stereotypes that exist regarding Asian-American students?
9. What were the chief characteristics of the charter school movement in the twentieth century?
10. What is the relationship between diet and exercise?

ACTIVITY 2.3: OPERATIONAL DEFINITIONS

2, 3, 4, 5, 6, 8, and 9 are operational definitions.

ACTIVITY 2.4: JUSTIFICATION

1 is the stronger justification, not because it is longer but because it gives a number of reasons as to why the author thinks the study is important.

Chapter 3: Variables and Hypotheses

ACTIVITY 3.1: DIRECTIONAL VS. NON-DIRECTIONAL HYPOTHESES

1. D
2. ND
3. D
4. D
5. ND

ACTIVITY 3.2: TESTING HYPOTHESES

1. Quality of professor is related to amount (or degree) of interest in students.
2. Parental admonition is related to likelihood of kids using drugs.
3. Gender is related to level of management position to which appointed.

There are many possible restatements. Here are a few.

1. Professors who receive high ratings from students (a 4 or 5 on a 1-5 rating scale where 5 is high and 1 is low) spend more than two hours per week in their offices and never miss holding office hours.
2. Parents who say to their kids, "You may not use drugs" are more likely to have kids who smoke marijuana than parents who say to their kids "I trust you to make your own decisions about the wisdom of using drugs."
3. There are no women CEOs in any of the 500 companies listed this year in *Fortune* magazine.

ACTIVITY 3.3: CATEGORICAL VS. QUANTITATIVE VARIABLES

1. CV
2. QV
3. CV
4. CV
5. QV
6. CV
7. QV
8. QV

ACTIVITY 3.4: INDEPENDENT AND DEPENDENT VARIABLES

1. Independent variable = seeing vs. not seeing the film
   Dependent variable = attitudes toward sharing candy
   Constant: grade level

2. Independent variable = teaching materials
   Dependent variable = knowledge about events of the Civil War
   Constant: grade level; subject matter

3. Independent variable = presence of computers vs. no computers
   Dependent variable = student achievement
   Constant: grade level

Chapter 4: Ethics and Research

ACTIVITY 4.1: ETHICAL OR NOT?

1. Yes; it is unethical to require students to participate in a study without their consent.
2. The dilemma here is between the rights of the patients and the responsibilities of the U.S. Food and Drug Administration. The U.S. FDA must ensure that the drugs have been adequately tested before the general public is permitted to use them. Against this must be balanced the rights of terminally ill patients to any kind of treatment that might offer them a

chance for a longer life. The question at issue is whether the cost to the patients in this case (i.e., death) possibly outweighs the possible knowledge gain about an effective treatment for AIDS. The decision is not a simple one, however. A drug that has not been thoroughly tested may be discovered to have serious, unanticipated side effects that actually worsen a patient's condition instead of improving it. Furthermore, society may lose in that properly controlled tests of a new drug are necessary if we are to build up a base of knowledge about AIDS in order to eventually find ways to control or cure this disease.

3. This study violated practically every ethical standard there is — from informed consent to deception to imposing physical harm on the participants.

ACTIVITY 4.2: SOME ETHICAL DILEMMAS

1. The question at issue here is whether deception is ever justified. Most researchers would agree that if deception involves some risk to others, it is unethical. Some feel if there is no risk to the participants in a study, as is indicated here, deceiving subjects is not unethical. Some researchers point out that it is impossible to study some things, such as behavior of patients in hospitals, without deceiving them. Others argue that casual observation is not unethical, but that it is unethical to violate a person's privacy deliberately (e.g., through the use of binoculars). And some say that deception is never justified.

2. There is no question here that research is needed on both genders. The number of reported heart attacks of women has been increasing considerably in recent years, and data are needed as to the ways in which these attacks are similar to and different from heart attacks suffered by males.

3. Opinions differ here, but in my opinion, all of this information should be given to potential subjects in clinical trials.

ACTIVITY 4.3: SOME VIOLATIONS OF ETHICAL PRACTICE

1. f
2. g
3. e
4. a
5. c

ACTIVITY 4.4: WHY WOULD THESE RESEARCH PRACTICES BE UNETHICAL? AUTHORS' SUGGESTED ANSWERS

1. "We are required to ask you to sign this consent form. You needn't read it; it's just routine." *Participants are being asked, in effect, to give their consent without being informed of what the study is about (and accordingly of any risks they might incur).*

2. "A few cases seemed quite different from the rest, so we deleted them." *The results of the study may be quite different if these cases are included. Hence without their inclusion, any results that are reported may be misleading.*

3. "Yes, as a student at this university you are required to participate in this study." *No one (especially students) is ever required to participate in a study.*

4. "There is no need to tell any of the parents that we are modifying the school lunch diet for this study." *This statement assumes that the parents of the students who will be involved in the study will have no objection. They might.*

5. "Requiring students to participate in class discussions might be harmful to some, but it is necessary for our research." *No participant in a study should be exposed to any sort of harm, physical or psychological, unless they are aware of such harm and are willing to undergo the risk involved.*

ACTIVITY 4.5: DRUG TESTING: AUTHORS' SUGGESTED ANSWERS

The Center for Bioethics at the University of Minnesota advocates using inmates only when the research could benefit prisoners as individuals or as a group. Prisoner advocacy groups point out that not all prisoners involved in research have been unwitting or unwilling participants. Jackie Walker of the American Civil Liberties Union states "Our position is that prisoners should not be excluded from trials that are efficacious, that are going to improve their health and that they would normally have access to if they were members of the community, but we also don't want prisoners to be used as guinea pigs for trials that companies wouldn't complete in the community." (Taken from a detailed account by S. J. A. Talvi. *In These Times*, January 7, 2002.)

Chapter 5: Reviewing the Literature

ACTIVITY 5.2: WHERE WOULD YOU LOOK?

1. *Review of Educational Research*
2. *Encyclopedia of Educational Research*
3. The current issue of *Books in Print* (to locate some books that might discuss research on the topic)
4. Either *Psychological Abstracts* or *PsycINFO*
5. *Dissertation Abstracts*
6. A professional journal in the field of social studies (e.g., *Theory and Research in Social Education*)
7. A textbook in educational sociology
8. *Readers' Guide to Periodical Literature*

Chapter 6: Sampling

6.1: IDENTIFYING TYPES OF SAMPLING

1. b
2. c
3. g
4. a
5. d
6. e
7. f
8. f
9. g
10. e

ACTIVITY 6.2: DRAWING A RANDOM SAMPLE

The results of this exercise will depend on which line in the Table of Random Numbers you decide to use. You should find, however, that as your sample size increases, the characteristics of your sample will approach (and in some cases match) the characteristics of the population. I include an example for sample of 10 below, using the first line from the random numbers table.

STUDENT NUMBER	GENDER	SCHOOL	IQ
83	F	Cortez	104
57	M	Beals	101
95	F	Cortez	95
29	M	Adams	96
78	F	Cortez	111
49	M	Beals	111
37	F	Beals	128
20	F	Adams	104
15	M	Adams	109
77	M	Cortez	111

AVERAGES

N = 10	M	F	A	B	C	IQ
Average	.5	.5	.3	.3	.4	98
Population	.49	.51	.33	.31	.36	109.8

Notice that my sample is actually quite similar to the population in most respects, except that it has a markedly lower IQ average. Were I to enlarge the size of my sample, the chances are that the IQ average would increase. Can you see why?

ACTIVITY 6.3: WHEN IS IT APPROPRIATE TO GENERALIZE?

1. No, it would not. Because only *unsuccessful* hijackers are included in the sample.
2a. All career women between the ages of 30 and 50
2b. Those women in the local area who could be contacted and who would be willing to be interviewed
2c. This might be difficult. You could try to obtain a list of the women in this age range employed in local firms and randomly select from the list. This would reduce the generalizability of your findings, of course.
2d. For starters, age, socioeconomic level, where employed, job description (or at least titles).

ACTIVITY 6.4: TRUE OR FALSE? AUTHORS' SUGGESTED ANSWERS

1. T
2. F
3. T
4. T
5. T
6. F
7. T
8. T
9. F
10. F

Chapter 7: Instrumentation

ACTIVITY 7.1: MAJOR CATEGORIES OF INSTRUMENTS AND THEIR USES

1. g
2. a
3. d
4. f
5. b
6. e

ACTIVITY 7.2: WHICH TYPE OF INSTRUMENT IS MOST APPROPRIATE?

1. Q
2. AT
3. I
4. PC
5. RS
6. RS
7. I
8. AT
9. TS
10. TS
11. RS
12. I
13. Q
14. PC
15. TS

ACTIVITY 7.3: TYPES OF SCALES

1. d
2. d
3. b
4. a
5. d
6. a
7. c
8. a
9. c

ACTIVITY 7.4: NORM-REFERENCED VS. CRITERION-REFERENCED INSTRUMENTS

1. C
2. C
3. N
4. C
5. N
6. C
7. N
8. C
9. N

ACTIVITY 7.6: DEVELOPING A RATING SCALE: AUTHORS' SUGGESTED ANSWERS

Only a few of the indicators that were originally developed were converted directly into the rating scale. All of the items except #2 and #11 relate directly to one or more indicators. For example, Item #1 encompasses two indicators: "Are students free to move outside without an adult present?" and "Can students leave the classroom on their own, or must they request permission?" Note that in most cases the wording of the indicator has been changed in the transition.

Items #2 and #11 do not relate to specific indicators, but rather emerged during the conversion process. A decision by this student to focus on items that can be directly observed did cause her to eliminate many indicators, particularly those under the headings of curriculum and parental participation.

Rating scales can be substantially improved by giving explicit descriptions of each point on the scale, as in the following example for Item #1:

1. Students are observed to move around without teacher permission

1	2	3	4	5
(Never)	(Less than 11)	(11-30 instance)	(31-50 instances)	(More than 50 instances)

Chapter 8: Validity and Reliability

ACTIVITY 8.1: INSTRUMENT VALIDITY

Many answers are can be given here. Here are some possibilities:

1. To measure the degree to which a person enjoys modern art, you might:
   - use a rating scale to have a person rate (on a scale of 1-low, to 5-high) various types of paintings (modern and other)
   - interview a person in depth about his or her feelings about modern art

2. To measure the level of anxiety that exists among university students during final exams, you might:
   - use an existing anxiety scale to have a person rate (on a scale of 1-low to 5-high) how anxious they are just before a final exam
   - interview students in depth about their feelings of anxiety just before a final exam
   - observe students while they are taking exams

3. To measure the attitudes of local residents toward the building of a new ballpark in downtown San Francisco, you might:
   - mail out a questionnaire to a randomly selected sample of residents in which you ask them to respond to questions about the building of the ballpark
   - interview a random sample of residents' questions concerning their feelings about the building of the ballpark

ACTIVITY 8.2: INSTRUMENT RELIABILITY (1)

These data indicate that the test is reliable. With few exceptions, students performed similarly on both administrations of the test. Later (in Chapter 10), we will discuss a better way to analyze such data.

ACTIVITY 8.3: INSTRUMENT RELIABILITY (2)

1. c
2. d
3. a
4. d
5. b
6. c

ACTIVITY 8.4: WHAT KIND OF EVIDENCE? AUTHORS' SUGGESTED ANSWERS

1. Criterion-related
2. Content-related
3. Content-related
4. Construct-related
5. Criterion-related
6. Content-related

ACTIVITY 8.5: WHAT CONSTITUTES CONSTRUCT-RELATED EVIDENCE OF VALIDITY? AUTHORS' SUGGESTED ANSWERS

1. Many possibilities will suggest themselves. Here are a few of ours. In an attempt to establish construct validity for the paper and pencil test of honesty he or she is developing, the researcher might compare scores on his or her test with:

   - *ratings* by employers testifying to an individual's behavior in the workplace.
   - *whether,* when given an opportunity to lie or steal something of value, an individual is observed refusing to do so.
   - *statements* by teachers or friends as to the degree of honesty an individual displays.
   - *scores* of a group of convicted felons on the test.

2. In trying to establish construct validity for a test designed to measure interest in chemistry, the researcher might compare scores of an individual on his or her test with:

   - *number of books* on chemistry voluntarily checked out from the library.
   - *number of questions* asked in class about chemistry.
   - *frequency of voluntary attendance* of lectures on the subject of chemistry.
   - *number of volunteer chemistry projects* completed over a year's time.
   - *ratings* of individual's interest in chemistry as made by friends, teachers and/or others.

Chapter 9: Internal Validity

ACTIVITY 9.1: THREATS TO INTERNAL VALIDITY

1. *Mortality.* If the students who dropped out had a greater decrease in achievement motivation than those who remained, their loss will affect the male group more than the female group. The remaining male group will appear to have less of a decline in motivation than is really the case for the whole group.
2. *Data collector characteristics.* Responses, either positive or negative, regarding a military career may be influenced by the way the officers are dressed.
3. *Regression.* Since all of the students who took the second test were excellent students to begin with, their lower average score on the test two weeks later may be due to the fact that their scores regressed downward toward the mean.
4. *Instrumentation.* The fact that the researcher changes the instrument turns it into a new instrument, which could account for any differences.
5. *Maturation.* The students are eight months older.
6. *Location.* Responses may be affected by the interviews being conducted in such markedly different locations.

ACTIVITY 9.2: WHAT TYPE OF THREAT?

1. h
2. g
3. a
4. b
5. c
6. d

ACTIVITY 9.3: CONTROLLING THREATS TO INTERNAL VALIDITY

1. *Instrument decay.* Either standardize the instrumentation process, or schedule data collection times so that the data collector does not get fatigued.
2. *Subject characteristics.* Either use random assignment or (if possible) match subjects.
3. *Loss of subjects (mortality).* This is the most difficult of all threats to control. The best way, of course, is to do one's best to ensure subjects do not drop out of the study. If possible, one may be able to argue that those who dropped out were not significantly different from those who remained.
4. *Data collector characteristics.* Use the same data collectors throughout the study.
5. *Location.* Keep the location constant.
6. *Regression.* Use an equivalent comparison group by means of random assignment or matching.
7. *Implementation.* In an intervention-type methods study, have each method taught by all the teachers in the study. Or, if possible, provide detailed training and observe the implementers to ensure they do not differ on some pertinent characteristic.
8. *Attitude of subjects.* Treat all groups as if they were "special."

Chapter 10: Descriptive Statistics

ACTIVITY 10.1: CONSTRUCT A FREQUENCY POLYGON

Your completed frequency polygon should look like the one shown here.

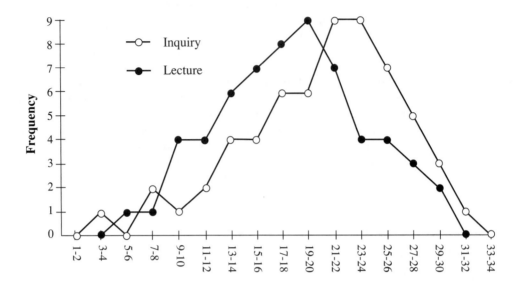

The lecture group performed, overall, at a lower level than the inquiry group. A greater number of students in the lecture group scored toward the low end of the distribution of scores. Fewer scored toward the high end. The difference can be illustrated further. For example, we find 25 cases above a score of 22 in the inquiry group compared with only 13 cases above that score in the lecture group. There are 23 cases below a score of 17 in the lecture group, compared with 14 cases in the inquiry group. The curve for the lecture group is more symmetrical, whereas the inquiry curve has a few cases at the low end of the scale. As you can see, frequency polygons are of considerable help in communicating all of the information contained in a group of scores.

ACTIVITY 10.2: COMPARING FREQUENCY POLYGONS

1. Experimental (Curriculum) group = **5** percent; Comparison group = **3** percent.
2. Experimental (Curriculum) Group = **3** percent; Comparison group = **2** percent.
3. We would say yes because the curriculum group had more cases of high scores (e.g., 32 percent vs. 14 percent above a score of 15), and fewer scores in the middle (e.g., 57 percent vs. 71 percent between scores of 8 and 14).

ACTIVITY 10.3: CALCULATING AVERAGES

1. The mean = 20.5
2. The median = 15.5
3. The mean for Set A = 51, and the median = 50

The mean for Set B = **51**, and the median = **50**.

We see that the means and the medians are identical. However, the scores in Set B are much more spread out. This is confirmed once we find the range, the difference between the highest and lowest scores in each set. For Set A, the range is **15** points. For Set B, the range is **94** points!

ACTIVITY 10.4: CALCULATING THE STANDARD DEVIATION

The standard deviation for this set is 14.08.

ACTIVITY 10.5: CALCULATING A CORRELATION COEFFICIENT

1. 135 (6) = 810
2. 24 (30) = 720
3. 810 − 720 = 90
4. 114 (6) = 684
5. 24^2 = 576
6. 684 − 576 = 108
7. 172 (6) = 1032
8. 30^2 = 900
9. 1032 − 900 = 132
10. 108 (1032) = 14,256
11. Square root of 14,256 = 119.4
12. 90/119.4 = .75 This is a substantial correlation, indicating that students with more pencils also have more pens. Surprise!

ACTIVITY 10.6: ANALYZING CROSSBREAK TABLES

1. Most of the counselors who used a Gestalt approach received their training at Happy Valley State, with College of the Specific a respectable second. Most of those who used a behavior modification approach received their training at Multiversity II, followed by Happy Valley State. Most of those who used a Rogerian approach were trained at College of the Specific.
2. Table 10.6 reveals that more than half of the teachers (17 out of 29, or almost 60 percent) rated paraprofessionals as "excellent." None rated them as "poor," and only five rated them as "fair." The paraprofessionals did not rate themselves as highly as did the teachers, with only 12 of 28 (43 percent) rating themselves as "excellent." With regard to participant cooperation, 12 of 30 teachers (40 percent) rated such cooperation as "excellent," or "good," while 18 of 28 paraprofessionals (64 percent) did so.

ACTIVITY 10.7: COMPARING Z-SCORES

1. James, as he scored two standard deviations above the mean in his group, while Felicia scored only one standard deviation above the mean in her group.
2. a. z = **-1**
   b. z = **0**
   c. z = **+0.5**
3. a. raw score = **55**
   b. raw score = **120**
   c. raw score = **80**

Chapter 11: Inferential Statistics

ACTIVITY 11.1: PROBABILITY

Since the probability of getting four heads on any given sample is only .06, this outcome for the first sample would lead me to tentatively accept the hypothesis that the coin is dishonest. Any other outcome would clearly not support the hypothesis.

The procedure you followed in this exercise is essentially that used in deriving probabilities in any statistical inference test. This is, the outcome from a particular sample is compared to a distribution of possible outcomes and its probability is determined.

Researchers generally take certain probabilities as indicative of a nonchance relationship. If the probability of obtaining a particular result (outcome, relationship) is less than .05 (one chance in 20), it is customary to take it as *statistically significant* or probably not due to chance). Clearly, if the probability is less than 5 percent (e.g., 1 percent), we are more confident that we are not simply dealing with chance. These values (1 percent and 5 percent) are frequently spoken of as *levels of significance*.

Consequently, when a research report states that a particular relationship was significant at the .05 level, it means that the chance of the finding being simply a fluke, due to the particular sample that was used, was less than 5 in 100. It means that the result (outcome, relationship) is worth noting and tentatively acceptable as a reproducible relationship for a specified population. Note, however, as we mentioned in the text (see page 000) that statistical significance is not the same thing as practical significance. A correlation of .23, for example, can under certain circumstances be statistically significant. However, it is usually too low to be of practical use.

ACTIVITY 11.2: LEARNING TO READ A *T*-TABLE

A sample with **10 d.f.** would require a *t*-value of **2.764** to be statistically significant at the **.01** level.

A sample with **25 d.f.** would require a *t*-value of **1.708** to be considered statistically significant at the **.05** level; to be statistically significant at the **.01** level would require a *t*-value of **2.485.**

ACTIVITY 11.3: CALCULATE A *T*-TEST

	INQUIRY GROUP	LECTURE GROUP
Mean	87	85
Standard deviation (SD)	2	3
Standard error of the mean (SEM)	0.4	0.6
Standard error of the difference (SED)	.72	

$\text{SEM}_{\text{inquiry}} = 2/5 = 0.4$ $\text{SEM}_{\text{lecture}} = 3/5 = 0.6$

SED = sq. root of $(0.4)^2 + (0.6)^2$ = sq. root of $(.16 + .36)$ = sq. root of $.52 = .72$

$$t = \frac{\text{Mean}_{\text{inquiry}} - \text{Mean}_{\text{lecture}}}{SED} = 87 - 85\ /\ .72 = 2\ /\ .72 = 2.78$$

Degrees of freedom (df) = $(n_1) + (n_2) = (26 + 26) - 2 = 50.$ Thus the result (the difference in means) of **2** points is statistically significant at the **.01** level (indicating it is a real difference, and not just a fluke due to chance). It is doubtful, however, that a difference of only **2** points would be considered practically significant.

ACTIVITY 11.4: PERFORM A CHI-SQUARE TEST

TABLE 11.4

UNIVERSITY	NUMBER OF STUDENTS ENROLLING IN PHYSICAL EDUCATION COURSES	NUMBER OF STUDENTS PARTICIPATING IN INTRAMURAL SPORTS	TOTALS
Alpha	70 (60)	30 (40)	100
Beta	130 (120)	70 (80)	200
Kappa	160 (180)	140 (120)	300
Totals	360	240	600

$(70 - 60)^2/60 = 10^2/60 = 100/60 = 1.67$
$(30 - 40)^2/40 = -10^2/40 = 100/40 = 2.50$
$(130 - 120)^2/120 = 10^2/120 = 100/120 = 0.83$
$(70 - 80)^2/80 = -10^2/80 = 100/80 = 1.25$
$(160 - 180)^2/180 = -20^2/180 = 400/180 = 2.22$
$(140 - 120)^2/120 = 20^2/120 = 400/120 = 3.33$
Chi-square = **11.80**

To determine the degrees of freedom (d.f.), multiply the number of rows minus one (r – 1) times the number of columns minus one (c – 1). In this case, it would be **(3 – 1) x (2 – 1) = 2**. The chi-square table indicates that, with two d.f., a value of **5.99** is required for a result to be statistically significant. Is the value you obtained (**11.80**) statistically significant? Yes _X_ No ____

ACTIVITY 11.5: CONDUCT A *T*-TEST

1. Were the results statistically significant? This will depend on whether or not the results reach or exceed the proportions listed for the various degrees of freedom.
2. What basic assumption must be met to justify using a *t*-test? That the population is normally distributed on the characteristic of interest.
3. Was it met? Yes _____ No _____ Explain why it was or was not.

_____

_____

Chapter 12: Statistics in Perspective

ACTIVITY 12.1: STATISTICAL VS. PRACTICAL SIGNIFICANCE

1. Anything that can occur by chance 20 times out of 100 (a 20% chance of occurring just by chance) is not statistically significant. Whether the result is practically significant cannot be determined by its statistical significance.
2. A 20 percent increase seems like a lot to us. We would imagine that this would be practically significant.

3. Even though the decrease is only 3 percent, most people in the medical profession would likely say this would be important — be practically significant.
4. Very doubtful. One percent would not be considered much of an increase.
5. This would not be. Being able to tie one's shoes three weeks earlier than other five-year-olds would make little difference to most (all?) parents.
6. No. A correlation of .18, although not occurring by chance, is too small to be considered important.

ACTIVITY 12.2: APPROPRIATE TECHNIQUES

1. c
2. e
3. f
4. d
5. i
6. h
7. b
8. g

ACTIVITY 12.3: INTERPRET THE DATA IN ACTIVITY 11.5:

1. This will depend on the size of the difference.
2. Whether the results are likely to have been attained by chance.
3. Delta.
4. Whether the difference in means is sizable in comparison to the variability within the groups. Generally, a **.5** value or greater for delta is taken to be meaningful.

Chapter 13: Experimental Research

ACTIVITY 13.1: GROUP EXPERIMENTAL RESEARCH QUESTIONS

2. Which is more effective in reducing the anxiety of clients—client-centered or traditional therapy?
3. Does personal counseling improve student achievement?
7. Do students like history more if taught by the case study or the inquiry method?

ACTIVITY 13.2: DESIGNING AN EXPERIMENT

1. Because they would have no idea whether or not it was the new drug that produced any results.

2.

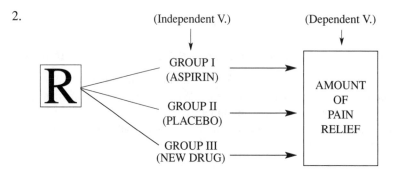

3. No. They might react differently than if they did not know which drug they were getting.

4. Possibly. Those administering the treatments might behave differently toward those receiving the drug if they know who they are, and this might influence symptoms.

ACTIVITY 13.3: CHARACTERISTICS OF EXPERIMENTAL RESEARCH

1. i
2. d
3. b
4. g
5. f
6. a
7. c
8. e

ACTIVITY 13.4: RANDOM SELECTION VS. RANDOM ASSIGNMENT

1. RA
2. B
3. RS
4. O

Note that numbers 3 and 4 are not experiments.

Chapter 14: Single-Subject Research

ACTIVITY 14.1: SINGLE-SUBJECT RESEARCH QUESTIONS

Both (5) and (8) because they lend themselves to in-depth study of a single individual, and both suggest observation as the method of data collection.

ACTIVITY 14.2: CHARACTERISTICS OF SINGLE-SUBJECT RESEARCH

1. b
2. d
3. c
4. h
5. g
6. a
7. f
8. i

ACTIVITY 14.3: ANALYZE SOME SINGLE-SUBJECT DATA

The treatment appears to have been effective with behaviors 1 and 2 because frequencies increased after the treatment was introduced. Effectiveness with behavior 3 is unclear because frequencies increased in observations 9 and 10 before the treatment was introduced, but then increased only slightly thereafter.

Chapter 15: Correlational Research

ACTIVITY 15.1: CORRELATIONAL RESEARCH QUESTIONS

1. Does early success in school lead to financial success in adulthood?
6. Is teacher praise related to student achievement?

ACTIVITY 15.2: WHAT KIND OF CORRELATION?

1. positive
2. negative
3. positive
4. not
5. positive
6. negative
7. negative
8. negative
9. not

ACTIVITY 15.3: THINK UP AN EXAMPLE

There are many possibilities. Here are a few.
1. strong positive: drug use and arrest record
2. strong negative: alcohol use and school grades
3. weak positive: liking for mystery novels and liking for adventure novels
4. weak negative: age of a car and its gas mileage
5. little or none: eating carrots and reading ability

ACTIVITY 15.4: MATCH THE CORRELATION COEFFICIENT TO ITS SCATTERPLOT

a. r = .90
b. r = .65
c. r = -.90
d. r = -.75
e. r = .35
f. r = .00
g. r = .-50
h. r = -.10

ACTIVITY 15.5: CALCULATE A CORRELATION COEFFICIENT

$$r = \frac{(5)(1328) - (81)(78)}{\sqrt{[(5)(1373) - (81^2)][(5)(1300) - (78^2)]}}$$

$$r = \frac{(6640) - (6318)}{\sqrt{[(6865) - (6561)][(6500) - (6084)]}}$$

$$r = \frac{322}{\sqrt{(304)(416)}} =$$

$$r = \frac{322}{\sqrt{355.6}} = \underline{.91}$$

This would indicate a very high relationship between reading and writing for these students.

ACTIVITY 15.6: CORRELATION IN EVERYDAY LIFE : AUTHORS' SUGGESTED ANSWERS

Many different relationships might be suggested. Here are ours:

1. "A fool and his money are soon parted" suggests a <u>negative</u> relationship between *foolishness* and *savings*.
2. As the twig is bent, so grows the tree" suggests a <u>positive</u> relationship between *early experiences* and *future behavior*.
3. "You can't grow grass on a busy street" suggests a <u>positive</u> relationship between *baldness* and *thoughtfulness*.
4. "Virtue is its own reward" suggests there is <u>no</u> relationship between *virtue* and *worldly rewards*.
5. "What fails to destroy me makes me stronger" suggests a <u>positive</u> relationship between *non-fatal adversity* and *psychological strength*.
6. "To get along, go along" suggests a <u>positive</u> relationship between *success* and *conformity*.
7. "You can't make an omelet without breaking some eggs" suggests a <u>positive</u> relationship between *progress* and *suffering*.
8. "You can't make a silk purse out of a sow's ear" suggests a <u>negative</u> relationship between *early limitations* and *future success*.
9. "All that glitters is not gold" suggests a <u>negative</u> relationship between *appearance* and *quality*.
10. "If at first you don't succeed, try, try again" suggests a <u>positive</u> relationship between *persistence* and *success*.

Chapter 16: Causal-Comparative Research

ACTIVITY 16.1: CAUSAL-COMPARATIVE RESEARCH QUESTIONS

3. How do elementary school teachers teach phonics?
4. Are two-year-old girls more aggressive than two-year-old boys?

ACTIVITY 16.2: ANALYZE SOME CAUSAL-COMPARATIVE DATA

The females do have a higher average score. The difference, however, is only three points (82.9 vs. 79.5). The importance of this can be assessed by calculating the effect size (see page 000 in the text). Causation is highly questionable due to the possible effect of such extraneous variables as age, background in mathematics, class attendance, and/or GPA. Generalizing beyond this one class is clearly inappropriate.

ACTIVITY 16.3: CAUSAL-COMPARATIVE VS. EXPERIMENTAL HYPOTHESES: AUTHORS' SUGGESTED ANSWERS

Hypothesis #1: This hypothesis could be studied using either methodology. The experimental method would require that teachers be trained in each method and students randomly assigned to each method. The causal-comparative method would require the researcher to locate classes already being taught by teachers using the different methods.

Hypothesis #2: This hypothesis could be studied only by identifying groups of male homosexuals and heterosexuals and obtaining information on the sexual history of each. The experimental method, clearly, is not possible. A third method, a longitudinal study in which the researcher followed a group of boys throughout their early years, would provide better information, but it would be extremely difficult to carry out.

Hypothesis #3: This hypothesis could be studied most appropriately by means of an experiment. Existing examples of the simulation-of-pregnancy technique, as required by the causal-comparative approach, are likely to be rare. Furthermore, the nature of the intervention is such that the more powerful experimental method could likely be used without great expense or inconvenience.

Chapter 17: Survey Research

ACTIVITY 17.1: SURVEY RESEARCH QUESTIONS

1. How do sophomore students feel about the new counseling program?
4. How much college tuition are parents able and willing to pay?
6. Do professors think it is ethical to require graduate students to participate in a professor's research project?

ACTIVITY 17.2: TYPES OF SURVEYS

1. d
2. h
3. g
4. f
5. a
6. i
7. b
8. e

ACTIVITY 17.3: OPEN VS. CLOSED-ENDED QUESTIONS

There are many possible closed-ended questions that you might suggest. Here are a few:

1. Which of the following was your favorite subject when you were in elementary school?
   a.   social studies
   b.   reading
   c.   physical education
   d.   English
   e.   other

2. Use the scale below to rate each of the qualities that follow
   a.   Very Important (Very Imp)
   b.   Important (Imp)
   c.   Somewhat important (Some Imp)
   d.   Slightly important (Slight Imp)
   e.   Not important (Not Imp)

A good teacher is fair	Very Imp	Imp	Some Imp	Slight Imp	Not Imp
A good teacher is friendly	Very Imp	Imp	Some Imp	Slight Imp	Not Imp
A good teacher is helpful	Very Imp	Imp	Some Imp	Slight Imp	Not Imp
A good teacher is organized	Very Imp	Imp	Some Imp	Slight Imp	Not Imp
A good teacher is smart	Very Imp	Imp	Some Imp	Slight Imp	Not Imp

3. Which of the following factors contributed most to the election of George W. Bush in 2000?
   a.   money
   b.   reputation as Governor of Texas
   c.   personality
   d.   election fraud
   e.   his educational background

4. Which of the following is the main reason that many poor people in the United States today cannot improve their status?
   a.   Many are sick.
   b.   Many are homeless.
   c.   Many have no skills.
   d.   Many are lazy.
   e.   none of the above

Chapter 18: The Nature of Qualitative Research

ACTIVITY 18.1: QUALITATIVE RESEARCH QUESTIONS

3. How do elementary school teachers teach children to read?
5. What kinds of things do history teachers do as they go about their daily routine?
9. What methods do the volunteer tutors use in the after-school tutoring program?

ACTIVITY 18.2: QUALITATIVE VS. QUANTITATIVE RESEARCH

1. Qualitative
2. Quantitative
3. Quantitative
4. Qualitative
5. Quantitative
6. Quantitative
7. Quantitative
8. Qualitative
9. Qualitative
10. Qualitative
11. Quantitative

ACTIVITY 18.3: APPROACHES TO QUALITATIVE RESEARCH

1. b
2. e
3. c
4. a
5. d
6. b
7. c
8. d

Chapter 19: Observations and Interviewing

ACTIVITY 19.1: OBSERVER ROLES

1. d
2. c
3. a
4. a
5. d
6. a

ACTIVITY 19.2: TYPES OF INTERVIEWS

1. c
2. a
3. c
4. d
5. c
6. a
7. d

ACTIVITY 19.3: TYPES OF INTERVIEW QUESTIONS

1. c
2. a
3. e
4. d
5. d
6. b
7. b

Chapter 20: Content Analysis

ACTIVITY 20.1: CONTENT ANALYSIS RESEARCH QUESTIONS

3. Is violence on television different from violence in classical drama?
5. Are women or men portrayed more favorably in 1930 movies?
7. How do the ingredients in recipes found in 1940s cookbooks compare with those found in 1990s cookbooks?

ACTIVITY 20.3: ADVANTAGES VS. DISADVANTAGES OF CONTENT ANALYSIS

1. T
2. T
3. F
4. F
5. F
6. T
7. F
8. T
9. F
10. F

ACTIVITY 20.4: CONTENT ANALYSIS CATEGORIES: AUTHORS SUGGESTED ANSWERS

1. <u>Coverage of minority groups in social studies textbooks.</u> Possible categories might include *hero, victim, domestic, partner, leader, follower, etc.*
2. <u>How characters are portrayed in Saturday morning television cartoon programs.</u> Possible categories might include *funny, exciting, violent, dangerous, dumb, etc.*
3. <u>Issues discussed in newspaper editorials.</u> Possible categories might include *crime, homelessness, the Presidency, transportation, airports, etc.*
4. <u>Themes used in magazine advertisements.</u> Possible categories might include *glamour, danger, sexiness, style, sleekness, casual, sports, etc.*
5. <u>Emotions presented in popular songs.</u> Possible categories might include *love, dreams, loneliness, sadness, romance, mystery, etc.*

Chapter 21: Ethnographic Research

ACTIVITY 21.1: ETHNOGRAPHIC RESEARCH QUESTIONS

2. What is the social structure of children attending nursery school?
3. How do beginning counselors interact with teachers?
5. How do middle school teachers plan their daily routine?

ACTIVITY 21.2: TRUE OR FALSE?

1. T
2. F
3. F
4. T
5. T
6. F
7. T
8. T
9. T
10. T
11. F

ACTIVITY 21.3: DO SOME ETHNOGRAPHIC RESEARCH

I suspect that you found this to be a difficult assignment. Don't be disappointed, however, since even experienced researchers not trained in ethnography often find this difficult. Perhaps you had difficulty determining what was important and what was not. Quite likely you were unable to record everything that went on, and probably you were not always sure about what to record and what to ignore. You also probably found it difficult not to impose your own interpretations on the various events as they occurred. What do you think about this method now?

Chapter 22: Historical Research

ACTIVITY 22.1: HISTORICAL RESEARCH QUESTIONS

1. What was life like for a woman teacher in the 1920s?
5. What were the beginnings of the modern social studies?
7. How were women portrayed in 1930s fiction?
9. How has the age of children leaving home changed between the years 1920 and 1980?

ACTIVITY 22.2: PRIMARY OR SECONDARY SOURCE?

1. P
2. P
3. S
4. P
5. S
6. P
7. S
8. P
9. S

ACTIVITY 22.3: WHAT KIND OF HISTORICAL SOURCE?

1. a
2. d
3. d
4. a
5. a
6. a
7. a
8. b
9. b
10. c

ACTIVITY 22.4: TRUE OR FALSE?

1. T
2. F
3. F
4. T
5. T
6. T
7. F
8. T
9. T
10. T
11. T

Chapter 23: Action Research

ACTIVITY 23.1: ACTION RESEARCH QUESTIONS

2. Is the content found in the literature anthologies in our district biased, and if so, how?
3. Would filmstrips help our elementary school teachers teach multiplication to third-graders?
6. How might we improve the quality of our school's social studies programs?
7. Is the use of detention successful with our elementary school students?
8. What are the effects of giving the students with serious behavior problems at Adams Elementary School choices about how to behave in class?

ACTIVITY 23.2: TRUE OR FALSE?

1. T
2. F
3. T
4. F
5. F
6. T
7. T
8. T
9. F
10. T
11. T
12. F

Chapter 24: Writing Research Proposals and Reports

ACTIVITY 24.1: PUT THEM IN ORDER

1. Table of contents
2. Purpose of the study
3. Justification of the study
4. Research question
5. Definition of terms
6. Review of related literature
7. Description of the research design
8. Description of the sample
9. Description of the instruments used
10. Explanation of the procedures followed
11. Discussion of internal validity
12. Description of the methods of data analysis used
13. Description of findings
14. Discussion of findings and conclusions
15. Suggestions for further research

Problem Sheets

Problem Sheet 1: Type of Research

1. A possible topic or problem I am thinking of researching is:

   _____

   _____

   _____

   _____

   _____

   _____

   _____

2. The type of research that seems most appropriate to this topic or problem is: *(circle one)*

   a.   An experiment

   b.   A correlational study

   c.   A causal-comparative study

   d.   A survey using a written questionnaire

   e.   A survey using interviews of several individuals

   f.   An ethnographic study

   g.   A case study

   h.   A content analysis

   i.   A historical study

3. What questions (if any) might a critical researcher raise with regard to your study?

   _____

   _____

   _____

   _____

   _____

   _____

Problem Sheet 2: The Research Question

1. My (restated) research problem is

   _____

   _____

2. My research question is:

   _____

   _____

3. The following are the key terms in the problem or question that are not clear and thus need to be defined:

   a. _____

   b. _____

   c. _____

   d. _____

   e. _____

   f. _____

4. Here are my constitutive definitions of these terms:

   _____

   _____

   _____

   _____

5. Here are my operational definitions of these terms:

   _____

   _____

   _____

   _____

6. My justification for investigating this question/problem (why I would argue that it is an important question to investigate) is as follows:

   _____

   _____

   _____

   _____

   _____

Problem Sheet 3: The Research Hypothesis

1. My research question is: _____

   _____

   _____

2. I intend to use a hypothesis to investigate this question. Yes _____ No _____

3. If no, my reasons are as follows: _____

   _____

   _____

   _____

   _____

4. If yes, my hypothesis is: _____

   _____

   _____

   _____

5. This hypothesis suggests a relationship between at least two variables.

   They are _____ and _____

6. More specifically, the variables in my study are:
   a. Dependent _____
   b. Independent _____

7. The dependent variable is (check one) categorical _____ quantitative _____

   The independent variable is (check one) categorical _____ quantitative _____

8. Possible extraneous variables that might affect my results include:
   a. _____
   b. _____
   c. _____
   d. _____
   e. _____

Problem Sheet 4: Ethics and Research

1. My research question is: _____

_____

_____

2. The possibilities for harm to participants (if any) are as follows: _____

_____

_____

_____

I would handle these problems as follows: _____

_____

_____

3. The possibilities of problems of confidentiality (if any) are as follows: _____

_____

_____

_____

I would handle these problems as follows: _____

_____

_____

4. The possibilities of problems of deception (if any) are as follows: _____

_____

_____

_____

I would handle these problems as follows: _____

_____

5. If you think your proposed study would fit the guidelines for exempt status, state why here.

_____

_____

_____

_____

Problem Sheet 5: Review of the Literature

1. The question of hypothesis in my study is: _____

   _____

   _____

2. The general reference(s) I consulted was (were): _____

   _____

   _____

3. The database I used in my search was: _____

   _____

4. The descriptors (search terms) I used were (list single descriptors and combinations in the order in which you did your search):

   _____

   _____

   _____

   _____

5. The results of my search using these descriptors were as follows:

SEARCH #	DESCRIPTOR(S)	RESULTS

6. Attached is a printout of my search (attach to the back of this sheet).

7. The title of one of the abstracts located using the descriptors identified above is:

   _____

   (Attach a copy of the abstract)

8. The titles of the studies I read (note cards are attached) were:
   a. _____
   b. _____
   c. _____

Problem Sheet 6: Sampling Plan

1. My intended sample (subjects who would participate in my study) consists of (tell who and how many):

   _____

   _____

   _____

2. Demographics (characteristics of the sample) are as follows:

   a. Age range _____

   b. Sex distribution _____

   c. Ethnic breakdown _____

   d. Location (where are these subjects?) _____

   e. Other characteristics not mentioned above that you deem important (use a sheet of paper if you need more space)

   _____

   _____

   _____

   _____

3. Type of sample: simple random _____ stratified random _____

   cluster random _____ two-stage random _____ convenience _____

   purposive _____

4. I will obtain my sample by: _____

   _____

   _____

5. External validity (I will generalize to the following population):

   a. To what accessible population? _____

   b. To what target population? _____

   c. If not generalizable, why not? _____

6. Ecological validity (I will generalize to the following settings/conditions):

   a. Generalizable to what setting(s)? _____

   b. Generalizable to what condition(s)? _____

   c. If not generalizable, why not? _____

Problem Sheet 7: Instrumentation

1. The question or hypothesis in my study is _____

   _____

2. The types of instruments I plan to use to measure my variables are: _____

   _____

3. Circle one of the following:
   a. I plan to use an existing instrument.
   b. I plan to develop an instrument.

4. If I need to develop an instrument, here are two examples of the kind of questions I would ask (or tasks I would have students perform) as part of my instrument:

   a._____

   b._____

5. These are the existing instruments I plan to use: _____

   _____

6. The independent variable in my study is _____

   I would describe it as follows (circle the term in each set that applies)

   [quantitative or categorical] [nominal or ordinal or interval or ratio]

7. The dependent variable in my study is _____

   I would describe it as follows (circle the term in each set that applies)

   [quantitative or categorical] [nominal or ordinal or interval or ratio]

8. My study does not have independent/dependent variables. The variable(s) in my study is (are)

   _____

9. For each variable above that yields numerical data, I will treat it as follows (check one in each column):

INDEPENDENT	DEPENDENT	OTHER
Raw score		
Age/grade equivalents		
Percentile		
Standard score		

10. I do not have any variables that yield numerical data in my study _____

Problem Sheet 8: Instrument Validity and Reliability

1. I plan to use the following *existing* instruments: _____

   _____

   _____

   _____

   In summary, I have learned the following about the validity and reliability of scores obtained with these instruments.

   _____

   _____

   _____

2. I plan to *develop* the following about the validity and reliability of scores obtained with these instruments.

   _____

   _____

   _____

   I will try to ensure reliability and validity of results obtained with these instruments by:

   _____

   _____

   _____

3. For each instrument I plan to use:

   a. This is how I will collect evidence to check internal consistency: _____

   _____

   _____

   b. This is how I will collect evidence to check reliability over time (stability): _____

   _____

   _____

   c. This is how I will collect evidence to check validity: _____

   _____

   _____

Problem Sheet 9: Internal Validity

1. My question or hypothesis is: _____

   _____

2. I have placed an X in the blank in front of four of the threats listed below that apply to my study. I explain why I think each one is a problem and then explain how I would attempt to control for the threat.

THREATS

_____ Subject characteristics	_____ Mortality	_____ Location
_____ Instrumentation	_____ Testing	_____ History
_____ Maturation	_____ Subject	_____ Regression
_____ Implementation	_____ Attitude	_____ Other

Threat 1: _____ Why? _____

_____

I will control by _____

_____

Threat 2: _____ Why? _____

_____

I will control by _____

_____

Threat 3: _____ Why? _____

_____

I will control by _____

_____

Threat 4: _____ Why? _____

_____

I will control by _____

_____

Problem Sheet 10: Descriptive Statistics

1. The question or hypothesis of my study is: _____

   _____

2. My variables are: (1) _____

   (2) _____ (others) _____

3. I consider variable 1 to be: quantitative _____ or categorical _____

4. I consider variable 2 to be: quantitative _____ or categorical _____

5. I would summarize the results for each variable checked below (indicate with a check mark):

VARIABLE 1:	**VARIABLE 2:**	**OTHER:**
a. Frequency polygon		
b. Box plot		
c. Mean		
d. Median		
e. Range		
f. Standard deviation		
g. Frequency table		
h. Bar graph		
i. Pie chart		

6. I would describe the relationship between variables 1 and 2 by (indicate with a check mark):

   a. Comparison of frequency polygons _____

   b. Comparison of averages _____

   c. Crossbreak table(s) _____

   d. Correlation coefficient _____

   e. Scatterplot _____

Problem Sheet 11: Inferential Statistics

1. The question or hypothesis of my study is: _____

   _____

2. The descriptive statistic(s) I would use to describe the relationship I am hypothesizing would be: _____

   _____

   _____

   _____

3. The appropriate inference technique for my study would be: _____

   _____

   _____

   _____

4. Circle the appropriate word in the sentences below.
   a. I would use a *parametric* or a *nonparametric* technique because: _____

   _____

   b. I *would* or *would not* do a significance test because _____

   _____

   _____

   c. I *would* or *would not* calculate a confidence interval because: _____

   _____

   _____

   _____

   _____

5. The type of sample used in my study is: _____

6. The type of sample used in my study places the following limitation(s) on my use of inferential statistics:

   _____

   _____

   _____

   _____

Problem Sheet 12: Statistics in Perspective

1. The question or hypothesis of my study is: _____

_____

_____

_____

2. My expected relationship(s) would be described using the following descriptive statistics:

_____

_____

_____

_____

3. The inferential statistics I would use are: _____

_____

_____

_____

_____

_____

_____

4. I would evaluate the magnitude of the relationship(s) I find by: _____

_____

_____

_____

_____

_____

5. The changes (if any) in my use of descriptive or inferential statistics from those I described in Problem Sheets 10 and 11 are as follows: _____

_____

_____

_____

_____

_____

_____

Problem Sheet 13: Research Methodology

1. The question or hypothesis of my study is: _____

_____

_____

_____

2. The methodology I intend to use is: _____

_____

_____

_____

_____

3. A brief summary of *what* I intend to do, *when, where,* and *how* is as follows: _____

_____

_____

_____

_____

_____

_____

_____

_____

_____

4. The major problems I foresee at this point include the following: _____

_____

_____

_____

_____

_____

_____

_____

_____

_____

Popular Complete Smart Series

Complete
Canadian
Curriculum

Grade

5

Contents   Grade 5

Mathematics

English

Social Studies

Science

MATHEMATICS

* The Canadian penny is no longer in circulation. It is used in the units to show money amounts to the cent.

Numbers to 100 000 (1)

- Write, compare, and order whole numbers to 100 000.
- Write numbers in expanded form and in words.
- Identify the value of a digit in a 5-digit whole number.

Count and write the numbers. Then write the 5-digit numbers in the blocks.

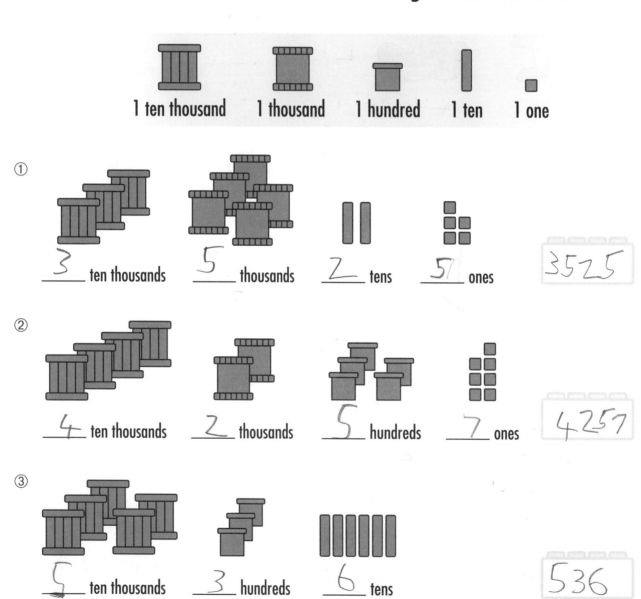

① ___3___ ten thousands ___5___ thousands ___2___ tens ___5___ ones | 3525

② ___4___ ten thousands ___2___ thousands ___5___ hundreds ___7___ ones | 4257

③ ___5___ ten thousands ___3___ hundreds ___6___ tens | 536

5-digit Numbers:

Standard form
43 692

Forty-three thousand six hundred ninety-two

Expanded form:
40 000 + 3000 + 600 + 90 + 2

Write the numbers in words.

④ 36 453   30000 + 6000 + 400 + 50 + 3

⑤ 64 078   60000 + 4000 + 70 + 80 + 8

⑥ 90 156   90000 + 7000 + 700 + 50 + 6

⑦ 28 714   20000 + 8000 + 700 + 70 + 4

⑧ 59 203   50000 + 9000 + 200 + 30 + 3

Write each number in expanded or standard form.

⑨ 34 785 = 30000 + 4000 + 700 + 80 + 5

⑩ 76 059 = 70000 + 600 + 50 + 90 − 9

⑪ 52 306 = 50000 + 2000 + 300 + 60 + 6

⑫ 80 548 = 80000 + 0000 + 500 + 40 + 8

⑬ 25267 = 20 000 + 5000 + 200 + 60 + 7

⑭ 41058 = 40 000 + 1000 + 50 + 8

⑮ 30074 = 30 000 + 70 + 4

⑯ 58962 = 50 000 + 8000 + 900 + 60 + 2

Place Value Chart:

56 293

Ten Thousand	Thousand	Hundred	Ten	One
5	6	2	9	3

5 means 50 000;
6 means 6000;
2 means 200;
9 means 90;
3 means 3.

Write the meaning of each digit.

⑰ 27 854

2 means _2 0000_.
7 means _7000_.
8 means _800_.
5 means _50_.
4 means _4_.

⑱ 36 819

3 means _30000_.
6 means _6000_.
8 means _800_.
1 means _10_.
9 means _9_.

⑲ 65 923

6 means _60000_.
5 means _5000_.
9 means _900_.
2 means _20_.
3 means _3_.

⑳ 75 196

7 means _70000_.
5 means _5000_.
1 means _100_.
9 means _90_.
6 means _6_.

Write the numbers.

㉑ Write two 5-digit numbers which

    a.   have a 5 in its ten thousands place.

    b.   have a 9 in its hundreds place.

_56293_
_90156_

㉒ Write two 5-digit numbers which have a 7 in its thousands place and are greater than 60 000.

_67000_

Comparing 5-digit numbers:

e.g. 27 869 28 113

Compare • 2 7 8 6 9   • 2 7 8 6 9
               2 8 1 1 3   2 8 1 1 3
                 ↑   ↑
               same   8 > 7

Compare the digits in the ten thousands place. If they are the same, compare the digits in the thousands place and so on. The number with the greater digit is greater.

27 869 (<) 28 113

Put ">" or "<" in the circle.

㉓ 45 273 (<) 74 511

㉔ 28 593 (>) 21 499

㉕ 30 639 (<) 36 930

㉖ 68 847 (<) 68 874

㉗ 53 276 (>) 35 276

㉘ 40 083 (>) 40 003

㉙ 50 600 (<) 60 500

㉚ 31 233 (<) 31 332

Put the numbers in order.

㉛  *from least to greatest*   37 254   73 524   75 324   32 754

32754   37254   73524   75324

㉜  *from greatest to least*   40 068   40 680   48 060   48 680

40068 40680 48060 48680

Use the digits on the balls to form different 5-digit numbers. Then put the numbers in order from least to greatest and write them on the lines.

㉝ 65000 60500 60050 6005

56000 50600 50060 50006

Numbers to 100 000 (2)

37 596 fish →

There are about 40 000 fish.

- Follow patterns to find the missing numbers.
- Develop a better understanding of place value of 5-digit numbers.
- Round 5-digit numbers.
- Solve problems involving numbers.

Fill in the missing numbers.

① 68 050 — 68 100 — 68 150 — *68 200* — *68 250* — 68 300

② 40 005 — 50 005 — *60 005* — *70 005* — 80 005 — *90 005*

③ 78 250 — 79 250 — *80 250* — *81 250* — *82 250* — 83 250

④

	96 118		50 118	*49 118*	48 118
93 318	*95 118*				*49 118*
94 318	*94 218*	94 118	*94 018*		*50 118*
95 318	93 118				51 118
96 318	*92 118*	82 118	72 118	*62 118*	*52 118*
97 318	*91 118*				53 118
	90 118				
89 218	*89 118*	*89 018*	*88 918*	88 818	88 718
	88 118				

Write the numbers.

⑤ a number 3000 more than 45 888   *48888*

⑥ a number 20 000 more than 73 645   *93645*

⑦ a number 500 less than 67 833   *68333*

⑧ a number 20 less than 58 624   *58644*

⑨ | How many numbers are there between 79 997 and 80 004? What are they?

    6 ; *79998 79999 80000 80001 80002 80003*

⑩ | What number is 44 444 more than eleven thousand one hundred eleven? Write the answer in standard form and in words.

    55555 ; *fifteen thousand five hundred fifteen*

Write three sentences to describe the relationships between any two numbers in each group.

> *37 808 is 80 less than 37 888.*

⑪
| 36 888 |
| 37 808 \ 37 888 |
| \ 36 088 |

37888 is 1000 more than 36888
36088 is 800 less than 36888
37888 is 80 more than 37808

⑫
| 59 650 |
| 60 650   70 650 |
| 59 550 |

70650 is 11000 more than 59650
59550 is 100 less than 59650
70650 is 11000 more than 60650

Rounding to the nearest ten thousand:

e.g. 3$\underline{8}$ 625 $\xrightarrow{\text{round up}}$ **40 000**

↑
8 > 5

1st Look at the digit in the thousands place.

2nd If it is 5 or greater, round the number up; otherwise, round the number down.

8$\underline{4}$ 173 ⟶ **80 000**

↑
4 < 5

round down

Round each number to the nearest ten thousand.

⑬ 46 534 __50000__

⑭ 17 225 __20000__

⑮ 93 108 __90000__

⑯ 88 622 __90000__

⑰ 77 655 __80000__

⑱ 60 213 __60000__

⑲ 35 271 __40000__

⑳ 44 306 __40000__

Round each number to the nearest thousand.

㉑ 37 246 __38000__

㉒ 46 850 __47000__

㉓ 62 109 __62000__

㉔ 98 764 __99000__

㉕ 53 324 __52000__

㉖ 73 052 __73000__

㉗ 44 623 __45000__

㉘ 11 088 __11000__

㉙
 36 450 cm

 14 375 mL

 12 225 g

 $40 860

a.   The height of the building is about __36450__ cm.

b.   The capacity of the cooler is about __14375__ mL.

c.   The bag of potatoes weighs about __12225__ g.

d.   The ring costs about $ __40860__ .

Help David write each number in numerals and round it to the nearest thousand.

...thirty-six thousand four hundred eighteen dollars were collected in the fundraising campaign...

...ABC Company has sold eighty-nine thousand seven hundred five packs of chocolate...

...twenty-one thousand five hundred sixteen men and seventeen thousand three hundred two women were asked about their favourite songs...

...there were twelve thousand two hundred seven people who visited Shark Land last week and seventeen thousand six hundred people this week...

③⓪

Exact: $ _36418_

About: $ _36000_

③①

Exact: _89705_ packs

About: _90000_ packs

③②

Exact: _27516_ 🧍

About: _27000_ 🧍

Exact: _17302_ 🧍

About: _17000_ 🧍

③③ **Shark Land**

a.

	Last Week	This Week
Exact	12207 visitors	17600 visitors
About	12000 visitors	18000 visitors

b.

About how many people in all visited me in these two weeks?

about _30000_ people

Addition and Subtraction of 4-Digit Numbers

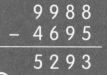

$$\begin{array}{r} 9\,9\,8\,8 \\ -\;4\,6\,9\,5 \\ \hline 5\,2\,9\,3 \end{array}$$

- Add or subtract 4-digit numbers.
- Estimate or check the answers.
- Solve word problems.

$9988

$4695

I cost $5293 more than you.

Find out the number of toy cars a factory produced last year. Do the addition. Then circle the correct answers.

①
$$\begin{array}{r} 1\,1 \\ 4\,7\,5\,2 \\ +\quad\;8\,9\,4 \\ \hline 5\,6\,4\,6 \end{array}$$

②
$$\begin{array}{r} 1 \\ 2\,5\,6\,3 \\ +\;1\,3\,0\,9 \\ \hline 3\,8\,7\,2 \end{array}$$
3872 +5503 9375

③
$$\begin{array}{r} 1 \\ 5\,1\,1\,4 \\ +\;2\,6\,3\,7 \\ \hline 7\,7\,5\,1 \end{array}$$

④
$$\begin{array}{r} 1\,1 \\ 1\,8\,8\,4 \\ +\;5\,6\,7\,6 \\ \hline 6\,5\,7\,0 \end{array}$$

⑤
$$\begin{array}{r} 1\,1 \\ 4\,0\,6\,0 \\ +\;1\,9\,4\,7 \\ \hline 6\,0\,0\,7 \end{array}$$

⑥
$$\begin{array}{r} 1\,1\,1 \\ 3\,8\,0\,5 \\ +\;1\,6\,9\,8 \\ \hline 5\,5\,0\,3 \end{array}$$

⑦ 2562 + 1768 = __4330__

⑧ 594 + 2677 = __6277__

⑨ 3815 + 3815 = __7630__

⑩ 1890 + 3274 = __5164__

⑪ 4206 + 189 = __4395__

⑫ 3105 + 2916 = __6021__

⑬ Which toy cars were produced the most?

⑭ How many and were produced in all?

523   **8267**   **7267**

Do the subtraction.

⑮
$$
\begin{array}{r}
5\,7\,13\,13 \\
6\,2\,4\,3 \\
-\ 1\,5\,9\,6 \\
\hline
4\,6\,4\,7
\end{array}
$$

⑯
$$
\begin{array}{r}
1\,7\,6\,14\,14 \\
2\,7\,5\,4 \\
-\ 1\,8\,8\,6 \\
\hline
8\,6\,8
\end{array}
$$

⑰
$$
\begin{array}{r}
4\,9\,9\,14 \\
5\,0\,0\,4 \\
-\ 3\,6\,9\,7 \\
\hline
1\,3\,0\,7
\end{array}
$$

⑱
$$
\begin{array}{r}
3\,10\,7\,11 \\
4\,0\,8\,1 \\
-\ 3\,6\,5\,4 \\
\hline
4\,2\,7
\end{array}
$$

⑲
$$
\begin{array}{r}
2\,7\,9\,16 \\
3\,3\,0\,6 \\
-\ 2\,5\,1\,7 \\
\hline
7\,8\,9
\end{array}
$$

⑳
$$
\begin{array}{r}
4\,10\,11\,16 \\
5\,1\,1\,6 \\
-\ \ 9\,2\,5 \\
\hline
4\,1\,9\,1
\end{array}
$$

㉑ 2603 – 1564 = __1039__

㉒ 5077 – 4653 = __424__

㉓ 9468 – 7430 = __2038__

㉔ 2566 – 888 = __1678__

Find the difference between the items.

㉕

Cookies 4252 g 1474 g

$$
\begin{array}{r}
3\,11\,14\,12 \\
4\,2\,5\,7 \\
-\ 1\,4\,7\,4 \\
\hline
2\,7\,7\,8
\end{array}
$$

The difference is __2778__ .

㉖

$6014 $5247

$$
\begin{array}{r}
5\,9\,10\,14 \\
6\,0\,1\,4 \\
-\ 5\,2\,4\,7 \\
\hline
7\,6\,7
\end{array}
$$

The difference is __767__ .

㉗

Juice 1500 mL 275 mL

$$
\begin{array}{r}
12 \\
0\,\ \ \,7\,5 \\
1\,5\,0\,0 \\
\hline
7\,7\,5
\end{array}
$$

The difference is __775__ .

㉘

2870 cm 1023 cm

$$
\begin{array}{r}
10\,0\,11\,13 \\
2\,8\,7\,0 \\
-\ 1\,0\,2\,3 \\
\hline
1\,5\,3\,3
\end{array}
$$

The difference is __1533__ .

㉙

Tickets Sold	
Mon	3682
Tue	4723

$$
\begin{array}{r}
5\,16\,11\,12 \\
3\,6\,8\,2 \\
4\,7\,2\,3 \\
\hline
1\,9\,5\,9
\end{array}
$$

The difference is __1959__ .

㉚

Eggs
White: 2764
Brown: 5657

$$
\begin{array}{r}
8\,\ \ 5\,14 \\
2\,7\,6\,4 \\
-\ 5\,6\,5\,7 \\
\hline
3\,1\,0\,7
\end{array}
$$

The difference is __3107__ .

Round each number to the nearest thousand to do the estimate. Then find the exact answer.

③¹
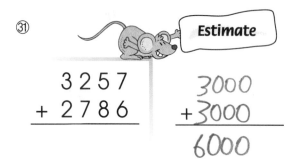

$$
\begin{array}{r}
3\,2\,5\,7 \\
+\ 2\,7\,8\,6 \\
\hline
\end{array}
$$

Estimate
$$
\begin{array}{r}
3000 \\
+3000 \\
\hline
6000
\end{array}
$$

③²
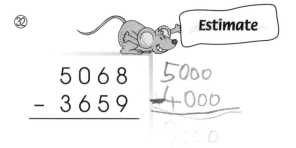

$$
\begin{array}{r}
5\,0\,6\,8 \\
-\ 3\,6\,5\,9 \\
\hline
\end{array}
$$

Estimate
$$
\begin{array}{r}
5000 \\
-4000 \\
\hline
9000
\end{array}
$$

③³
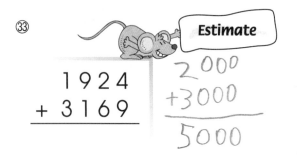

$$
\begin{array}{r}
1\,9\,2\,4 \\
+\ 3\,1\,6\,9 \\
\hline
\end{array}
$$

Estimate
$$
\begin{array}{r}
2000 \\
+3000 \\
\hline
5000
\end{array}
$$

③⁴
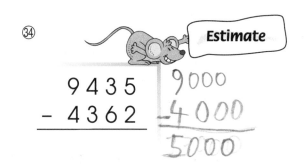

$$
\begin{array}{r}
9\,4\,3\,5 \\
-\ 4\,3\,6\,2 \\
\hline
\end{array}
$$

Estimate
$$
\begin{array}{r}
9000 \\
-4000 \\
\hline
5000
\end{array}
$$

Check the answer of each question. Put a check mark in the space provided if the answer is correct; otherwise, put a cross and find the correct answer.

③⁵

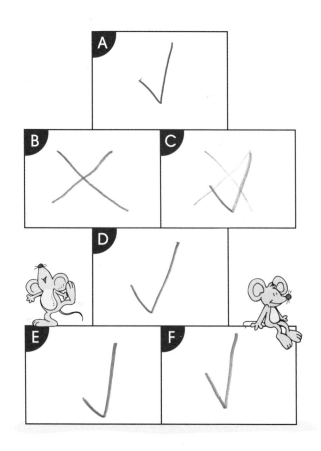

A $3257 + 1464 = \underline{4721}$

B $8016 - 477 \ = \underline{8539}$ (with small *3* above)

C $1594 + 2806 = \underline{4410}$

D $5253 - 2478 = \underline{2775}$

E $7000 - 2885 = \underline{4115}$

F $946 + 4193 \ = \underline{5039}$

Read what the children say. Help them solve the problems.

There were 4262 men and 3788 women who visited the library last week.

765 books and 432 audio items were delivered to homebound users last year.

There are 4663 hardcover and 982 paperback storybooks in the children's section.

㉟ How many people visited the library last week?

4262 + 3788 = 8050   8050

㊲ How many more men than women visited the library last week?

4262 - 3788 = 474   474

㊳ How many storybooks are there in the children's section?

4663 + 982 = 5645   5645

㊴ If 3405 children's storybooks are borrowed, how many storybooks will be left in the library?

4663 - 982 = 2681   2681

㊵

I'm responsible for the library delivery service. How many items in all did I deliver to homebound users last year?

765 + 432 = 1197

1197

Multiplication

- Multiply 2-digit numbers by 2-digit numbers.
- Solve problems involving multiplication.

> I have 13 necklaces. I have 156 beads in all.

```
   13
 x 12
 ----
   26
  130
 ----
  156
```

12 beads

Fill in the missing numbers to complete the steps to do multiplication. Then find the answers.

①

Multiply by the ones.   **Multiply by the tens.**

```
   3                3              3
  3 4              3 4            3 4             3 4           3 4
x  2 8          x  2 8          x  2 8          x 2 8        x 2 8
-------         -------         -------         -------       -------
  2 7 2           2 7 2           2 7 2           2 7 2         2 7 2
                                  1 3 8 0           6 8 0         6 8 0
                                                                -------
                                                                  9 5 2
```

34 x 28 = __952__

②

Multiply by the ones.   **Multiply by the tens.**

```
   2                2              4              4             2
  6 9              6 9            6 9            6 9           6 9
x  5 3          x  5 3          x  5 3          x 5 3        x 5 3
-------         -------         -------         -------       -------
      7           2 0 7           2 0 7           2 0 7         2 0 7
                                    5 0           3 4 5 0       3 4 5 0
                                                                -------
                                                                3 6 5 7
```

69 x 53 = __3657__

Do the multiplication.

③
```
        2
      2 7
  x   1 4
  ─────────
    1 0 8
    2 7 0
  ─────────
    3 7 8
```

④
```
        7
      3 8
  x   2 9
  ─────────
    3 4 2
    6 6 0
  ─────────
    1 0 2
```

⑤
```
      2
      6
      4 7
  x   3 9
  ─────────
    4 2 3
    1 4 1 0
  ─────────
    2 8 3 3
```

⑥
```
      3 4
  x   2 2
  ─────────
    1 6 8
    6 8 0
  ─────────
    7 4 8
```

⑦
```
      5 3
  x   3 2
  ─────────
    1 0 6
    1 5 9 0
  ─────────
    1 6 9 6
```

⑧
```
      3
      4
      6 8
  x   4 5
  ─────────
    1 3 4 0
    2 7 2 0
  ─────────
    3 0 6 0
```

⑨ 42 x 16 = __672__

⑩ 37 x 13 = __457x__   481

⑪ 61 x 45 = __2745__

⑫ 55 x 34 = __1820__

⑬ 73 x 23 = __1675__

⑭ 18 x 26 = __468__

⑮ 52 x 19 = __988__

⑯ 49 x 49 = __2401__

⑰ 18 x 67 = __1206__

⑱ 53 x 24 = __1272__

⑲ 35 x 48 = __1680__

⑳ 27 x 82 = __2274__

Fill in the missing numbers.

㉑
```
      3 4
  x   2 6
  ─────────
    2 0 4
    6 8 0
  ─────────
    8 8 4
```

㉒
```
      3 9
  x   4 7
  ─────────
    4 1 3
    2 3 6 0
  ─────────
    2 7 7 3
```

Look at the pictures. Complete the tables. Then answer the questions.

⑳

	Chicken Burgers		Detergent	
No. of Boxes	No. of Burgers	Cost	No. of Loads	Cost
15	180	$270	510	$195
29	348	$366	983	$367
47	564	$658	1598	$611
58	696	$732	1972	$754

㉔

	Candies		Balloons	
No. of Bags	No. of Candies	Cost	No. of Balloons	Cost
18	936	$288	1296	$276
26	1352	$426	1872	$372
34	1768	$544	2448	$408
85	4420	$1360	6120	$1020

㉕ Mrs. Green buys 16 boxes of detergent. How many loads are there in all?

34 × 16 = 544   544

㉖ Aunt Lucy buys 42 bags of balloons for her company. How many balloons are there in all?

72 × 42 = 3024   3024

Solve the problems.

㉗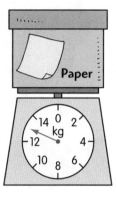

What is the total weight of 36 boxes of paper?

The total weight is _468kg_ .

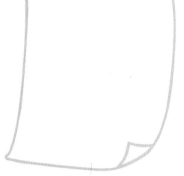

㉘

How much water do 28 bottles hold in all?

The total water is 1260L

㉙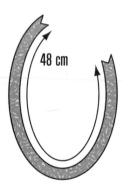

What is the total length of 33 ribbons?

The total length is 1578cm

㉚

How many pieces of dog treats are there in 22 boxes?

The total dog treats is 1496

I put 486 candies equally into 3 baskets.
Each basket holds 162 candies.

$$
\begin{array}{r}
162 \\
3\overline{)486} \\
3 \\
\hline
18 \\
18 \\
\hline
6 \\
6 \\
\hline
\end{array}
$$

Division (1)

- Divide 3-digit numbers by 1-digit numbers with no zero in the quotient.
- Use multiplication and addition to check answers.
- Solve problems involving division.

Do the division.

①
$$
\begin{array}{r}
184 \\
4\overline{)736} \\
4 \\
\hline
24 \\
24 \\
\hline
16 \\
16 \\
\hline
\end{array}
$$

②
$$
\begin{array}{r}
121 \\
7\overline{)847} \\
7 \\
\hline
49 \\
49 \\
\hline
7 \\
7 \\
\hline
\end{array}
$$

③
$$
\begin{array}{r}
124 \\
6\overline{)744} \\
-6 \\
\hline
14 \\
14 \\
\hline
24 \\
24 \\
\hline
\end{array}
$$

④ $351 \div 3 = \underline{117}$

⑤ $856 \div 4 = \underline{274}$

⑥ $632 \div 2 = \underline{316}$

⑦ $585 \div 5 = \underline{117}$

⑧ $938 \div 7 = \underline{134}$

⑨ $768 \div 6 = \underline{128}$

⑩ $976 \div 8 = \underline{122}$

⑪ $765 \div 3 = \underline{255}$

⑫

714 Stickers

Beads

6 Sheets

516

a. 3 girls share a box of beads equally.
   Each girl has $\underline{172 \times 117}$ beads.

b. A pack has 6 sheets of stickers. There
   are $\underline{274}$ stickers on each sheet.

Fill in the missing numbers.

⑬
```
        7 2 R 4
    7 ) 5 0 9
        4 9
        ___
        1 8
        1 4
        ___
          4
```

⑭
```
        2 8 7 R 2
    3 ) 8 6 3
       -6
       ____
       -2 6
       -2 4
       ____
         2 3
         2 1
         ____
           2
```

⑮
```
        1 2 5 R 6
    6 ) 7 5 1
        6
        ___
        1 5
        1 2
        ___
          3 6
          3 0
          ___
            6
```

Check the answer of each division sentence.   Put a check mark in the space provided if it is correct; otherwise, put a cross and write the correct answer.

⑯   475 ÷ 3

= __158 R 1__

Check 1st $\underset{\text{quotient}}{\underline{475}}$ × $\underset{\text{divisor}}{\underline{3}}$ = __474__

2nd $\underset{\text{the answer above}}{\underline{158}}$ + $\underset{\text{remainder}}{\underline{1}}$ = __475__

⑰   716 ÷ 5

= __144 R 4__

Check 1st __716__ × __5__ = __720__

2nd __144__ + __4__ = __724__

⑱   647 ÷ 4

= __161 R 3__

Check 1st __647__ × __4__ = __644__

2nd __161__ + __3__ = __647__

⑲   927 ÷ 6

= __153 R 5__

Check 1st __927__ × __6__ = __918__

2nd __153__ + __5__ = __923__

Steps to do division:

$$4 \overline{)3\ 2\ 8} \leftarrow \text{3 < 4; consider 1 more digit}$$

$$4 \overline{)\begin{array}{c}8\ 2\\ 3\ 2\ 8\\ 3\ 2\end{array}} \leftarrow \text{There are 8 4's in 32.}$$
$$\begin{array}{c}8\\ 8\end{array}$$

$328 \div 4 = \underline{\textbf{82}}$

Divide the things equally. Show your work. Then fill in the blanks.

⑳ **525** cm – **7** pieces

Each: _75_ cm

 364 g – **4** bowls

Each: _91_ g

 753 mL – **8** glasses

Each: _752_ mL

Juice left: _1_ mL

 466 blocks – **9** towers

Each: _50_ blocks

Blocks left: _7_

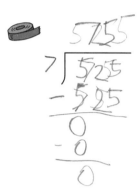
```
      75 5
 7 ) 5 2 5
   - 5 2 5
        0
      - 0
        0
```

```
     9 6
 9 ) 3 6 4
   - 3 6 4
        0
      - 0
        0
```

```
     9 8 R?
 8 ) 7 5 3
   - 7 2 2
        9
      - 8
        1
```

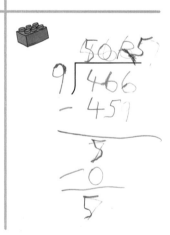
```
     5 0 R5
 9 ) 4 6 6
   - 4 5 ?
        5
      - 0
        5
```

Do the division.

㉑ $394 \div 5 = \underline{78R4}$ ㉒ $627 \div 8 = \underline{78R3}$

㉓ $564 \div 9 = \underline{62R6}$ ㉔ $463 \div 7 = \underline{66R7}$

㉕ $165 \div 6 = \underline{28R3}$ ㉖ $274 \div 4 = \underline{68R2}$

㉗ $583 \div 7 = \underline{83R2}$ ㉘ $391 \div 8 = \underline{48R7}$

Solve the problems.

㉙
488 children

a. 3 children in a group

- *162* groups

- *2* children left

b. 7 children in a group

- *483* groups

- *5* children left

㉚
755 flowers

a. 4 flowers in a vase

- *188* vases

- *3* flowers left

b. 6 flowers in a vase

- *750* vases

- *5* flowers left

㉛ Judy, Marco, and Tiffany share a box of 413 chocolate eggs equally. How many chocolate eggs does each child have? How many chocolate eggs are left?

413 ÷ *3* = *137R22*

Each child has *137* chocolate eggs. *2* chocolate eggs are left.

㉜ Each bag has 8 gumballs. If Jason wants to give 178 gumballs to his friends, how many bags of gumballs does he need to buy?

178 ÷ *8* = *23R2*

He needs to buy *22* gumballs. *2* gumballs are left.

㉝

> *This jumbo lollipop is on sale now. Its sale price is $2 less. If Mrs. White pays $125 for lollipops, how many lollipops can she get? What is her change?*

125 ÷ *2* = *62R1*

She can get 62 lollipops. Her change is 2.

My dress has 3 layers! There are 104 flowers on each layer.

$$3 \overline{)312} \quad \begin{array}{r} 104 \\ \hline 3 \\ \hline 12 \\ 12 \end{array}$$

Division (2)

- Divide 3-digit numbers by 1-digit numbers with zeros in the quotient.
- Solve problems involving division.

312

Complete the long division.

①
$$\begin{array}{r} 109 \\ 4 \overline{)436} \\ 4 \\ \hline 36 \\ 36 \\ \hline \end{array}$$

②
$$\begin{array}{r} 107 \text{ R } 5 \\ 6 \overline{)647} \\ 6 \\ \hline 47 \\ 42 \\ \hline 5 \end{array}$$

③
$$\begin{array}{r} 106 \text{ R } 2 \\ 5 \overline{)532} \\ 5 \\ \hline 32 \\ 30 \\ \hline 2 \end{array}$$

④
$$\begin{array}{r} 120 \text{ R } 0 \\ 7 \overline{)842} \\ 7 \\ \hline 14 \\ 14 \\ \hline 0 \end{array}$$

⑤
$$\begin{array}{r} 120 \text{ R } 0 \\ 8 \overline{)965} \\ 8 \\ \hline 16 \\ 16 \\ \hline 0 \end{array}$$

⑥
$$\begin{array}{r} 260 \text{ R } 0 \\ 3 \overline{)781} \\ 6 \\ \hline 18 \\ 18 \\ \hline 0 \end{array}$$

⑦
$$\begin{array}{r} 101 \\ 5 \overline{)505} \\ 5 \\ \hline 5 \\ 5 \\ \hline \end{array}$$

⑧
$$\begin{array}{r} 101 \text{ R } 6 \\ 7 \overline{)706} \\ 7 \\ \hline 6 \end{array}$$

⑨
$$\begin{array}{r} 105 \\ 6 \overline{)630} \\ 6 \\ \hline 30 \\ 30 \\ \hline \end{array}$$

Do the division.

⑩
```
     16R4
  8 ) 8 5 2
      8
      ──
      52
      48
      ──
      4
```

⑪
```
     150R0
  3 ) 4 5 1
      3
      ──
      15
      15
      ──
      0
```

⑫
```
     2 4R2
  4 ) 8 3 4
      8
      ──
      34
      32
      ──
      2
```

⑬ 845 ÷ 7 = __120R0__

⑭ 543 ÷ 5 = __58 R3__

⑮ 542 ÷ 3 = __100R2__

⑯ 617 ÷ 6 = __62 R5__

⑰ 535 ÷ 5 = __107__

⑱ 763 ÷ 7 = __109__

⑲ 942 ÷ 9 = __16 R6__

⑳ 561 ÷ 4 = __140R0__

㉑ 724 ÷ 6 = __110R5__

㉒ 963 ÷ 8 = __120R0__

Look at the picture. Solve the problems.

㉓ a.

If 4 boys share a box of stickers equally, how many stickers will each boy get? How many stickers will be left?

__822 ÷   4__ = __205R2__

Each boy will get __205__ stickers.

__2__ stickers will be left.

Stickers
822

b.

If 6 girls share a box of stickers equally, how many stickers will each girl get? How many stickers will be left?

__822 ÷   6__ = __137__

Each girl will get __137__ stickers. __0__ stickers will be left.

e.g.

$$5 \overline{)302} \leftarrow \text{3 < 5; consider 1 more digit}$$

$$\begin{array}{r} 6\ 0\ \text{R}\ 2 \\ 5\overline{)3\ 0\ 2} \\ 3\ 0 \\ \hline 2 \end{array}$$

$302 \div 5 = \underline{\textbf{60R2}}$

Remember to put a zero in the quotient.

Look at the picture. Solve the problems.

㉔ Mrs. Smith buys a pack of spaghetti for her family of 4 people. How many grams of spaghetti does each person have on average?

$\underline{832 \div 4} = \underline{208R3}$

$\underline{208\ 9}$

832 g

$2

454 g

$5

㉕ If Jason puts a box of macaroni equally into 5 bowls, how many grams of macaroni are there in each bowl? How many grams are left?

$\underline{454 \div 5} = \underline{90R4}$

$\underline{90R4}$; $\underline{9\text{rams}}$

Ed's Grocery Store
This week's specials

㉖ Mrs. Green spends $100 on buying lettuce for her restaurant. How many heads of lettuce does she buy in all?

$\underline{100 \div 2} = \underline{50}$ $\underline{\$50}$

㉗ The bakery has collected $350 from selling French loaves. How many French loaves have been sold in all?

$\underline{350 \div 5} = \underline{70}$ $\underline{\$70}$

㉘ A loaf is cut into 9 pieces. If Mr. Shaw needs 365 slices of bread, how many loaves of bread does he need to buy?

$\underline{365 \div 9} = \underline{40R5}$ $\underline{40R5}$

Solve the problems. Do the long division in the spaces provided.

㉙  If Maria cuts the ribbon into 4 equal lengths, how long is each piece? How much ribbon is left?

Each piece is ___80___ cm. ___2___ cm of ribbon is left.

㉚ Each teaspoon can hold 9 g of sugar. How many teaspoons of sugar are there in one bag? How much sugar is left?

E̶a̶c̶h̶ sugar is 700 ~~teaspoon of~~ g, 5 g of sugar is left.

㉛ Aunt Lucy uses 6 mL of dish detergent every day to do the dishes. How many days does a bottle of dish detergent last?

125 days of the bottle of dish detergent last

㉜ Katie saves $8 each month for the dress. How many months does it take Katie to save enough money to buy the dress?

15 months will take Katie to save enough money to buy the dress

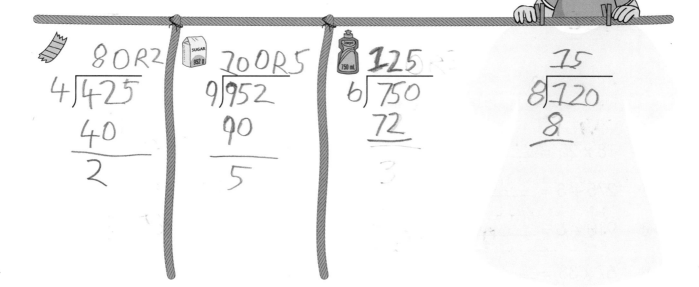

```
   8 0 R 2
4 ) 4 2 5
  4 0
     2
```

```
   7 0 0 R 5
9 ) 9 5 2
  9 0
     5
```

```
   1 2 5
6 ) 7 5 0
  7 2
```

```
    1 5
8 ) 1 2 0
  8
```

More about Multiplication and Division

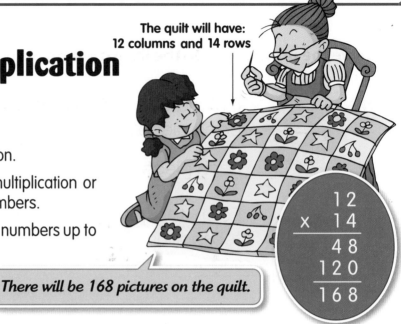

The quilt will have:
12 columns and 14 rows

There will be 168 pictures on the quilt.

```
   12
 x 14
   48
  120
  168
```

- Do basic multiplication or division.
- Solve problems involving the multiplication or division of multi-digit whole numbers.
- Solve problems involving whole numbers up to 100 000 or 2-step problems.

Find the answers.

①
```
    36
 x  24
   144
   720
   864
```

②
```
    79
 x  15
   395
   790
  1185
```

③
```
    27
 x  48
   216
  1080
  1296
```

④
```
     58 R1
 9 ) 523
     45
     73
     02
      1
```

⑤
```
     112 R2
 6 ) 674
     66
     14
     02
      2
```

⑥
```
     203 R3
 4 ) 815
     80
     15
     12
      3
```

⑦ 18 x 25 = __450__

⑧ 64 x 19 = __1216__

⑨ 275 ÷ 3 = __90R5__

⑩ 504 ÷ 5 = __100R4__

⑪ 910 ÷ 6 = __91R2__

⑫ 28 x 41 = __1148__

⑬ 67 x 33 = __2211__

⑭ 451 ÷ 4 = __112R3__

Look at the pictures. Solve the problems.

⑮   a.   A box has 945 pieces of gum. How many packs
of gum are there in a box?

$945 \div 9$ = _105_   _105 pcs_

b.   How much do 15 packs of gum cost?

15×9 = _1140_   _135 pcs_

c.   If Leo and his family consume 2 packs of gum
every day, how many packs of gum do Leo
and his family consume in March?

31×2 = _62_   _62 pcs_

9 pcs Chewy

76¢

⑯

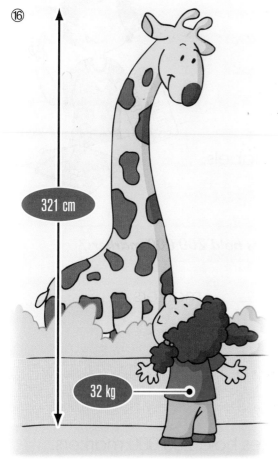

321 cm

32 kg

a.   The giraffe is 3 times the height of Sue.
How tall is Sue?

$327 \div 3$ = _707_
_707cm_

b.   The giraffe is 18 times as heavy as Sue.
How heavy is the giraffe?

32×18 = _576_
_576 kg_

c.   Sue visited 7 zoo animals in
112 minutes. How much time did she
spend visiting each animal?

$112 \div 7$ = _16_
16 min

Read what the people say. Help them solve the problems.

⑰

How many boxes hold 100 000 sheets of paper?

- 1 package: __500__ sheets
- 8 packages: __4000__ sheets
- 1 box: __4000__ sheets
- 5 boxes: __20,000__ sheets ◄
- 20 boxes: __80,000__ sheets ◄

┐make 100 000 sheets

__525__ boxes hold 100 000 sheets of paper.

⑱

A sheet has 20 labels. How many packs do I need for 100 000 labels?

X
- 1 sheet: __18__ labels
- 8 sheets: 744 labels
- 1 package: 18 labels
- 5 packses; 100 000 labels
- 20 packages; 100 0000 labels

20x10 sheet; 200 label
1 Pack; 200 label
100 Pack; 20,000 labels
500 Pack; 100,000 label
500 Packs

She needs __500__ packs for 100 000 labels.

⑲

How many boxes hold 200 000 markers?

X 25
- 1 pack: __25__ markers
- 8 packs; 200 markers
- 1 box; 25 markers
- 5 boxes; 200000 markers
- 20 boxes; 200000 markers

1 box; 400

__500__ boxes hold 200 000 markers.

Solving 2-step problems:

How much do 8 boxes of cookies cost?

1st $8 \div 2 = 4$ ← Find the number of 2's in 8.

2nd $\$5 \times 4 = \$20$ ← Find the cost.

8 boxes cost $20.

Solve the problems. Show your work.

⑳

How much do 81 boxes of juice cost?

$81 \div 3 = 27$

$27 \times 2 = 54$

81 boxes of juice cost $ ___ 54 ___ .

㉑

How much do 78 muffins cost?

$78 \div 6 = 13$

$13 \times 4 = 52$

78 muffins cost $ ___ 52 ___ .

㉒

How much do 52 CDs cost?

$52 \div 4 = 13$

$13 \times 29 = 372$

52 CDs cost $ ___ 377 ___ .

㉓

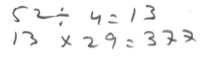

What is the total area of 96 small pieces of cloth?

$96 \div 4 = 24$

$24 \times 5 = 120$

The total area is ___ 120 ___ dm².

Area: 5 dm²

Length, Distance, and Time

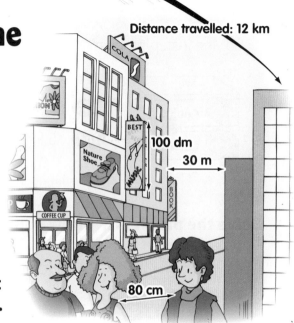

Distance travelled: 12 km

100 dm

30 m

80 cm

- Choose the most appropriate standard unit to measure length, height, width, and distance, using mm, cm, dm, m, or km.

- Do unit conversions.

- Find time intervals to the nearest second and elapsed time.

Choose the most appropriate standard unit to do each measurement. Write it on the line.

km   m   dm   cm   mm

① the thickness of a dime ___mm___

② the length of your arm ___dm___

③ the length of your thumb ___cm___

④ the distance between Toronto and New York ___km___

⑤ the width of a swimming pool ___m___

⑥ the length of a tunnel ___m___

⑦ the thickness of a lunch box ___km___

⑧ the height of Mount Everest ___m___

⑨

a. the distance between the girls

___cm___

b. the distance between the girls and the whale

___cm___

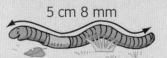

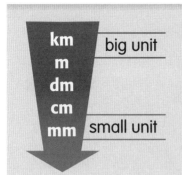

km	big unit
m	
dm	
cm	
mm	small unit

The relationships between the units:

1 km = 1000 m

1 m = 10 dm = 100 cm

1 dm = 10 cm

1 cm = 10 mm

e.g.

5 cm 8 mm

5 cm 8 mm = 50 mm + 8 mm
= 58 mm

The worm is 58 mm long.

Fill in the blanks.

⑩ 4 m = _4 00_ cm

⑪ 8 km = _8000_ m

⑫ 6 dm = _60_ cm

⑬ 9 cm = _90_ mm

⑭ 8000 m = _8_ km

⑮ 60 cm = _6_ dm

⑯ 700 cm = _7_ m

⑰ 50 mm = _5_ cm

⑱ 7 km 8 m

= _7080_ m + 8 m _7008_

= _7008_ m

⑲ 9 cm 8 mm

= _90_ mm + 8 mm

= _798_ mm

⑳ 5 dm 6 cm

= _50_ cm + 6 cm

= _56_ cm

㉑ 4 m 9 cm

= _400_ cm + 9 cm

= _409_ cm

Do the conversion. Show your work. Then circle the greater measurement.

㉒

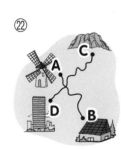

A to B : 4 km (20) m

C to D : (4150) m

㉓ Sam's height : 1 m (15) cm

Teddy's height : (9) dm 8 cm

You can find time intervals to the nearest second by using an analogue clock.

e.g. Start eating a cookie   Finish the cookie   Time taken

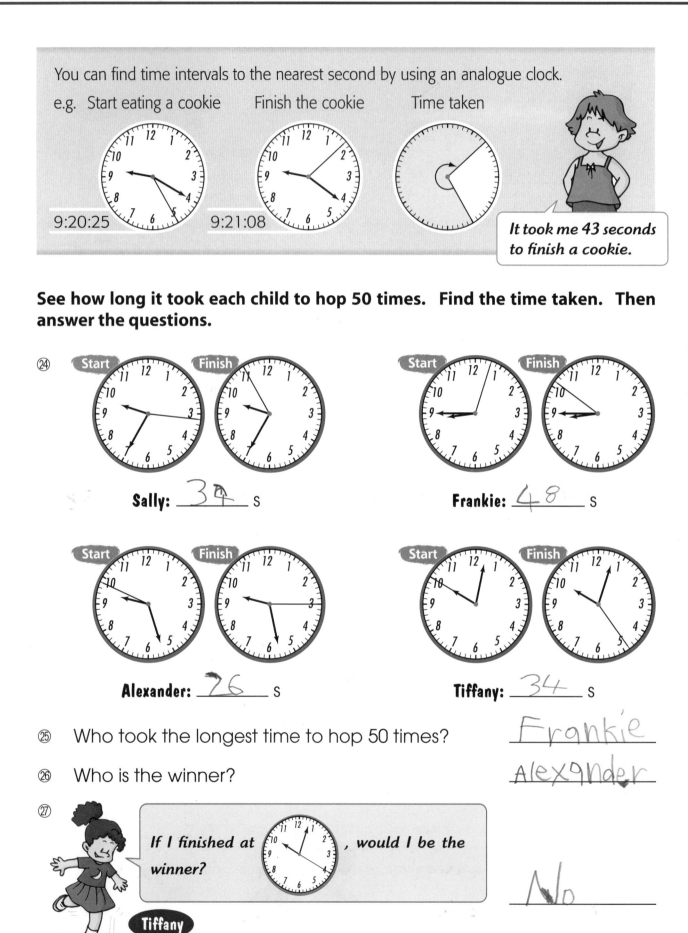

9:20:25   9:21:08

It took me 43 seconds to finish a cookie.

See how long it took each child to hop 50 times. Find the time taken. Then answer the questions.

㉔

Start   Finish

Sally: _3 4_ s

Start   Finish

Frankie: _4 8_ s

Start   Finish

Alexander: _2 6_ s

Start   Finish

Tiffany: _34_ s

㉕ Who took the longest time to hop 50 times?   _Frankie_

㉖ Who is the winner?   _Alexander_

㉗ *If I finished at* [clock] *, would I be the winner?*

Tiffany

_No_

We can use subtraction to find time intervals. Sometimes we need to find the time interval in 2 steps.

e.g. 8:46 a.m. ⟶ 4:20 p.m.

1st 8:46 ⟶ noon

$$12:00$$
$$-\quad 8:46$$
$$\overline{\quad 3:14}$$

(3 h 14 min)

2nd noon ⟶ 4:20 p.m.
(4 h 20 min)

Time interval:
3 h 14 min + 4 h 20 min
= 7 h 34 min

The time interval is 7 h 34 min.

Find the travelling time of each train from Villa Village to Cook City. Then answer the question.

㉘

Train	Departure Time	Arrival Time	Travelling Time
A	8:25 a.m.	12:07 p.m.	6:18
B	6:53 a.m.	11:51 a.m.	5:02
C	10:12 a.m.	3:54 p.m.	6:58
D	11:29 a.m.	4:16 p.m.	7:13

㉙ Which train is the fastest? _____A_____

Ask your parent to give you a calendar. Then find the durations with the help of it.

㉚ From Sep 1 to Nov 30 • __3__ months or __13__ weeks

㉛ From Apr 3 to May 7 • __5__ weeks or __35__ days

㉜ From Apr 1 to Jun 30 • __3__ months or __13__ weeks

㉝

If I start working on Project A on Mar 8, 2015 and the deadline is on Mar 7, 2017, how much time do I have to spend on this project?

__2__ years or __24__ months

Perimeter and Area (1)

- Measure and record the perimeters and areas of regular and irregular polygons.
- Draw polygons with a given area or perimeter.
- Solve problems about perimeter or area.

Your face has an area of about 144 cm².

Find the perimeter of each polygon.

①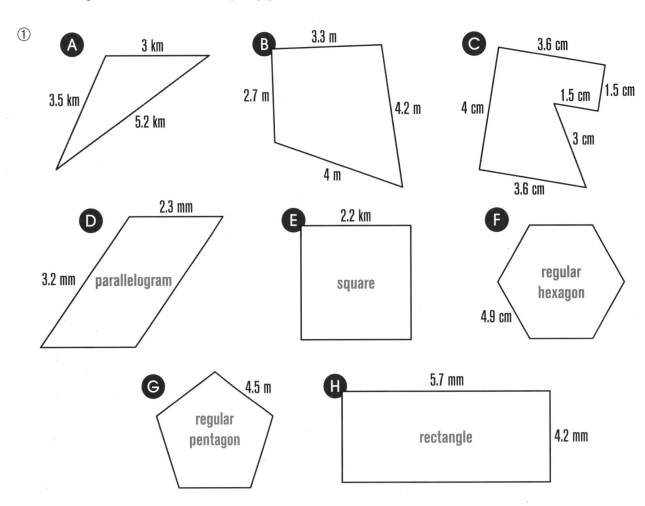

A — 3 km, 3.5 km, 5.2 km

B — 3.3 m, 2.7 m, 4.2 m, 4 m

C — 3.6 cm, 1.5 cm, 1.5 cm, 4 cm, 3 cm, 3.6 cm

D — parallelogram — 2.3 mm, 3.2 mm

E — square — 2.2 km

F — regular hexagon — 4.9 cm

G — regular pentagon — 4.5 m

H — rectangle — 5.7 mm, 4.2 mm

Perimeter

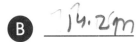  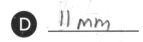

A 11.7 km   B 14.2 m   C 17.2 cm   D 11 mm

E 8.8 km   F 29.4 cm   G 22.5 m   H 19.8 mm

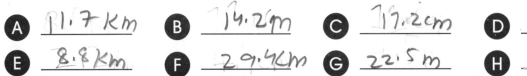

Find the area of each shape.

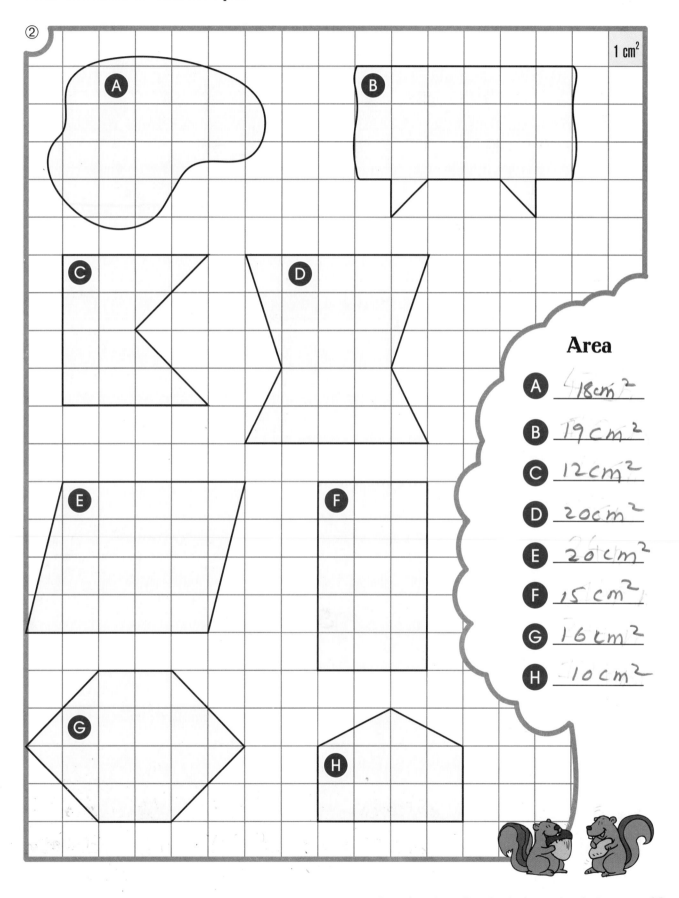

②

1 cm²

A

B

C

D

E

F

G

H

Area

A ___4 18cm²___

B ___19 cm²___

C ___12 cm²___

D ___20 cm²___

E ___20 cm²___

F ___15 cm²___

G ___16 cm²___

H ___10 cm²___

Draw 4 different rectangles, each with a perimeter of 20 cm. Then find the area of each rectangle and write the answer in it.

③

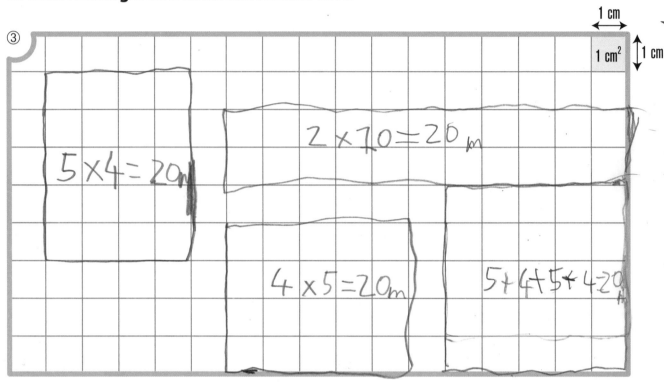

1 cm

1 cm² 1 cm

$5 \times 4 = 20$ m

$2 \times 10 = 20$ m

$4 \times 5 = 20$ m

$5 + 4 + 5 + 4 = 20$

Draw 3 different rectangles, each with an area of 24 cm². Then find the perimeter of each rectangle and write the answer in it.

④

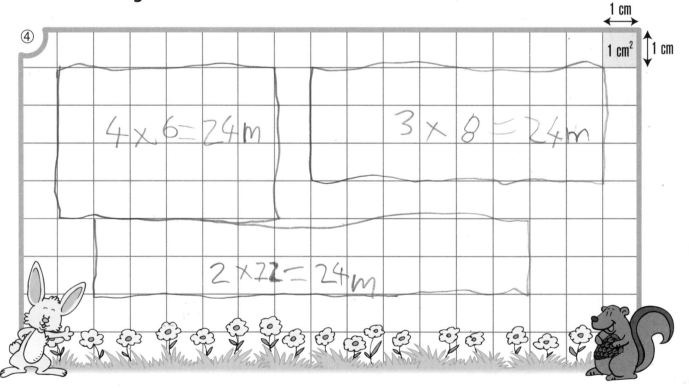

1 cm

1 cm² 1 cm

$4 \times 6 = 24$ m

$3 \times 8 = 24$ m

$2 \times 22 = 24$ m

Solve the problems.

⑤

8 cm

square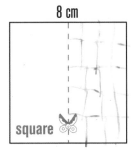

> If I cut along the dotted line to get two identical rectangles, what is the perimeter of each rectangle?

_24cm_

⑥

15 cm

13 cm

rectangle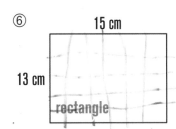

> If I want to cut a square with the greatest area from this rectangle, what is the perimeter of that square?

_52cm_

⑦

Area: 36 cm²

parallelogram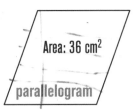

> If 42 parallelograms are needed to cover a carpet, what is the area of the carpet?

1512cm²

⑧

Area: 126 cm²

trapezoid

> I've used 3 triangles of the same size to form this trapezoid. What is the area of each triangle?

42cm²

⑨

20 cm

18 cm   18 cm

36 cm   36 cm

42 cm

> What is the "perimeter" of my dog?

_170cm_

Perimeter and Area (2)

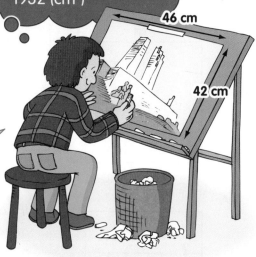

Area of the rectangle:
= 46 x 42
= 1932 (cm²)

46 cm

42 cm

- Use formulas to find the perimeters and areas of rectangles.

- Solve problems related to perimeters or areas.

The area of my picture is 1932 cm².

Read what Emily says. Then fill in the blanks and follow Emily's method to find the perimeters of the rectangles.

①

A rectangle has 2 lengths and 2 widths. The perimeter of a rectangle is the sum of 2 lengths and 2 widths.

8 cm

5 cm

- 2 lengths: ___16___
- 2 widths: ___16___

Perimeter = ___16___ + ___510___ = ___22___

My perimeter is ___26___ .

②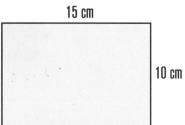

15 cm

10 cm

- 2 lengths: ___30___

- 2 widths: ___20___

Perimeter = ___32___ + ___20___

= ___50___ (cm)

③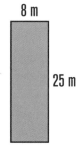

8 m

25 m

- 2 lengths: ___16___

- 2 widths: ___50___

Perimeter = ___16___ + ___20___

= ___30___ (cm)

Formula for finding the perimeter of a rectangle:

Perimeter = 2 x length + 2 x width

width

length

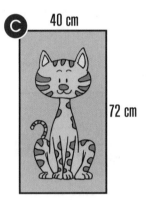

9 cm

16 cm

Perimeter = 2 x 16 + 2 x 9
= 32 + 18
= 50

The perimeter of the rectangle is 50 cm.

Use the formula to find the perimeter of each rectangle.

④ **A** 16 cm

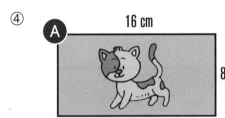

8 cm

B 12 m

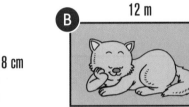

7 m

C 40 cm

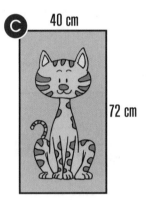

72 cm

D 13 cm

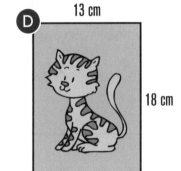

18 cm

E

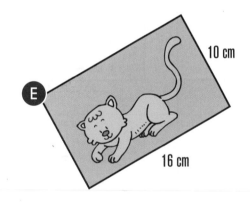

10 cm

16 cm

F 32 m

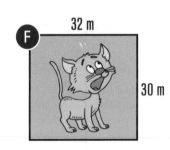

30 m

A Perimeter

= 2 x 16 + 2 x 8

= 32 + 16

= 48cm

B Perimeter

= 2 x 12 + 2 x 7

= 24 + 14

= 38

C Perimeter

= 2 x 40 + 2 x 72

= 80 + 244

= 224

D Perimeter

= 2 x 13 + 2 x 18

= 26 + 36

= 62

E Perimeter

= 2 x 16 + 2 x 10

= 32 + 20

= 52

F Perimeter

= 2 x 32 + 2 x 30

= 64 + 60

= 124

Formula for finding the area of a rectangle:

Area = length x width

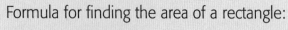

width

length

9 cm

16 cm

Area = 9 x 16

= 144

The area of the rectangle is 144 cm².

Find the lengths and widths of the rectangles. Then find the areas of the rectangles by counting and using the formula.

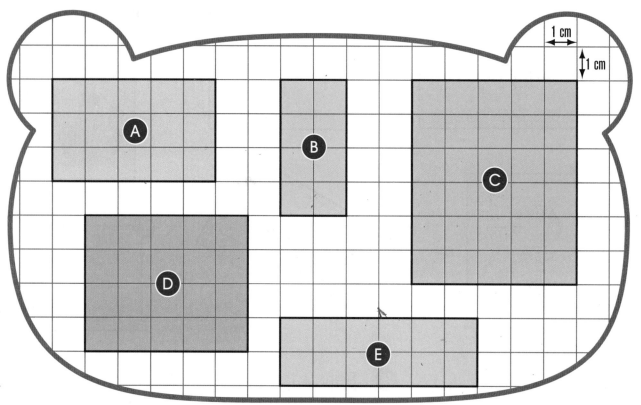

1 cm

1 cm

⑤

Area

	Length	Width	By counting	By using formula
Ⓐ	5	3	15	The area of the rectangle is 15cm²
Ⓑ	2	4	8	The area of the rectangle is 8cm²
Ⓒ	5	6	30	The area of the rectangle is 30cm²
Ⓓ	5	4	20	The area of the rectangle is 20cm²
Ⓔ	6	2	12	The area of the rectangle is 12cm²

Solve the problems.

⑥ What is the length of the rectangle?

Area = 153 cm² | 9 cm

The length is _17cm_ .

⑦ If the length of the poster is 10 cm longer than the width,

a. what is the length?

48 + 10 = 58 = 58 cm

The length is _58 cm_ .

48 cm

b. what is the perimeter of the poster?

2 × 58 + 2 × 48 = 116
116 + 9 = 212

The perimeter of the poster is _212_ .

⑧ a. What is the area of the picture?

24 × 36 = 864

The area is _864_ .

24 cm

Architecture
Today

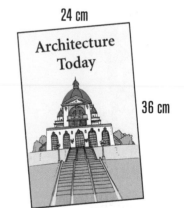

36 cm

b. What is the perimeter of the picture?

The perimeter is _120_ .

⑨

> The width of my favourite picture is 32 cm.
> If its perimeter is 118 cm, what is its length?

Its length is _22 cm²_ .

Mass, Capacity, and Volume

It can hold 4 layers of 40 centimetre cubes.

Volume
= 40 x 4
= 160 (cm³)

- Choose the most appropriate standard unit to measure mass (e.g. mg, g, kg, or t).

- Understand the relationships between capacity and volume by comparing the volume of an object with the amount of liquid it can contain or displace.

- Use a formula to find the volume of a rectangular prism.

My volume is 160 cm³.

Complete the diagram and fill in the blanks with the short forms of the given units.

gram (g)	kilogram (kg)	milligram (mg)	tonne (t)

① **Big Unit**

mg

kg

t

g

Small Unit

② **Relationships between the units:**

a. 1 t = 1000 __kg__

1 kg = 1000 __g__

1 g = 1000 __mg__

4 t = 4000 __kg__

6 kg = 6000 __g__

7 g = 7000 __mg__

b. 5000 kg = 5 __t__

6000 mg = 6 __g__

4000 g = 4 __kg__

8000 g = 8 __kg__

9000 kg = 9 __t__

3000 mg = 3 __g__

Choose the appropriate unit for the mass of each object. Write "mg", "g", "kg", or "t".

③ a feather __mg__

④ an elephant __t__

⑤ a man __kg__

⑥ a pencil __g__

⑦ a pea __mg__

⑧ a whale __t__

⑨ an apple __g__

⑩ a watermelon __kg__

A centimetre cube is a cube with length, width, and height of 1 cm.

1 cm
1 cm
1 cm

Volume = 1 cm³

A cubic container with all edges 1 cm long can hold 1 millilitre of liquid.

1 cm
1 cm
1 cm

Capacity = 1 mL

The relationship between volume and capacity: **1 cm³ = 1 mL**

The children use centimetre cubes to show the capacity and volume of each container. Help them record the measurements. Then fill in the blanks.

⑪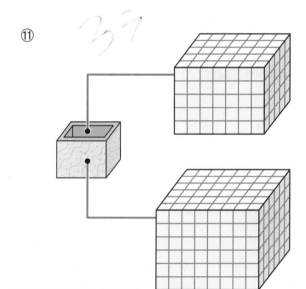

Capacity
- No. of cubes in each layer: _35_
- No. of layers: _5_
- Capacity: _175_ mL

Volume
- No. of cubes in each layer: _48_
- No. of layers: _7_
  Volume: _228_ cm³

⑫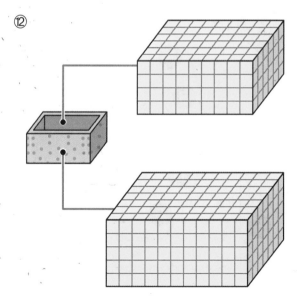

Capacity
- No. of cubes in each layer: _54_
- No. of layers: _4_
- Capacity: _216_ mL

Volume
- No. of cubes in each layer: _77_
- No. of layers: _5_
- Volume: _385_ cm³

Formula for finding the volume of a rectangular prism:

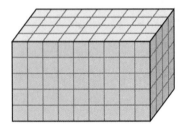

area of base ⟶

height

Volume = area of base x height

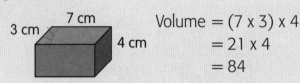

3 cm   7 cm

4 cm

Volume = (7 x 3) x 4
= 21 x 4
= 84

The volume of this prism is 84 cm³.

Look at each rectangular prism built with centimetre cubes. Fill in the blanks.

⑬

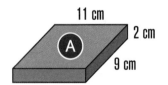

Area of Base = _36_ cm²

Height = _5_ cm

Volume = _36_ x _5_

= _180_ (cm³)

⑭

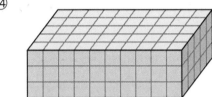

Area of Base = _50_ cm²

Height = _3_ cm

Volume = _50_ x _3_

= _150_ (cm³)

Find the volume of each rectangular prism.

⑮

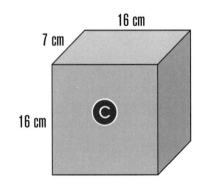

11 cm   2 cm
A
9 cm

16 cm
7 cm
C
16 cm

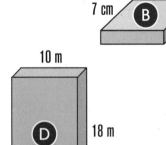

10 m

D   18 m

2 m

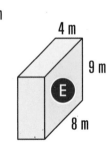

8 cm   2 cm
7 cm   B

4 m
9 m
E
8 m

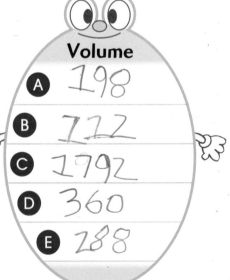

Volume

A   _198_

B   _222_

C   _1792_

D   _360_

E   _288_

Draw a line on each solid to cut it into two rectangular prisms. Find the volume of each prism. Then find the volume of the solid.

⑯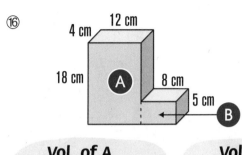

Vol. of A	Vol. of B
= __36__ x __12__	= __8__ x __5__
= __432__ (cm³)	= __40__ (cm³)

Vol. of the solid = __432__ + __40__
= __472__ (cm³)

⑰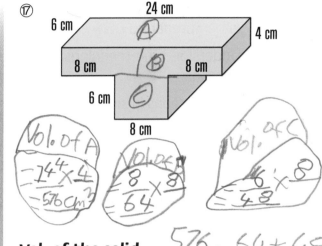

Vol. of A
_74⁴×4_
576 cm²

Vol. of B
_8×8_
_64_

Vol. of C
_6×8_
_48_

Vol. of the solid = __576__ + __64__ + __48__
= __688__ (cm³)

Help Elaine find the volume and the capacity of the aquarium with a thickness of 1 cm.

⑱ **Volume**

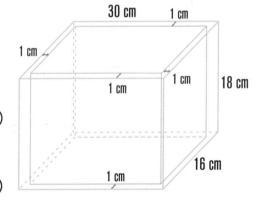

Length = 30 cm

Width = __16__ cm

Area = __30__ x __16__ = __480__ (cm²)

Height = __18__ cm

Volume = __480__ x __18__ = __8640__ (cm³)

Capacity

Length = 30 – 2 = 28 (cm)

Width = __16 – 2__ = __14__ (cm)

Height = __18 – 1__ = __17__ (cm)

Area = __28__ x __14__ = __392__ (cm²)

Volume = __392__ x __17__ = __17__ (cm³)

Capacity = __6664__ mL

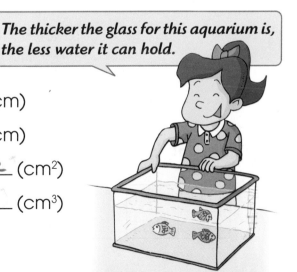

The thicker the glass for this aquarium is, the less water it can hold.

Fractions

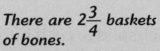

There are $2\frac{3}{4}$ baskets of bones.

- Identify and write different types of fractions: proper and improper fractions and mixed numbers.
- Understand the meanings of equivalent fractions.
- Write fractions in simplest form.
- Compare and order fractions.

Fill in the blanks with the given words. Then sort the fractions.

Improper fraction	Mixed number	Proper fraction

① **Types of Fraction**

In̲P̲r̲o̲p̲e̲r̲ fraction : a fraction with its numerator smaller than its denominator

e.g. $\frac{3}{7}$ $\frac{5}{6}$ $\frac{2}{4}$ ____ fraction

_I̲m̲p̲r̲o̲p̲e̲r̲_ : a fraction with its numerator equal to or greater than its denominator

e.g. $\frac{9}{5}$ $\frac{8}{7}$ $\frac{7}{5}$ $\frac{8}{8}$ ____ number

_M̲i̲x̲e̲d̲_ : a number made up of a whole number and a proper fraction

e.g. $2\frac{3}{4}$ $1\frac{1}{5}$ $3\frac{4}{9}$ $1\frac{1}{3}$ $2\frac{7}{10}$

$2\frac{3}{4}$

$\frac{3}{7}$

$1\frac{1}{5}$

$\frac{9}{5}$

$\frac{8}{7}$

$\frac{5}{6}$

$3\frac{4}{9}$

$\frac{2}{4}$

$1\frac{1}{3}$

$\frac{7}{5}$

$2\frac{7}{10}$

$\frac{8}{8}$

Write a fraction for the coloured part of each figure.

②

$\dfrac{3}{5}$

③ $\dfrac{4}{6}$

Write an improper fraction for the coloured parts of each group of diagrams.

④  $\frac{7}{2}$

⑤ 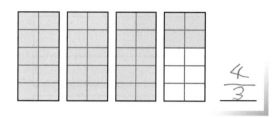 $\frac{4}{3}$

⑥ 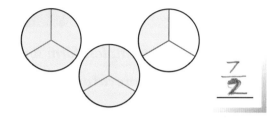 $\frac{5}{3}$

⑦ 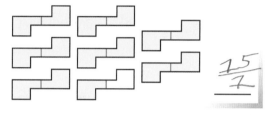 $\frac{15}{7}$

Draw lines to cut one of the diagrams in each group and colour the correct number of figures and parts to show the mixed number given.

⑧ $3\frac{4}{5}$

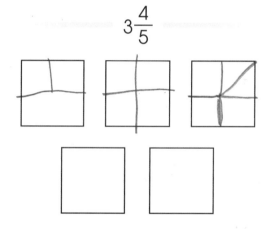

⑨ $4\frac{3}{10}$

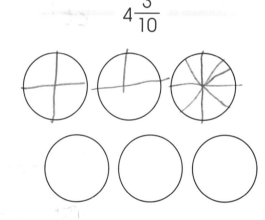

Write an improper fraction and a mixed number for the coloured parts of each group of diagrams.

⑩ A 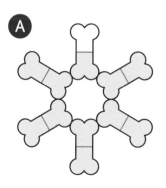   B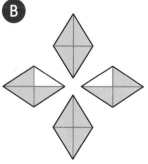

	Improper fraction	Mixed number
A	$\frac{17}{1}$	$4\frac{3}{5}$
B	$\frac{14}{2}$	$8\frac{3}{14}$

Equivalent fractions: fractions that represent the same part of a whole

e.g.

$\frac{1}{2}$ is coloured.

$\frac{2}{4}$ is coloured.

$\frac{4}{8}$ is coloured.

$\frac{1}{2}$, $\frac{2}{4}$, and $\frac{4}{8}$ are equivalent fractions.

$\frac{1}{2}$ is in simplest form since the numerator and the denominator have no more common factor except 1.

Colour the parts and write a fraction to show the coloured parts in each figure. Then write the equivalent fractions in the space provided.

⑪ Colour 2 parts : 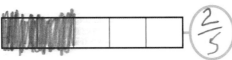 $\frac{2}{5}$

Colour 1 part : 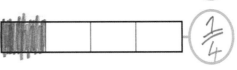 $\frac{1}{4}$

Colour 4 parts : 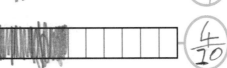 $\frac{4}{10}$

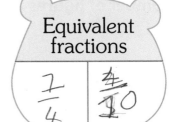

Equivalent fractions

$\frac{1}{4}$ | $\frac{4}{10}$

⑫ Colour 5 parts : 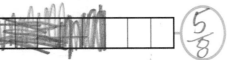 $\frac{5}{8}$

Colour 8 parts :  $\frac{8}{12}$

Colour 2 parts :  $\frac{2}{3}$

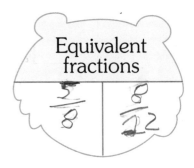

Equivalent fractions

$\frac{5}{8}$ | $\frac{8}{12}$

Circle the fractions in simplest form.

⑬

$\frac{6}{10}$ $\frac{4}{7}$ $\frac{3}{5}$

⑭

$\frac{3}{4}$ $\frac{9}{12}$ $\frac{5}{8}$

⑮

$\frac{3}{9}$ $\frac{7}{10}$ $\frac{1}{3}$

Steps to compare mixed numbers with the same denominator:

e.g. $4\frac{5}{8}$ $4\frac{6}{8}$

1st Compare the whole number parts. The one with a greater number is greater. If they are the same, go to step 2.

2nd Compare the fraction parts. The one with a greater numerator is greater.

1st $4\frac{5}{8}$ $4\frac{6}{8}$ — the same; compare the fraction parts

$5 < 6$

2nd $4\frac{5}{8}$ $4\frac{6}{8}$

$4\frac{6}{8}$ is greater.

Circle the greater fraction.

⑯ $\frac{7}{9} > \frac{3}{9}$

⑰ $1\frac{4}{5} > 3\frac{1}{5}$

⑱ $\frac{11}{8} > \frac{7}{8}$

⑲ $3\frac{1}{7} > 2\frac{6}{7}$

⑳ $4\frac{3}{6} > 3\frac{4}{6}$

㉑ $\frac{15}{9} < \frac{20}{9}$

Put the fractions in order. Then answer the question.

㉒ $1\frac{3}{5}$ $2\frac{1}{5}$ $\frac{4}{5}$

$2\frac{1}{5} > 1\frac{3}{5} > \frac{4}{5}$

㉓ $\frac{6}{12}$ $\frac{3}{12}$ $\frac{18}{12}$

$\frac{18}{12} > \frac{6}{12} > \frac{3}{12}$

㉔ $1\frac{5}{10}$ $1\frac{3}{10}$ $2\frac{1}{10}$

$1\frac{3}{10} < 1\frac{5}{10} < 2\frac{1}{10}$

㉕

Each bone is cut into 4 equal parts. If I have $3\frac{1}{4}$ bones, Tim has $\frac{15}{4}$, and Joe has $2\frac{2}{4}$, who has the most bones?

Gary

Number of bones in order from the most to the fewest: $3\frac{1}{4}$, $2\frac{2}{4}$, $\frac{15}{4}$

Gary has the most bones.

Decimals (1)

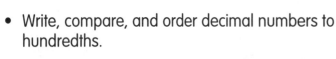

Can you see that 0.78 of the grid is coloured?

- Write, compare, and order decimal numbers to hundredths.
- Understand the place value in decimal numbers, the relationship between fractions and their equivalent decimal forms, and equivalent representations of a decimal number.
- Count forward or backward by hundredths.

Write a decimal for each diagram to show how much is coloured. Then write the decimal in words.

① **A**

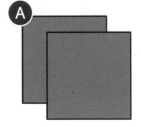

B

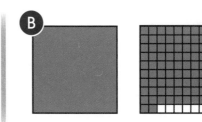

A _2.16_ ; _2_ and _16_ hundredths

B _1.92_ ; _1_ and 92 hundredths

C _4.8_ ; _4_ and 8 hundredths

D _3.36_ ; _3_ and 36 hundredths

E _4.30_ ; _4_ and 30 hundredths

C

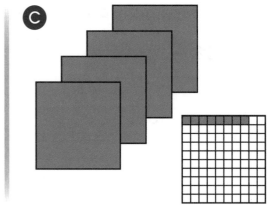

E

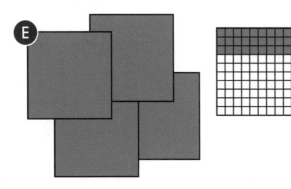

D

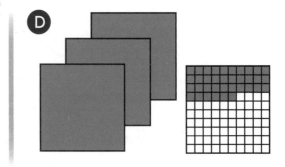

Place value: the value of a digit that appears in a number

e.g. 3.68

- "3" is in the ones place; it means 3.
- "6" is in the tenths place; it means 0.6.
- "8" is in the hundredths place; it means 0.08.

ones	tenths	hundredths
3 .	6	8

Draw and colour the diagrams to match each decimal given. Then write the decimal in words.

② **1.37**

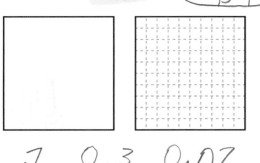

O	T	H
1	3	7

1   0.3   0.07

③ **1.84**

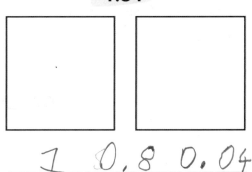

O	T	H
1	8	4

1   0.8   0.04

Write the meaning of each highlighted digit.

④ 4.2**8** __T 0.2__

⑤ 3.1**9** __O 3__

⑥ 2.6**5** __H 0.05__

⑦ 8.3**9** __H 0.09__

⑧ 4.5**3** __T 0.5__

⑨ 7.5**8** __H 0.08__

⑩ 2.7**1** __H 0.01__

⑪ 8.2**4** __O 8__

⑫ 4.1**3** __T 0.1__

Write as decimals. Then colour the greater one in each pair.

⑬ 4 and 27 hundredths 4.27

4 and 7 hundredths 4.7

⑭ 6 and 16 hundredths 6.16

1 and 66 hundredths 1.66

⑮ 3 and 11 hundredths 3.11

3 and 13 hundredths 3.13

⑯ 18 and 9 hundredths 18.9

9 and 18 hundredths 9.18

Fractions and Decimals

e.g.

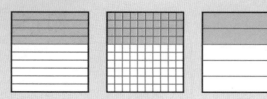

Fraction: $\dfrac{4}{10}$ = $\dfrac{40}{100}$ = $\dfrac{2}{5}$

Decimal: 0.4 = 0.40 ← equivalent decimals

$\dfrac{2}{5} = 0.40$; 0.40 is the equivalent decimal form of $\dfrac{2}{5}$.

Colour the diagrams to match the given ones. Then write a fraction and a decimal to tell how much of each diagram is coloured.

⑰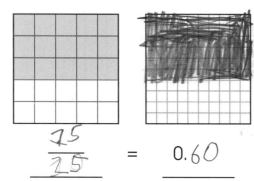

$\dfrac{15}{25}$ = 0.60

⑱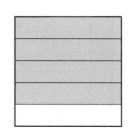

$\dfrac{4}{5}$ = 0.80

⑲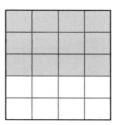

$\dfrac{12}{20}$ = 0.60

⑳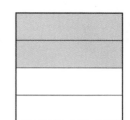

$\dfrac{2}{4}$ = 0.50

Circle the equivalent decimal form for each fraction.

㉑ $\dfrac{10}{25}$ (0.40) 0.04

㉒ $\dfrac{1}{2}$ 0.55 (0.50)

㉓ $\dfrac{12}{20}$ (0.60) 0.80

㉔ $\dfrac{9}{10}$ (0.90) 0.99

㉕ $\dfrac{5}{25}$ (0.40) (0.20)

㉖ $\dfrac{20}{50}$ (0.50) 0.40

Put the decimals in order.

㉗ 2.59 2.95 5.29 5.92   _5.92_ > _5.29_ > _2.95_ > _2.59_

㉘ 3.06 3.60 3.66 3.00   _3.66_ > _3.60_ > _3.06_ > _3.00_

㉙ 2.47 2.40 2.74 2.70   _2.74_ < _2.70_ < _2.47_ < _2.40_

㉚ 6.88 8.68 6.68 6.86   _8.68_ < _6.88_ < _6.86_ < _6.68_

Fill in the missing numbers.

㉛ 9.27 9.28 9.29 _9.30_ _9.31_ _9.32_ _9.33_ 9.34

㉜ 6.14 6.15 6.16 _6.17_ _6.18_ 6.19 _6.20_ _6.21_

㉝ 8.06 8.07 8.08 _8.09_ _8.10_ _8.11_ 8.12 _8.13_

㉞ 3.95 3.96 3.97 _3.98_ _3.99_ _4.00_ _4.01_ 4.02

㉟ 9.94 9.95 9.96 _9.97_ _9.98_ _9.99_ _10.00_ 10.01

Help Lucy use arrows to mark the locations of the bones on the number line. Then fill in the blanks.

㊱

> *The bones are at 5.96, 6.08, 5.99, 6.12, and 6.05.*

a.

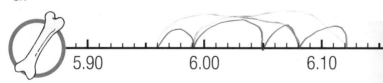

5.90   6.00   6.10

b. Which bone is closest to the one at 5.99?

_5.96_

c. Which bone is farthest from the one at 6.08?

_6.12_

Decimals (2)

I've never seen such a big bone in my life! It weighs 3.112 kg.

3 kg 112 g

- Round decimal numbers to the nearest tenth.
- Multiply decimal numbers by 10, 100, 1000, or 10 000.
- Divide decimal numbers by 10 or 100.
- Do conversion between different units.

kg	g		
3 .	1	1	2

Use arrows to place the decimals on the number lines. Then round each decimal to the nearest tenth.

①

4.11
3.92 | 4.17
3.96

a.

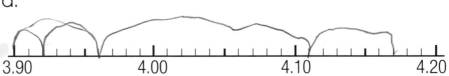

3.90   4.00   4.10   4.20

b. 4.11 __4.20__   c. 3.92 __3.90__

d. 4.17 __4.20__   e. 3.96 __4.00__

②

8.95
9.14 | 9.08
9.03

a.

8.90   9.00   9.10   9.20

b. 8.95 __9.00__   c. 9.14 __9.15__

d. 9.08 __9.10__   e. 9.03 __9.00__

Round each decimal to the nearest tenth.

③ 5.62 __5.60__   ④ 4.71 __4.70__   ⑤ 6.23 __6.20__

⑥ 10.54 __10.50__   ⑦ 15.82 __15.80__   ⑧ 20.27 __20.30__

⑨ 9.96 __10.00__   ⑩ 9.07 __9.20__   ⑪ 15.16 __15.20__

⑫ 8.08 __8.10__   ⑬ 3.44 __3.40__   ⑭ 2.93 __2.90__

Move the decimal point

A decimal
- x 10 ——— **1** place to the right
- x 100 ——— **2** places to the right
- x 1000 ——— **3** places to the right
- x 10 000 —— **4** places to the right

e.g. Multiply 3.25 by 10, 100, 1000, or 10 000.

3.25 x 10 = 32.5
3.25 x 100 = 325
3.250 x 1000 = 3250
3.2500 x 10 000 = 32500

Use arrows to show the movement of the decimal points. Then find the answers.

⑮ 6.25 x 10 = _62.5_

⑯ 3.28 x 100 = _328_

⑰ 4.06 x 1000 = _4060_

⑱ 5.13 x 10 000 = _51300_

⑲ 6.53 x 1000 = _6530_

⑳ 7.08 x 10 = _70.8_

㉑ 8.67 x 10 000 = _86700_

㉒ 9.62 x 100 = _962_

Look at the pictures. Fill in the blanks.

㉓ a. 10 bottles hold _07.5_ L of detergent.

b. 10 000 bottles hold _07500_ L of detergent.

㉔ a. 100 bags hold _085_ kg of candies.

b. 1000 bags hold _850_ kg of candies.

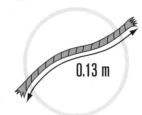

㉕ a. The total length of 10 strings is _07.3_ m.

b. The total length of 10 000 strings is _1300_ m.

Move the decimal point	e.g. Divide 4.6 by 10 or 100.
A decimal ÷ 10 — **1** place to the left	4.6 ÷ 10 = 0.46
÷ 100 — **2** places to the left	04.6 ÷ 100 = 0.046

Use arrows to show the movement of the decimal points. Then find the answers.

㉖ 8.54 ÷ 10 = _0.8854_

㉗ 06.7 ÷ 100 = _0.067_

㉘ 9.6 ÷ 100 = _0.096_

㉙ 5.29 ÷ 10 = _0.529_

㉚ 7.4 ÷ 10 = _0.74_

㉛ 3.8 ÷ 100 = _0.038_

㉜ 6.2 ÷ 100 = _0.062_

㉝ 5.6 ÷ 10 = _0.56_

Find the weight of each item. Then check the correct answer.

㉞

Each piece weighs _0.025_ kg.

Each piece weighs _00.8_ kg.

The heavier cookie

㉟

Each piece weighs _00.2_ kg.

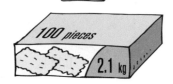

Each piece weighs _0.022_ kg.

The heavier cracker

Weight	Length/Distance	We can write measurements in an easier way with the help of the charts.
1 kg = 1000 g	1 km = 1000 m	
1 g = 1000 mg	1 m = 100 cm	e.g. 4 kg 16 g
	1 cm = 10 mm	= **4.016 kg**
Capacity		3 m 42 cm
1 L = 1000 mL		= **3.42 m**

e.g. 4 kg 16 g = **4.016 kg**

kg		g	
4 .	0	1	6

↑ decimal point

3 m 42 cm = **3.42 m**

m		cm
3 .	4	2

↑ decimal point

Write the measurements in decimals.

㊱ 3 kg 804 g = _3.804_ kg

kg		g	
3 .	8	0	4

㊲ 4 L 78 mL = _4.078_ L

L		mL	
4 .	0	7	8

㊳ 8 km 5 m = _8.005_ km

km		m	
8 .	0	0	5

㊴ 6 m 17 cm = _6.17_ m

m		cm
6 .	1	7

㊵ 5 cm 8 mm = _5.8_ cm

cm	mm
5 .	8

㊶ 9 kg 6 g = _9.006_ kg

kg		g	
9 .	0	0	6

Write each measurement in decimals. Then answer the questions.

㊷

A
2 kg 16 g

_2.076_ kg

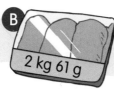
B
2 kg 61 g

_2.061_ kg

C
2 kg 6 g

_2.6_ kg

Which pack is the heaviest?

_A_

㊸

A 8 cm 9 mm _8.9_ cm

B 8 cm 5 mm _8.5_ cm

C 8 cm 8 mm _8.8_ cm

Which bone is the longest?

_A_

Addition and Subtraction of Decimals

- Add or subtract decimals to hundredths.
- Do estimates.
- Solve problems involving addition and subtraction of decimals.

1.25 m

0.16 m

$$\begin{array}{r} 1.2\,5 \\ +\ 0.1\,6 \\ \hline 1.4\,1 \end{array}$$

Teddy, can you believe that I'm 1.41 m tall?

Write a vertical addition or subtraction to match each sentence.

①

  Ⓐ The sum of 2.68 and 3.44 is 6.12.

  Ⓑ The difference of 5.14 and 2.99 is 2.15.

  Ⓒ 4.67 and 6.28 makes 10.95.

  Ⓓ Subtracting 2.13 from 8.07 is 5.94.

Ⓐ
$$\begin{array}{r} 1\ \ 1 \\ 2.68 \\ +\ 3.44 \\ \hline 6\cdot 22 \end{array}$$

Ⓑ
$$\begin{array}{r} 4\ 10\ 14 \\ 5.74 \\ -\ 2.99 \\ \hline 2.75 \end{array}$$

Ⓒ
$$\begin{array}{r} 1 \\ 4.67 \\ +\ 6.28 \\ \hline 10.95 \end{array}$$

Ⓓ
$$\begin{array}{r} 1 \\ 2.73 \\ -\ 8.07 \\ \hline 10.20 \end{array}$$

Find the answers.

②
$$\begin{array}{r} 1\ 1 \\ 6.5\,3 \\ +\ 2.4\,9 \\ \hline 9\cdot 02 \end{array}$$

③
$$\begin{array}{r} 1\ 1 \\ 4.2\,7 \\ +\ 3.9\,4 \\ \hline 8.21 \end{array}$$

④
$$\begin{array}{r} 1\ 12\ 11 \\ 2.3\,1 \\ -\ 0.6\,8 \\ \hline 1.63 \end{array}$$

⑤
$$\begin{array}{r} 3\ 16 \\ 7.4\,6 \\ -\ 5.3\,9 \\ \hline 2.07 \end{array}$$

⑥ 3.93 + 1.78 = __5.71__

⑦ 15.26 − 9.44 = __5.82__

⑧ 8.67 + 7.85 = __16.52__

⑨ 4.62 − 2.88 = __1.74__

⑩ 10.02 − 6.53 = __3.49__

⑪ 3.87 + 12.64 = __16.51__

⑫ 15.48 − 2.69 = __12.79__

⑬ 7.06 + 5.89 = __12.95__

Sometimes we need to find the equivalent decimals first before working out the vertical addition or subtraction.

e.g.

$3.64 + 9.6 =$ **13.24**

$$\begin{array}{r} 3.64 \\ +\ 9.60 \\ \hline 13.24 \end{array}$$ ← 9.6 = 9.60; the zero is a place holder.

$8 - 4.73 =$ **3.27**

$$\begin{array}{r} 8.00 \\ -\ 4.73 \\ \hline 3.27 \end{array}$$ ← 8 = 8.00; the zeros are place holders.

Find the sum and difference for each pair of numbers.

⑭ 4.79 6.3

Sum	Difference
$\begin{array}{r} 4.79 \\ +6.3 \\ \hline 10.109 \end{array}$	$\begin{array}{r} {}^{14}4.79 \\ -6.3 \\ \hline 8.49 \end{array}$

⑮ 9.2 11.08

Sum	Difference
$\begin{array}{r} 9.2 \\ +11.08 \\ \hline 20.28 \end{array}$	$\begin{array}{r} 9.2 \\ -11.08 \\ \hline 18.28 \end{array}$

⑯ 30.03 12.4

Sum	Difference
$\begin{array}{r} 30.03 \\ +1.24 \\ \hline 31.27 \end{array}$	$\begin{array}{r} 30.03 \\ -1.24 \\ \hline 29.79 \end{array}$

⑰ 5.86 20.5

Sum	Difference
$\begin{array}{r} 5.86 \\ +2.05 \\ \hline 7.91 \end{array}$	$\begin{array}{r} 5.86 \\ -2.05 \\ \hline 3.81 \end{array}$

Look at the pictures. Fill in the blanks.

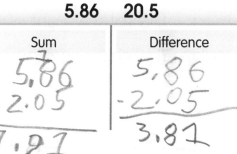

⑱ a. These two watermelons weigh **9.72** kg in all.

4.64 kg   5.8 kg

b. The big watermelon weighs **5.8** kg more than the small one.

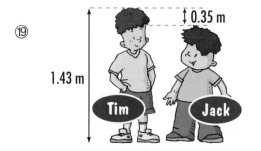

⑲

↕ 0.35 m

1.43 m

Tim   Jack

a. Jack is **0.35** m tall.

b. If Sue is 0.28 m taller than Jack, Sue is **1.43** m tall.

Look at the pictures. Round each decimal to the nearest tenth to do the estimate. Then answer the questions.

⑳

1.46 L   3.02 L

Estimate

$$\begin{array}{r} {}^{17}\!\!\!\not{1}.40 \\ -3.00 \\ \hline 8.40 \end{array}$$

Exact

$$\begin{array}{r} {}^{17}\!\!\!\not{1}.46 \\ -3.02 \\ \hline 8.44 \end{array}$$

a. The total capacity of these two pails is about __8.40__ L.

b. The pails can hold __8.44__ L of water.

㉑

4.65 kg   8.73 kg

Estimate

$$\begin{array}{r} 4.70 \\ +8.70 \\ \hline 12.140 \end{array}$$

Exact

$$\begin{array}{r} 4.65 \\ +8.73 \\ \hline 12.738 \end{array}$$

a. The total weight of these two pumpkins is about __12.140__ kg.

b. These two pumpkins weigh __12.738__ kg in all.

㉒

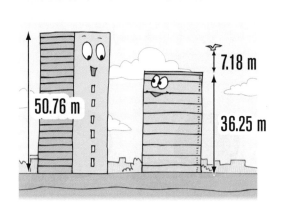

7.18 m

50.76 m

36.25 m

Estimate

$$\begin{array}{r} 50.80 \\ 36.30 \\ +7.20 \\ \hline 813.30 \end{array}$$

Exact

$$\begin{array}{r} 50.76 \\ 36.25 \\ +7.18 \\ \hline 813.779 \end{array}$$

a. There is a height difference of about __813.779__ m between the buildings.

b. The tall building is __50.76__ m taller than the short one.

c. The bird is about __36.30__ m above the ground.

d. The bird is __7.18__ m above the ground.

Solve the problems.

㉓  If Aunt Elaine uses 1.27 kg of flour to make a cake, how much flour will be left?

$2.63 - 1.27 = 3.9$ 3.9 kg

㉔  If James pays $50 for a season pass, what is his change?

$29.27 + 50 = 79.27$ $79.27

㉕ A chocolate bar weighs 1.08 kg. What is the total weight of two chocolate bars?

$1.08 + 2 = 1.10$ 1.10 kg

㉖ Aunt Sally has a ribbon that is 3.64 m long and she cuts it into 2 pieces. If one piece is 1.85 m long, how long is the other piece?

$3.64 + 2 + 85 = 4.169$ 4.169 m

㉗ Each bag of dog treats costs $36.74. How much do two bags cost?

$36.74 + 2 = 36.76$

$36.76

㉘ If Teddy gives 2.78 kg of treats to his friend, what will be the weight of the treats left?

$4.26 - 2.78 = 2.48$

2.48 kg

Money

- Read and write money amounts to $1000.
- Add and subtract money amounts to make purchases and changes.

It's so beautiful. It costs nine hundred sixty-five dollars and twenty-nine cents.

$965.29

Estimate and find the exact amount of money in each group.

①

A

B

C

D

Group	Estimate	Exact
A	370 dollars 0 cents	305 dollars 4 cents or $
B	270 dollars 2 cents	270 dollars 11 cents or $
C	250 dollars 60 cents	250 dollars 52 cents or $
D	110 dollars 30 cents	105 dollars 32 cents or $

Draw the fewest bills and coins to show how much each child collected for the fundraising campaign. Then answer the questions.

Key

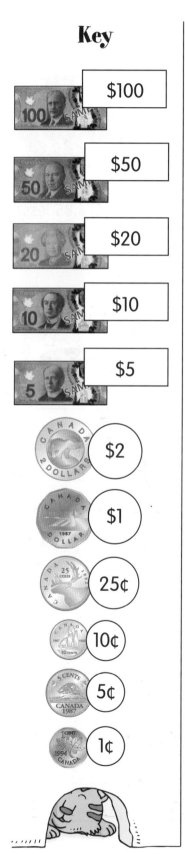

$100

$50

$20

$10

$5

$2

$1

25¢

10¢

5¢

1¢

② Tim $326.91

$700 $700 $20 $5 $1

25¢ 25¢ 25¢ 10¢ 5¢ 1¢

Jack $297.08

$700 $20 $50 $20 $20 $5 $2

5¢ 1¢ 1¢ 5¢

Katie $406.17

$100 $700 $700 $700 $5 $7

10¢ 5¢ 1¢ 1¢

③ How much did the boys collect in all?

$623.99

④ How much more did Katie collect than Jack?

1 0 0

Find the costs of the items. Then fill in the missing information on the receipts and answer the questions.

⑤

bookshelf

$127.49

coffee table

$192.64

armchair

It costs $218.54 more than a bookshelf.

task chair

It costs $76.85 less than a coffee table.

⑥

My Furniture Shop

ITEM	COST
Armchair	$278.54
Bookshelf	$127.49
Total	$538.67
Cash	$517.32
Change	$11.33

⑦

My Furniture Shop

ITEM	COST
Task Chair	$76.85
Coffee Table	$192.64
Total	$357.28
Cash	$300.28
Change	$57.00

⑧

If I want to buy two task chairs, how much do I need to pay?

76.85 + 76.85 = 153.70 $153.70

⑨

If I want to buy one coffee table and one bookshelf, how much do I need to pay?

127.49 + 192.64 = 220.13 $220.13

Solve the problems.

⑩ a. Uncle James buys two jackets. How much does he need to pay?

$259.52

b. Mr. Hunter pays $200 for a jacket. What is his change?

$129.76

$ 137.76

⑪ a. Jason has $157.88 only. If he wants to buy a lawn mower, how much more does he need?

3 36.37

b. If a snow blower costs $624.35 more than a lawn mower, how much does a snow blower cost?

$288.49

972.74

⑫

I paid 100 SAMPLE *for this necklace. Its original price was $965.29.*

Do you know how much I saved?

402.25 + 965.29 = 1367.54

$1367.54

2-D Shapes

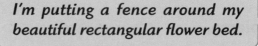

I'm putting a fence around my beautiful rectangular flower bed.

- Identify polygons, regular polygons, and other two-dimensional shapes.
- Draw 2-D shapes with the given measurements.
- Sort 2-D shapes by their geometric properties such as parallel sides, symmetry, etc.

Colour the regular polygons.
Then sort them. Write the letters.

①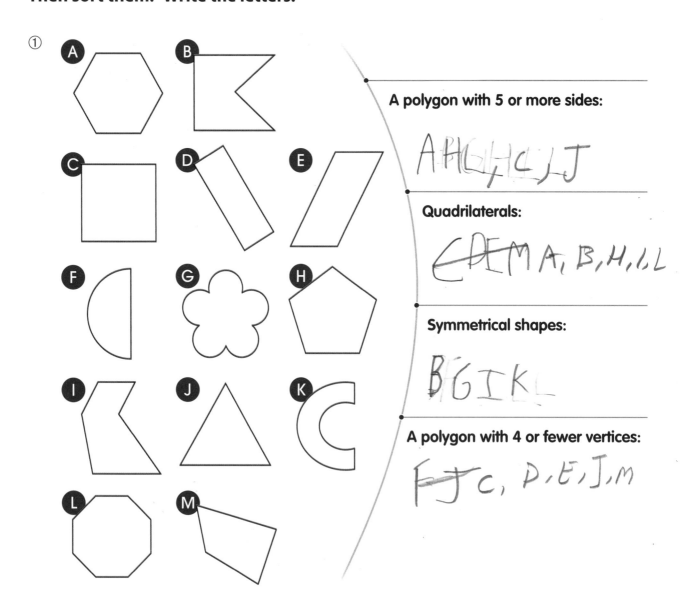

A polygon with 5 or more sides:

APHGHCJJ

Quadrilaterals:

CDEMA, B, H, LL

Symmetrical shapes:

BGIKL

A polygon with 4 or fewer vertices:

FJC, D, E, J, M

Read what the dogs say. Then draw the shapes.

② *a square with a side length of 4 cm*

a rectangle with lengths of 5 cm and widths of 3 cm

a triangle with sides of 5 cm and 3 cm

a quadrilateral with a right angle

a hexagon with a pair of parallel sides

a pentagon with two right angles

Draw lines on the shapes to match the sentences.

③ **A** The square is formed by nine congruent squares.

B The hexagon is formed by six congruent triangles.

C The trapezoid is formed by three congruent triangles.

D The rectangle is formed by six congruent rectangles.

E The triangle is formed by four small congruent triangles.

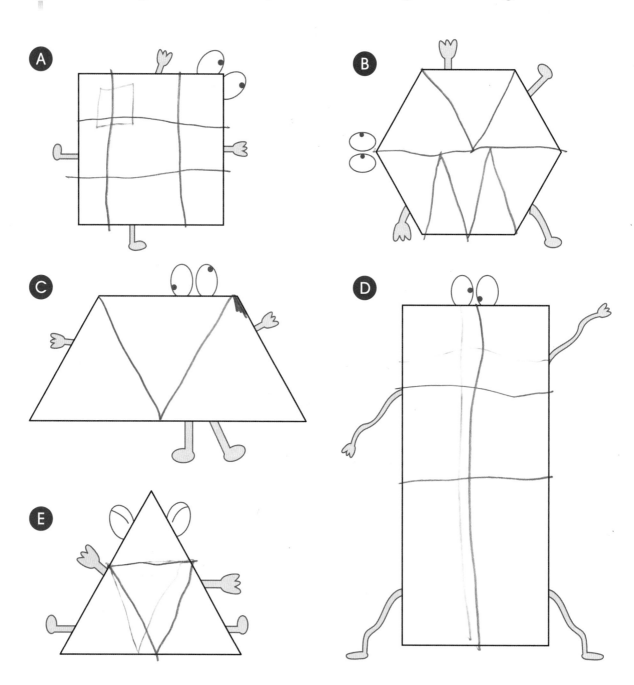

Read what the children and the animals say. Help them draw the shapes and lines. Then answer the questions.

④

Draw a big regular hexagon with sides of 4 cm. Then draw lines on it to show how it can be formed by six small congruent triangles.

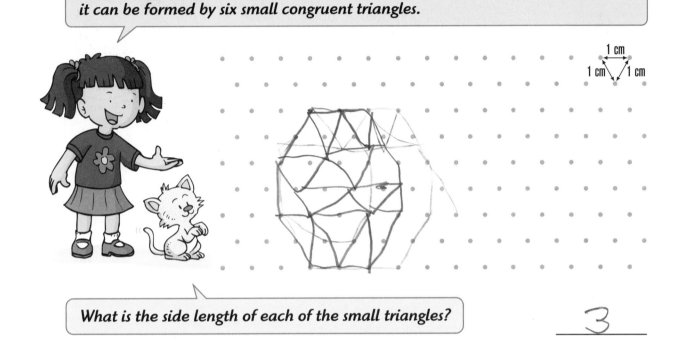

What is the side length of each of the small triangles?

3

⑤

Draw a big triangle with sides of 8 cm. Then draw lines on it to show how it can be formed by four small congruent triangles.

What is the side length of each of the small triangles?

8

Angles

I've got a hat with an obtuse angle.

120°

- Describe angles related to right angles or straight angles and find the measures.
- Identify and classify acute, right, obtuse, and straight angles.
- Measure angles and construct angles up to 90°, using a protractor.

Look at the angles. Complete the notes.

①

This is a __right__ angle.

A right angle is __90°__ .

②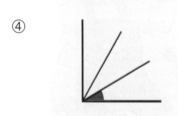

Two right angles form a __straight__ angle.

A straight angle is __280°__ .

③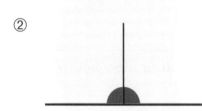

This angle is __obtuse__ of a right angle.

It is __90°__ .

④

This angle is __acute__ of a right angle.

It is __90°__ .

⑤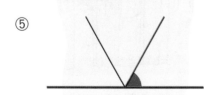

This angle is __acute__ of a straight angle.

It is __90°__ .

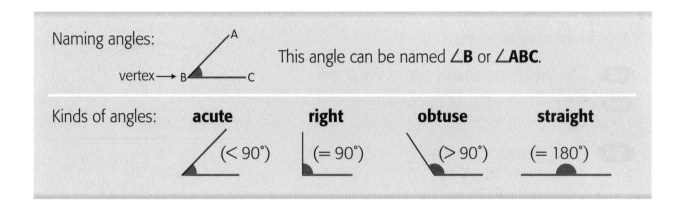

Naming angles:

vertex → B

This angle can be named ∠**B** or ∠**ABC**.

Kinds of angles:

acute	**right**	**obtuse**	**straight**
(< 90°)	(= 90°)	(> 90°)	(= 180°)

Name each angle. Then write what kind of angle it is.

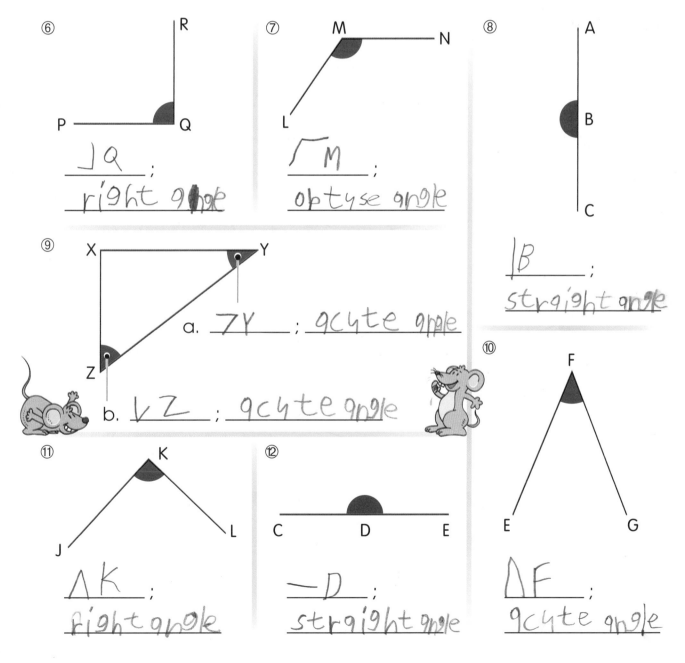

⑥

_JQ_ ;
right angle

⑦

_⌐M_ ;
obtuse angle

⑧

_|B_ ;
straight angle

⑨

a. _7Y_ ; _acute angle_

b. _∠Z_ ; _acute angle_

⑩

_∧F_ ;
acute angle

⑪

_∧K_ ;
right angle

⑫

_─D_ ;
straight angle

Steps to measure an angle:

1st Put the 0° line on one arm of the angle.

2nd Place the centre of the protractor at the vertex.

3rd Mark the reading of the angle and record it.

e.g.

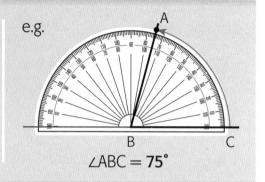

∠ABC = **75°**

Measure the size of each marked angle using a protractor.

⑬

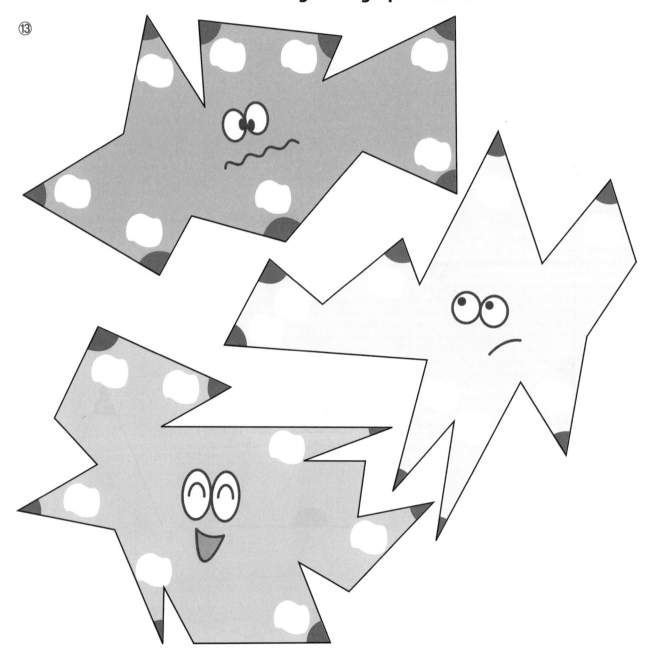

Draw and mark the angles.

⑭

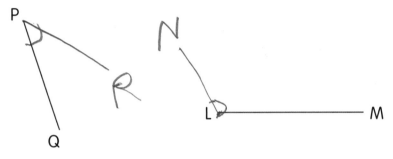

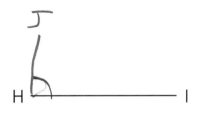

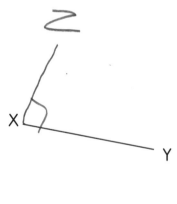

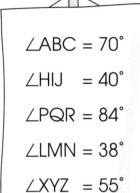

∠ABC = 70°

∠HIJ = 40°

∠PQR = 84°

∠LMN = 38°

∠XYZ = 55°

∠STU = 63°

∠EFG = 25°

Help the girl measure and record the size of each marked angle. Then circle the smallest one.

⑮

19

Triangles

- Identify triangles and classify them according to angles and side properties.
- Construct triangles with the given acute or right angles and side measurements.

Can I have an equilateral triangle sandwich?

Measure and record the angles of the triangles. Then fill in the blanks with the given words.

acute   obtuse   right

①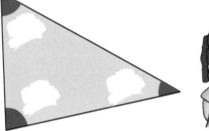

This triangle has 3 ___right___ angles. It is an ___acyte___ triangle.

②

This triangle has 2 ___acyte___ angles and 1 ___right___ angle. It is a ___right___ triangle.

③

This triangle has 2 ___acyte___ angles and 1 ___acyte___ angle. It is an ___acyte___ triangle.

Equilateral Triangle	Isosceles Triangle	Scalene Triangle
• 3 equal sides	• 2 equal sides	• no equal sides

Use a ruler to measure and record the sides of the triangles. Then name the triangles.

④

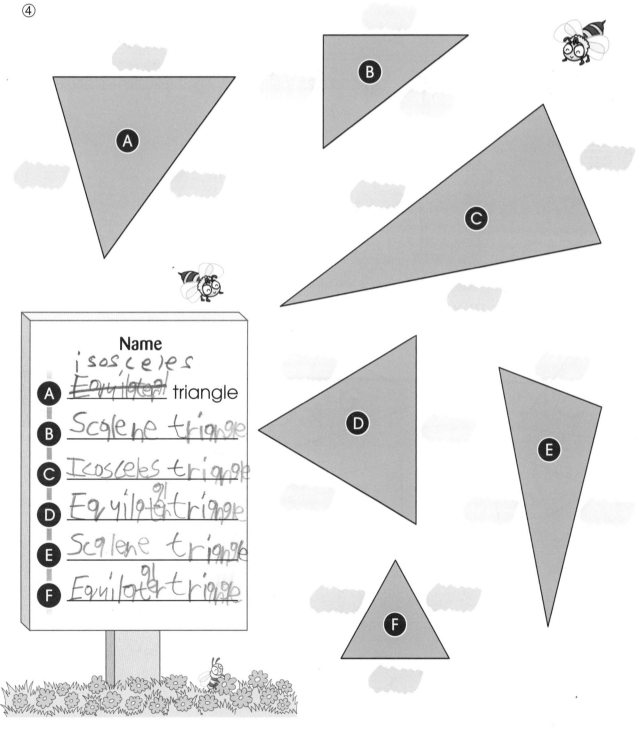

Name

A ~~Equilateral~~ *isosceles* triangle

B Scalene triangle

C Icosceles triangle

D Equilateral triangle

E Scalene triangle

F Equilateral triangle

Draw the triangles.

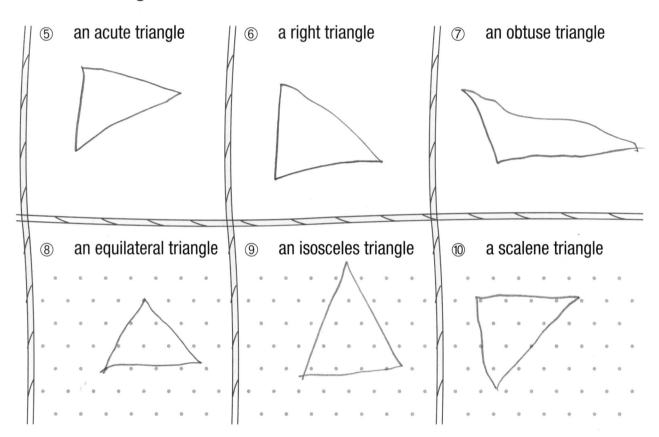

⑤   an acute triangle

⑥   a right triangle

⑦   an obtuse triangle

⑧   an equilateral triangle

⑨   an isosceles triangle

⑩   a scalene triangle

Sort the triangles. Write the letters.

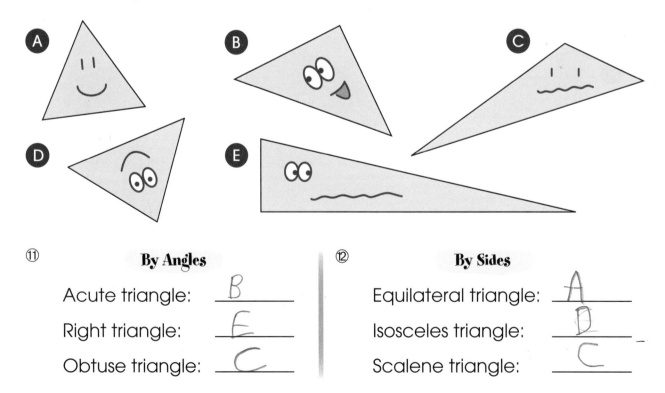

Ⓐ   Ⓑ   Ⓒ   Ⓓ   Ⓔ

⑪ **By Angles**

Acute triangle: _____B_____

Right triangle: _____E_____

Obtuse triangle: _____C_____

⑫ **By Sides**

Equilateral triangle: _____A_____

Isosceles triangle: _____D_____

Scalene triangle: _____C_____

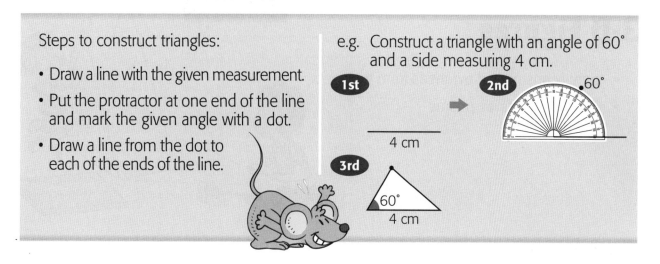

Steps to construct triangles:

- Draw a line with the given measurement.
- Put the protractor at one end of the line and mark the given angle with a dot.
- Draw a line from the dot to each of the ends of the line.

e.g. Construct a triangle with an angle of 60° and a side measuring 4 cm.

1st ———— 4 cm

2nd .60°

3rd 60° 4 cm

Draw the triangles. Then label them with the given letters.

⑬ A triangle with

Ⓐ an angle of 75° and a side measuring 3 cm

Ⓑ an angle of 28° and a side measuring 6 cm

Ⓒ an angle of 42° and a side measuring 5 cm

Draw a triangle with an angle of 125° and a side measuring 4 cm. Label it Ⓓ *.*

3-D Figures

- Identify prisms and pyramids from their nets.
- Construct nets of prisms and pyramids.

Pyramid Show

Rectangular Pyramid

Which nets make the coloured prisms?   Put a check mark in the correct circles.

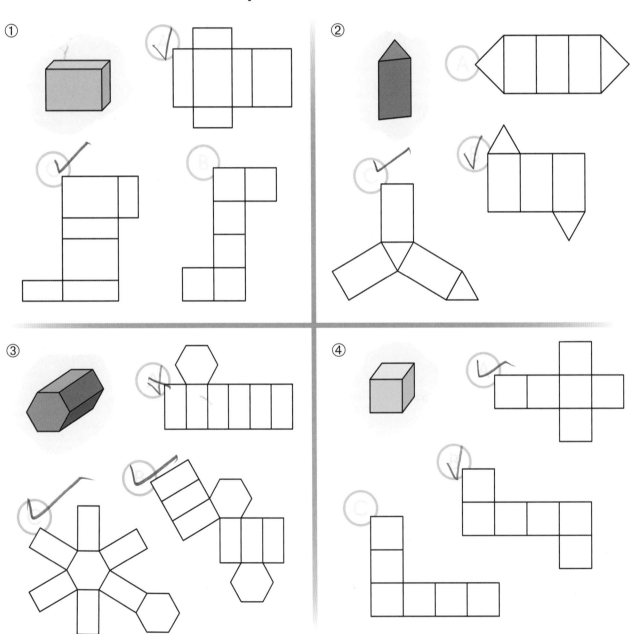

① ② ③ ④

Colour the nets that make the coloured pyramids.

⑤

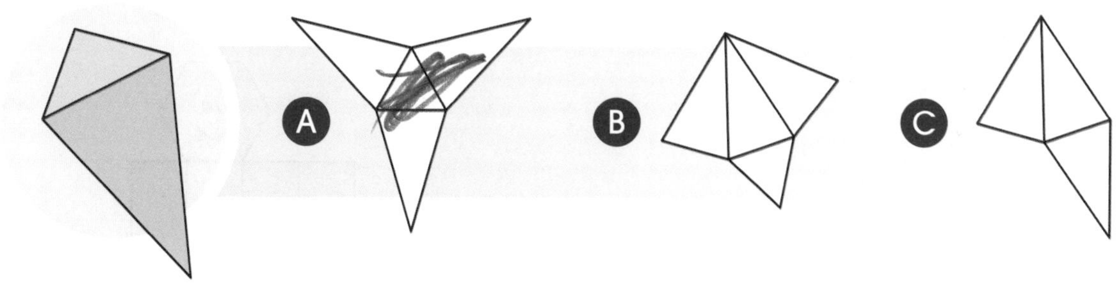

Ⓐ   Ⓑ   Ⓒ

⑥

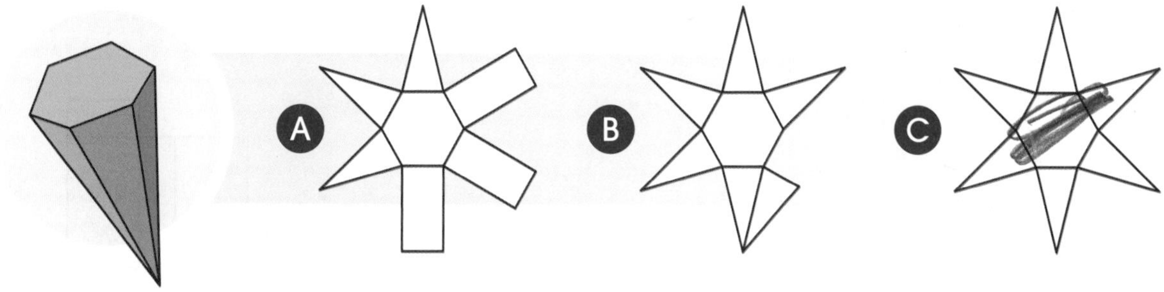

Ⓐ   Ⓑ   Ⓒ

⑦

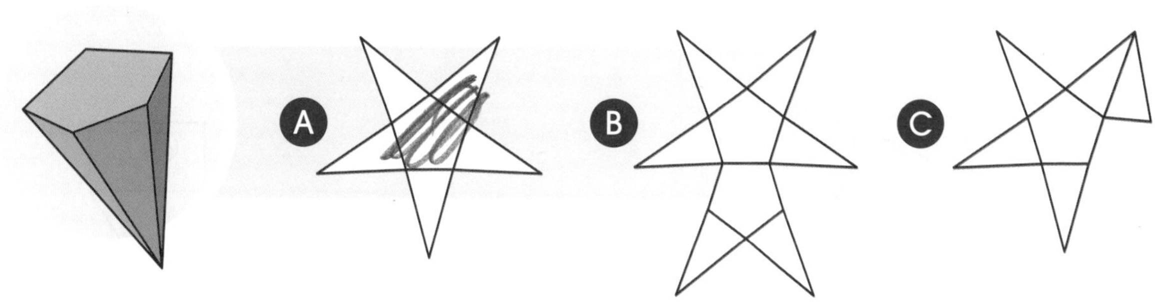

Ⓐ   Ⓑ   Ⓒ

⑧

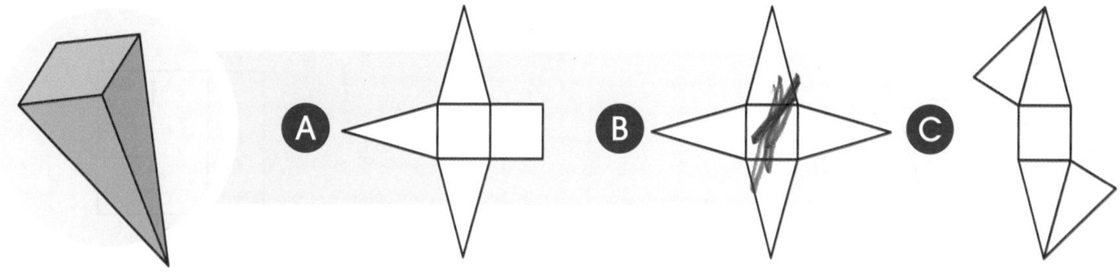

Ⓐ   Ⓑ   Ⓒ

⑨

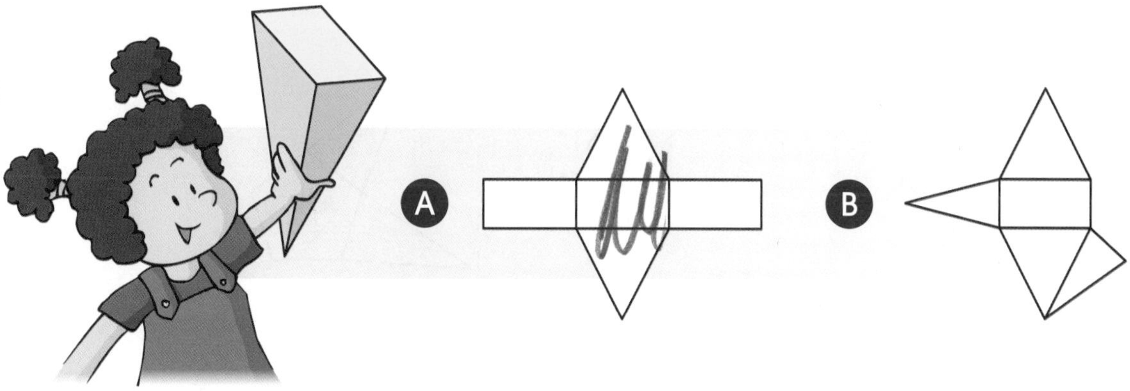

Ⓐ   Ⓑ

Draw the missing edges to complete the skeletons and the missing faces to complete the nets of the 3-D figures. Then match the skeletons with the nets that show the same figures.

⑩

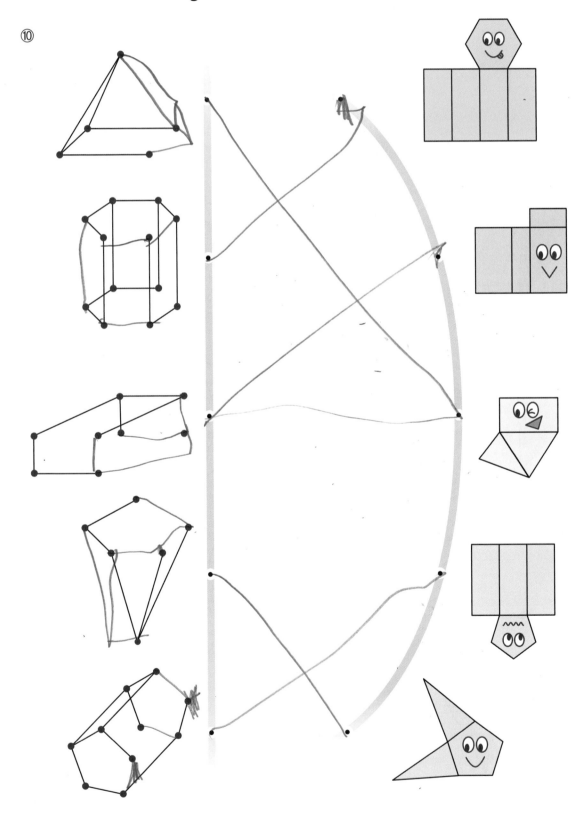

Draw the missing faces to complete the net of each 3-D figure. Then name the figure. Write the numbers and describe the shapes of the faces that it has.

⑪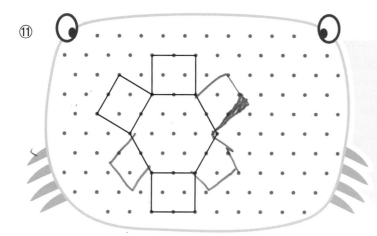

Name: Hexagonal Prism

It has 24 rectangular faces

and 6 hexagonal faces.

⑫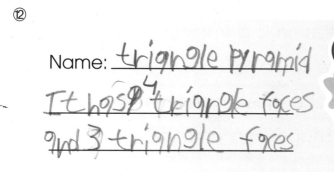

Name: triangle pyramid

It has 4 triangle faces

and 3 triangle faces

Draw the net of the 3-D figure that the girl is describing.

⑬

I've built a 3-D figure which has 12 edges, and all the faces that it has are rectangular.

Transformations

This is translation!

- Identify and draw translation images.
- Create and analyze designs by translating and/or reflecting a shape or shapes.

Circle the correct words to complete what Emily says. Then check the pictures that show translations.

①

A translation is a transformation that moves a figure to a new position. The figure (changes) / does not change its size, shape, or orientation.

Translation

②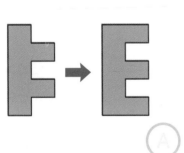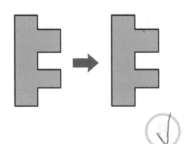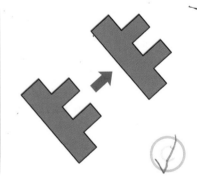

A

B ✓

C ✓

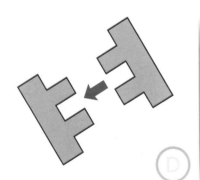 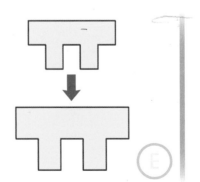 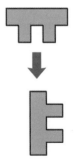

D

E

F

Follow the directions to draw the translation images of the given shapes.

③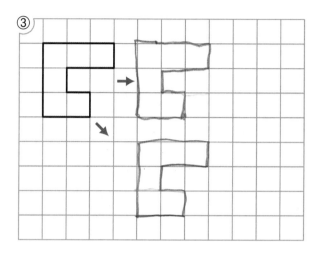

④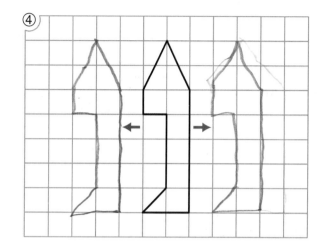

⑤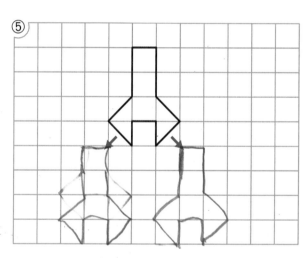

⑥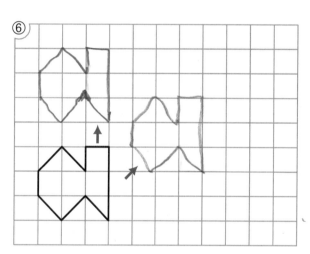

⑦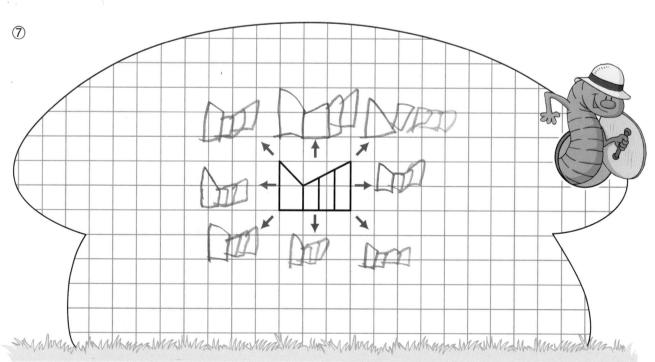

Create designs by

- translating
- reflecting
- translating and reflecting

Check the designs that are created by translating, reflecting, or translating and reflecting of a shape.

⑧

Create designs by translating, reflecting, and translating and reflecting the shapes.

⑨

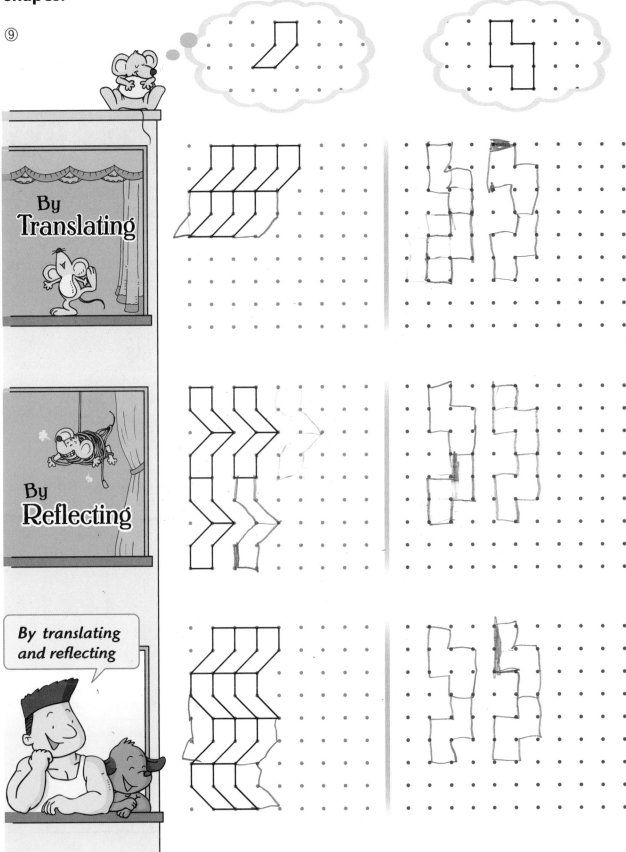

By **Translating**

By **Reflecting**

By translating and reflecting

22

Grids

- Locate an object using the cardinal directions (i.e. north, east, south, and west) and grids.
- Describe movement from one location to another.
- Read and describe grids used on maps.
- Draw maps on grid systems.

My house is covered by A1, B1, B2, B3, C1, C2, C3, D1, and D2. It has an area of about 9 square units.

Draw the things on the grid. Then circle the correct answers and answer the questions.

①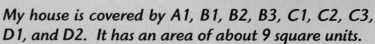

D4   A5   E1, G3

H5   A2, F6   B6, G2

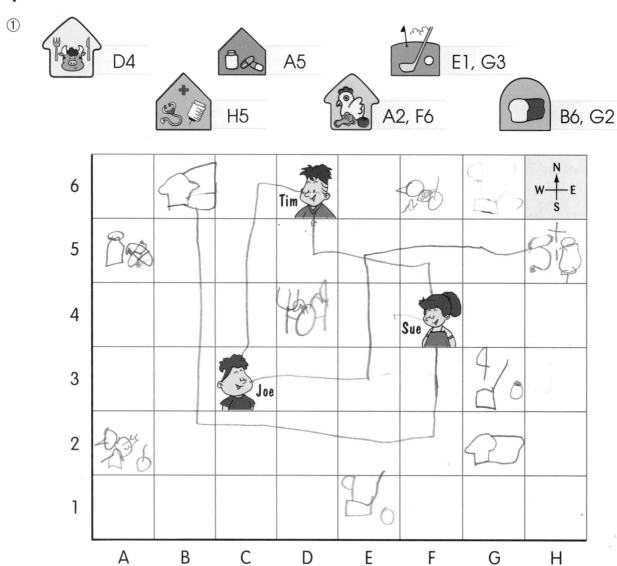

②

If I go 2 squares north and 2 squares west, do you know where I am going?

③

If I go 2 squares south and 1 square east, do you know where I am going?

④

We want to build a golf centre which has the same distance and is 2 squares away from the two golf courses. What are the possible locations?

south and west

⑤ Joe is at the clinic and he wants to go home. Draw the shortest path that he should take on the map and describe it.

He should go *3 squares west, 2 squares south and west*

⑥ Sue is at the bakery at B6 and she wants to go to the other bakery. Draw the shortest path that she should take on the map and describe it.

She should go 2 squares south, 4 squares west and 5 squares then hop

⑦ Tim wants to borrow some books from Joe and then give a present to Sue before going home. Describe the path that Tim should take to have the things done.

He should go 1 square west and 3 squares south. He should go 1 square south, 2 squares east and 1 square south.

Look at the zoo map. Answer the questions.

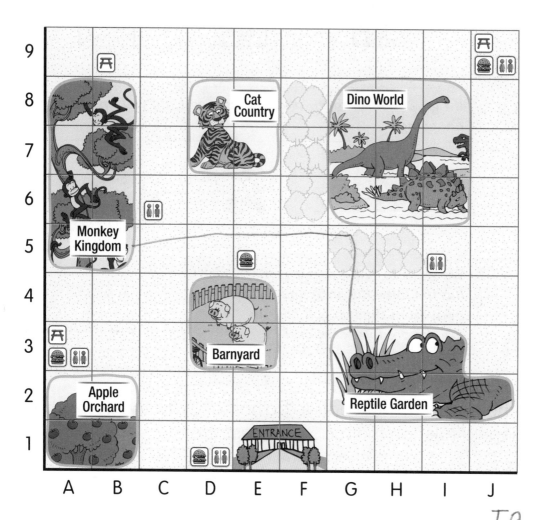

Apple Zoo

Washrooms

Picnic Site

Restaurant

⑧ Locations of the washrooms: C6 A3 D1 I5 J9

⑨ Locations of the restaurants: D1 A3 E5 J9

⑩

> *I'm at Reptile Garden. What's the shortest route to Monkey Kingdom?*

2 squares north and 5 squares west.

⑪ What is the area of each part in the zoo?

═══ **Area** ═══

Barnyard: _4_ square units   Reptile Garden: _7_ square units

Dino World: _9_ square units   Monkey Kingdom: _8_ square units

Cat Country: _4_ square units   Apple Orchard: _4_ square units

⑫ Which part of the zoo has the greatest area?

Dino world

⑬ There will be a big construction in the zoo.

Project 1 – Cutting down the trees from F6 to F8

• The entire Dino World will be extended 1 square west. What will be the new area of Dino World?

12 square units

Project 2 – Planting trees from G1 to J1

• What will be the area covered by the trees?

4 square units

Project 3 – Reptile Garden will be changed into a rectangle.

• How can that be done? What will be the new area?

8 square units

⑭

> *I'm going to make a donation to the zoo so that it can build an educational centre with an area of 2 square units beside Barnyard. What are the possible locations?*

West and North

Patterning

- Create, identify, and extend numeric and geometric patterns.
- Make a table of values for a pattern or build a model to represent a number pattern presented in a table of values.
- Make predictions related to growing and shrinking geometric and numeric patterns.

I love patterning.

Find out the pattern rule for each number pattern. Then write the next two numbers.

① 6   12   18   24   30   36

Pattern rule: 6 12 18 24 30 36 42 48

The next two numbers are __42__ and __48__ .

② 512   256   128   64   32   16

Pattern rule: 512 256 128 64 32 16.8 4

The next two numbers are __8__ and __4__ .

③ 575   550   525   500   475   450

Pattern rule: 575 550 525 500 475 450 425 400

The next two numbers are __425__ and __400__ .

④ 4   12   36   108   324   972

Pattern rule: 4 12 36 108 324 972 2916 8748

The next two numbers are __2916__ and __8748__ .

⑤ 172   167   162   157   152   147

Pattern rule: 172 167 162 157 152 147 142 137

The next two numbers are __142__ and __137__ .

MATHEMATICS

Make a table of values for each described number pattern. Then fill in the blanks.

⑥ Start with 15 and add 4 to each term to get the next term.

Term number	Term
1	15
2	19
3	23
4	27
5	37
6	35

The 8th term is _43_ .

⑦ Start with 20 and subtract 2 from each term to get the next term.

Term number	Term
1	20
2	18
3	16
4	14
5	12
6	10

The _11th_ term is 0.

⑧ Start with 6561 and divide each term by 3 to get the next term.

Term number	Term
1	6561
2	2189
3	219.1
4	218R1
5	217R1
6	216R1

The _100_ term is 1.

⑨ Start with 5 and multiply each term by 2 to get the next term.

Term number	Term
1	5
2	10
3	20
4	40
5	80
6	160

The 9th term is _1280_ .

Make a table of values for each number pattern. Then check the pictures that match the pattern.

⑩

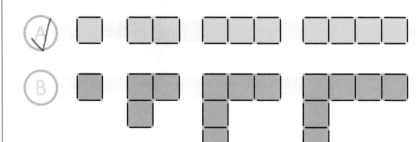

Start with 4 and add 3 to each term to get the next term.

Term number	Term
1	4
2	7
3	10
4	13

Ⓐ ✓

Ⓑ

⑪

Start with 21 and subtract 4 from each term to get the next term.

Term number	Term
1	21
2	17
3	13
4	9

Ⓐ

Ⓑ ✓

⑫

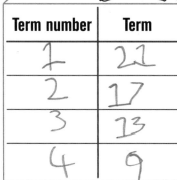

Start with 13 and subtract 4 from each term to get the next term.

Term number	Term
1	13
2	9
3	5
4	1

Ⓐ ✓

Ⓑ

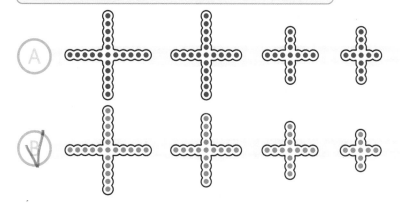

Follow the pattern to draw the next two pictures. Make a table of values to match the pictures. Then answer the questions.

⑬ a.

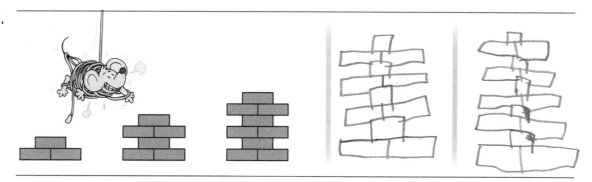

b.

Tower	No. of Blocks
1st	3
2nd	6
3rd	9
4th	12
5th	15

c.

How many blocks are there in the 8th tower?

24

⑭ a.

b.

Bone	No. of Squares
1st	32
2nd	30
3rd	28
4th	26
5th	24

c.

How many squares are there in the 7th bone?

20

Simple Equations

I know you can go 10 km in 1 h. Did you know that I can use $D = 10 \times t$ to tell how far you will go in a given time?

- Understand variables as changing quantities in an equation.
- Use symbols or letters to represent the unknown quantities to write equations that describe relationships involving simple rates.
- Find the missing numbers in equations.

$$D = 10 \times t$$
distance travelled   time

Look at the pictures. Then use equations to describe the relationships.

①  **$3 each**

Total cost = 3 x No. of hamburgers purchased

$$\underline{3} = 3 \times \underline{n}$$,

C = Total cost

n = No. of hamburgers purchased

②

Total no. of muffins = 6 x No. of boxes

$$\underline{6} = 6 \times \underline{1}$$,

$\underline{C}$ = Total no. of muffins

$\underline{n}$ = No. of boxes

③  Juice 2 L

Total amount of juice = 2 x No. of bottles

$$\underline{2} = 2 \times \underline{1}$$,

$\underline{C}$ = Total amount of juice

$\underline{n}$ = No. of bottles

④  A LUCKY Dog $9

Total cost = 9 x No. of books

$$\underline{9} = 9 \times \underline{1}$$,

$\underline{C}$ = Total cost

$\underline{n}$ = No. of books

Circle the symbols or letters in the equations. Match the equations with the situations. Then write what the symbols or letters represent.

⑤

$c =$ (100) $- n$

$c =$ ___Total left___

$n =$ ___No of candies___

Mrs. Smith divides 100 children into equal groups. She wants to know the number of children in each group.

$w =$ (100) $\times$

$w =$ ___Total weight___

 $=$ ___No of raisins___

I take some candies from a bag of 100 candies. There are some candies left in the bag.

$y =$ (100) $\div k$

$Y =$ ___Total of groups___

$K =$ ___No of children___

A watch costs $100. Jason wants to know how much he needs to pay for a watch and a doll.

▲ $=$ (100) $+ x$

△ $=$ ___Total cost___

$x =$ ___No of watch___

A box of raisins weighs 100 g. I want to know the total weight of some boxes of raisins.

Check the equations that can be used to represent each situation.

⑥

I have a bag of 40 cookies. If I eat some cookies, how many cookies will be left?

(A) ✓ $n = 40 - k$ (B) ✓ $40 - k = n$

(C) $40 + k = n$ (D) $n \times k = 40$

⑦

I earn $100 a day. If I work for a few days, how much will I earn?

(A) ✗ $c = 100 \times n$ (B) ✓ $c \times n = 100$

(C) ✓ $100 \div n = c$ (D) $100 \times n = c$

⑧

I have 12 stamps and 5 of them are from Canada. How many stamps are from other countries?

(A) $12 + 5 = s$ (B) ✓ $12 = 5 + s$

(C) ✓ $12 = 5 + \boxed{7}$ (D) $12 = \boxed{12} - 5$

⑨

If I take away 3 gifts from under the tree, there will be 7 gifts left. How many gifts are there under the tree?

(A) $n + 3 = 7$ (B) $7 + n = 3$

(C) $n - 3 = 7$ (D) ✓  $- 3 = 7$

(E) 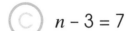 $= 7 - 3$ (F) $7 = s - 3$

Simplify the equations first if needed.	e.g. $k - 4 = 6 + 9$ ← Simplify 6 + 9 first.
	$k - 4 = 15$ ← Think: what number minus 4 is 15?
	$k = \underline{\textbf{19}}$

Find the unknowns.

⑩ $11 = 88 \div \blacksquare$

$\blacksquare = \underline{8}$

⑪ $9 \times \heartsuit = 144$

$\heartsuit = \underline{16}$

⑫ $\text{(bear)} - 8 = 22$

$\text{(bear)} = \underline{30}$

⑬ $50 - y = 34$

$y = \underline{16}$

⑭ $18 + k = 20$

$k = \underline{2}$

⑮ $h \times 7 = 126$

$h = \underline{18}$

⑯ $45 = \text{(flower)} \times 3$

$\text{(flower)} = \underline{15}$

⑰ $\text{(tree)} \div 8 = 24$

$\text{(tree)} = \underline{3}$

⑱ $138 \div m = 23$

$m = \underline{6}$

Simplify the equations. Then find the unknowns.

⑲ $m + 9 = 20 - 4$

$M = 16$

⑳ $b \div 4 = 3 + 3$

$b = 8$

㉑ $8 \times k = 144 \div 3$

$k = 48$

㉒ $y - 16 = 15 + 15 + 15$

$y = 45$

Graphs (1)

- Read and describe the data presented in charts and graphs, including broken-line graphs.

He really likes fish.

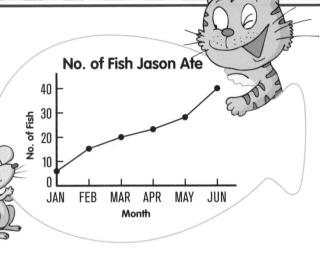

No. of Fish Jason Ate

Read the graph. Answer the questions.

No. of Boxes of Chocolates Sold Last Year

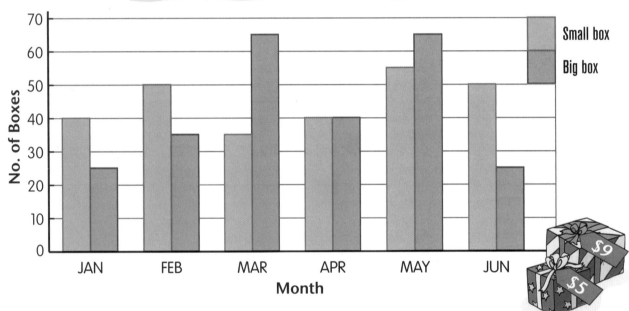

Small box

Big box

① How many kinds of packaging are there? ___2___

② How many boxes of chocolates were sold in March? ___100___

③ How many more big boxes of chocolates were sold in May than in June? ___40___

④ In which month were the most chocolates sold? ___March___

⑤ How much was collected from selling the chocolates in

    a. January?   b. April?   c. June?

    425   580   4.75

Broken-line Graph:

a graph formed by line segments that join points representing the data

I had lots of bones on Thursday.

No. of Bones the Dog Had

Uncle Jimmy has recorded the attendances at the local hockey matches. Look at the graph. Answer the questions.

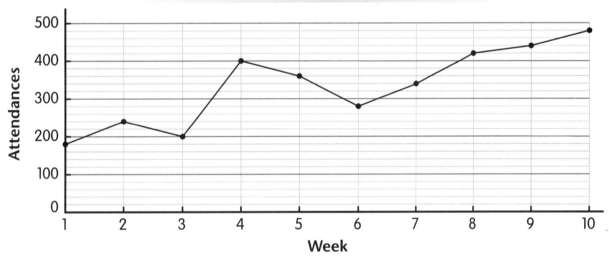

Attendances at the Local Hockey Matches

⑥ Which week had an attendance closest to 300? _____ 6

⑦ Which week had the largest attendance? _____ 10

⑧ How many more people were there

   a. in Week 4 than in Week 2? _____ 160

   b. in Week 8 than in Week 5? _____ 60

⑨ *The matches I took part in all had attendances of 400 or more. In which weeks did I play?*

4 8 9 10

Line Plot:

a graph that shows a mark (usually an "x") above a value on the number line for each entry in the data set

7 of the squirrels have 11 acorns each.

No. of Acorns the Squirrels Have

No. of Acorns

Mrs. White has recorded the heights of the children. Read the line plot. Then answer the questions.

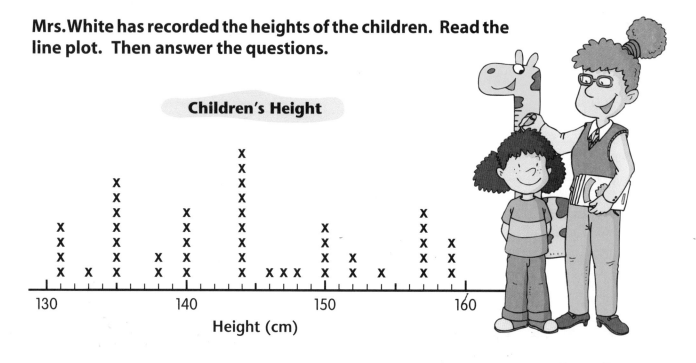

Children's Height

Height (cm)

⑩ What is the range of the data? _28 cm_

⑪ How many children are between 130 cm and 145 cm in height? _28_

⑫ How many children are over 155 cm in height? _8_

⑬ What is the most common height? _144_

⑭ What is the greatest height in the record? _159_

⑮ How many children were surveyed in all? _46_

Look at the graph showing the journey of Uncle Tim from his house to a campsite. Use the graph to answer the questions.

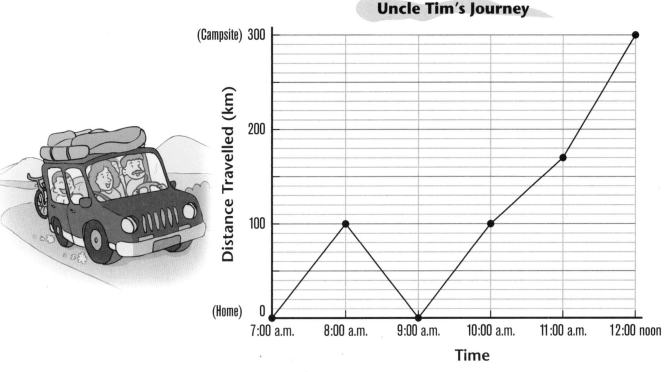

Uncle Tim's Journey

16 What time did Uncle Tim arrive at the campsite? _12:00_

17 What was the distance between Uncle Tim's house and the campsite? _300 and 0_

18 At 8:00 a.m., how far was Uncle Tim from his house? _150 km_

19 From 10:00 a.m. to 12:00 noon, how far did Uncle Tim travel? _2 hr_

20

> *After setting off, we found that our cat Lulu was not in the car. So I drove back home and picked her up. Do you know what time I started driving back home and what time I arrived home?*

_1:00 to 6:00_

Graphs (2)

- Complete graphs or make graphs to show data.
- Draw conclusions or describe the shape of a set of data presented in graphs.

No. of Treats in Each Box

No. of Treats

Joe did a survey of the reading habits of his friends. Look at the results and complete the line plot. Then answer the questions.

Reading Time (No. of hours in a week)	5	3	4	8	9	3	11	10	14	7
	5	9	11	3	4	3	5	3	5	9
	7	5	3	5	9	5	3	4	5	4

① **Children's Reading Time in a Week**

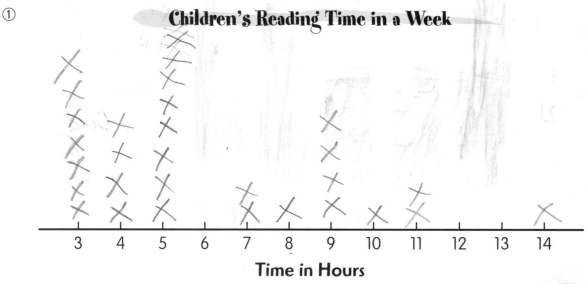

Time in Hours

② How many children read more than 6 h a week?

3 9nd 5

③ What conclusion can you draw from the line plot?

Childrens Reading time in a week.

See how many combos were sold last week. Complete the table by rounding each figure to the nearest 10. Then make a double bar graph to show the data and answer the questions.

④

No. of Orders		Sun	Mon	Tue	Wed	Thu	Fri	Sat
Combo 1	Actual	98	46	42	55	38	94	101
	Rounded	100	50	40	60	40	90	100
Combo 2	Actual	87	29	36	67	113	56	92
	Rounded	90	30	40	70	110	60	90

⑤

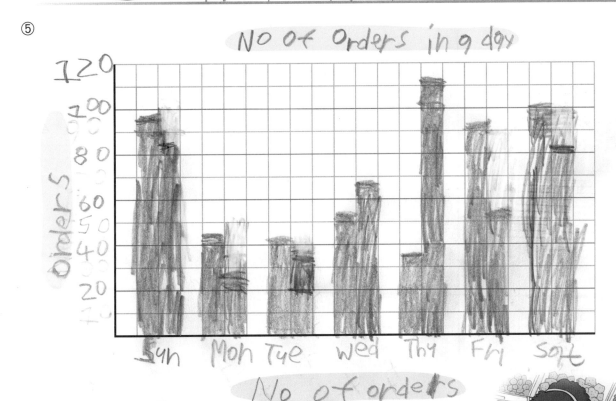

No of Orders in 9 day

Orders: 120, 100, 80, 60, 50, 40, 20

Sun Moh Tue wed Thy Fri Sat

No of orders

⑥

We had a promotion for Combo 2 last week. On which day do you think the promotion was held? Why?

Thursday because 113 is the biggest no.

⑦ What conclusion can you draw from the double bar graph?

No of orders in 9 day

The table shows the income of Douglas Bakery for each month last year. Round each figure to the nearest thousand and write the answer in the space provided. Then make a broken-line graph to show the data and answer the questions.

⑧ **Income ($)**

JAN	66 530
	70000
FEB	49 845
	50000
MAR	36 472
	40000
APR	33 617
	30000
MAY	28 825
	30000
JUN	30 334
	30000
JUL	31 149
	30000
AUG	30 816
	30000
SEP	37 113
	40000
OCT	38 605
	40000
NOV	47 018
	50000
DEC	68 076
	70000

⑨

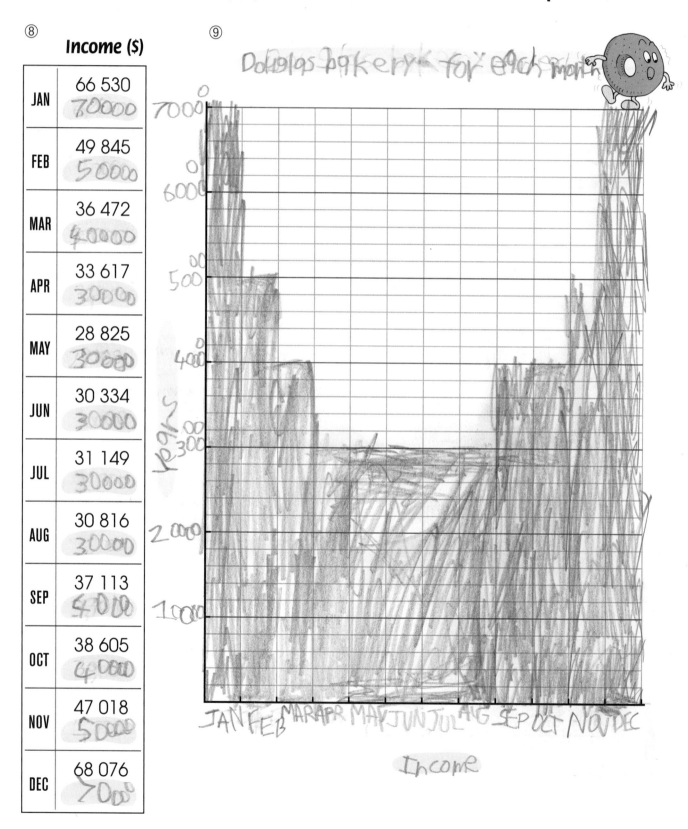

Dolglas bakery for each month

7000, 6000, 5000, 4000, 3000, years, 2000, 1000

JAN FEB MAR APR MAY JUN JUL AG SEP OCT NOV DEC

Income

⑩ In which month did the income reach $36 000?

March

⑪ In which months were the incomes over $60 000?

Jan & Dec

⑫ What was the difference in incomes between February and May?

March

⑬ What was the total income from October to December?

_160000_

⑭ What was the average daily income in June?

_30000_

⑮ In which month did Douglas Bakery have

    a. the highest income?

Jan & Dec

    b. the lowest income?

APR MAY JUN JUL AUG

⑯ If about half of the income in February was from selling strawberry cakes, about how many cakes were sold in February?

about _50000_

⑰ If 1000 pies were sold in October, about how much was collected from selling other items?

about _40 000_

⑱ What conclusion can you draw from the broken-line graph?

Douglas bakery for each month.

27

More about Graphs

The mean, the median, and the mode of the candies that I have are 8. Do you know how many candies are in each of my 3 boxes?

- Find the mean of a small set of data and use it to describe the shape of the data set across its range of values.

- Compare similarities and differences between two related sets of data by finding measures of central tendency, such as mean, median, and mode.

Help Judy find the mean number of the candies. Then find the mean of each group of data.

①

Find the total number of candies I have first. Then divide the sum by 4 to find the mean.

Total = 36 + 25 + 41
= 144
Mean = 144 ÷ 4 = 36

The mean number of the candies is 36 .

② 89 g 68 g 75 g 91 g 87 g 76 g

Total = 89 + 68 + 75 + 91 + 87 + 76
= 486
Mean = 486 ÷ 6 = 81
The mean weight is 81 .

③ 750 mL 600 mL 850 mL 750 mL 750 mL 850 mL 680 mL 650 mL

Total = 750+600+850+ 750+750+850+680 +650
= 5880
Mean = 5880 ÷ 8 = 735
The mean capacity is 735 .

e.g. The weights of a group of children: 42 kg 39 kg 42 kg 50 kg 37 kg 36 kg

Mean = (42 + 39 + 42 + 50 + 37 + 36) ÷ 6

= 246 ÷ 6

= 41

Put the data in order:

Mode

36 37 39 42 42 50

Median = (39 + 42) ÷ 2

= 40.5

The mean weight of the children is 41 kg, the median weight is 40.5 kg, and the mode weight is 42 kg.

Find the mean, median, and mode of each group of data.

④ 4 5 5 7 9 11

A

8 kg   4 kg   5 kg

9 kg   5 kg

7 kg   11 kg

B

80 muffins   29 muffins

29 muffins   42 muffins

28 muffins   50 muffins

	Mean	Median	Mode
A	7	3 4.7	5
B	43	35.1	29
C	240	13.2	27 25
D	60	2	887 83
E	45	2.5	0

C

$56 $27 $13

$27 $25 $40

$27 $25

E

0°C   8°C   12°C

4°C   7°C   6°C

0°C   5°C   3°C

D

7 m   6 m   8 m   3 m

8 m   8 m   7 m   8 m

2 m   3 m

Look at the bar graph. Find the mean number of the marbles that each group of children has and draw a line to show the mean on the graph. Then match the graphs with the correct descriptions.

⑤

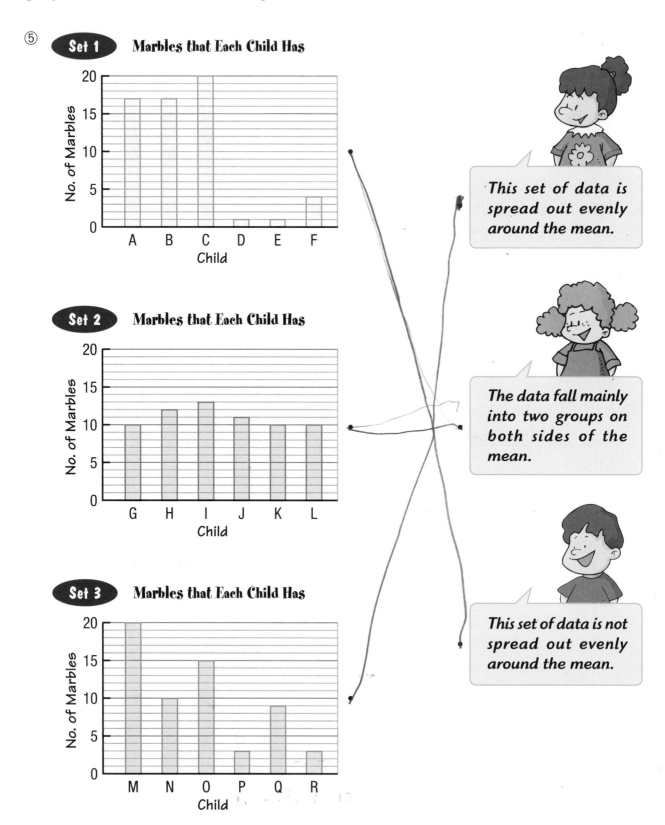

Set 1   Marbles that Each Child Has

Set 2   Marbles that Each Child Has

Set 3   Marbles that Each Child Has

This set of data is spread out evenly around the mean.

The data fall mainly into two groups on both sides of the mean.

This set of data is not spread out evenly around the mean.

Find the means, medians, and modes of the sets of data presented below. Then answer the questions.

⑥ a.

Mary's Scores in 10 Games

Stem	Leaves
5	3 3
8	6 7 7 7 7
9	0 1 9

Mean	Median	Mode
50	2	387

George's Scores in 10 Games

Stem	Leaves
7	0 6 7
8	0 0 2 5 6
9	1 3

Mean	Median	Mode
30	2	086

b. The mean scores of Mary and George are ___80___.

c. The range of Mary's scores is ___62___. Her median and mode are both ___62___, which is higher than the mean. Most of her data are (above) / below the mean.

d. The range of George's scores is ___38___. As the mean, median, and mode have a difference of 1 or 2 points, his data set should / (should not) be around the mean.

⑦

No. of Sausages Eaten Each Month

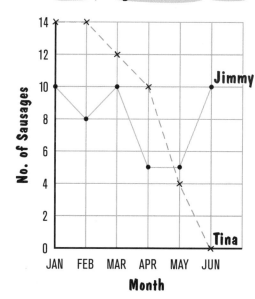

	Mean	Median	Mode
Jimmy	8	2.0	1085
Tina	6	11	14

Write a sentence to describe the graph.

The mean scores of Jimmy & Tina are 74. The range of Jimmy scores 25, The range of Tina scores 31. Which is Tina has the most score.

Probability

- Determine all the possible outcomes in a simple probability experiment.
- Use fractions to represent the probability that an event will occur in probability experiments.

> It's not fair! The probability of getting my favourite food is only $\frac{1}{4}$.

List out all the possible outcomes for each probability experiment.

① 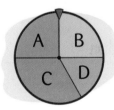 Toss a coin.

head, Tails

②  Roll a cube numbered 1 to 6.

1,2, 3,4,5 and 6

③  Spin the spinner.

A, B, C, D

④ Roll a cube numbered 1 to 6 two times and find the sum.

2,3,4,5,6,7,8,9,10 and 12

⑤ 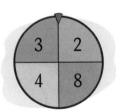 Spin the spinner two times and find the product.

17

4, 6, 8, 9, 12, 16, 24, 32, and 64

Probability: a number showing how likely it is that an event will happen

e.g. 2 2 2 7 8

$\text{Probability} = \dfrac{\text{No. of outcomes of a particular event}}{\text{Total no. of outcomes}}$

Probability of picking a 2

$= \dfrac{3}{5}$ ← There are 3 "2".
  ← There are 5 cards.

Write a fraction to describe the probability of each event.

⑥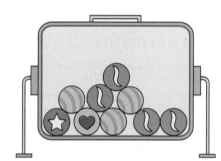

What is the probability of picking

a. a marble with a cat's eye? $\frac{4}{9}$

b. a marble with stripes? $\frac{3}{9}$

c. a marble with a star? $\frac{1}{9}$

⑦

What is the probability of picking

a. a card with an animal? $\frac{6}{12}$

b. a card with a vehicle? $\frac{2}{12}$

c. a card with a plant? $\frac{4}{12}$

⑧ What is the probability of landing on

a. a flower? $\frac{1}{8}$

b. a pencil? $\frac{4}{8}$

c. a car? $\frac{0}{8}$

d. a ring? $\frac{2}{8}$

e. a pail? $\frac{1}{8}$

28

Match the spinners with the correct tables. Then write fractions or draw pictures to complete the tables.

⑨

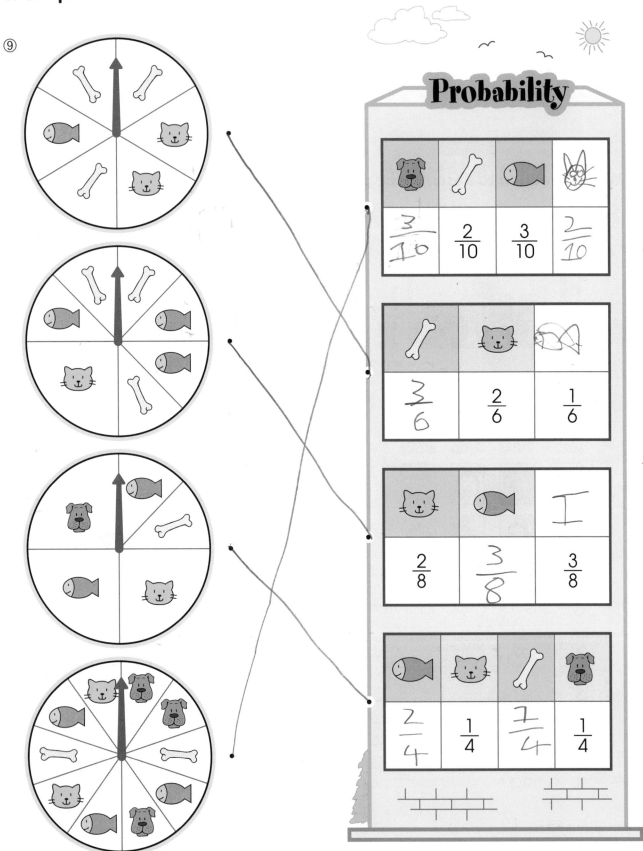

Probability

🐶	🦴	🐟	🐰
$\frac{3}{10}$	$\frac{2}{10}$	$\frac{3}{10}$	$\frac{2}{10}$

🦴	🐱	〰️
$\frac{3}{6}$	$\frac{2}{6}$	$\frac{1}{6}$

🐱	🐟	I
$\frac{2}{8}$	$\frac{3}{8}$	$\frac{3}{8}$

🐟	🐱	🦴	🐶
$\frac{2}{4}$	$\frac{1}{4}$	$\frac{7}{4}$	$\frac{1}{4}$

Draw things on the spinners to match the descriptions. Then answer the questions.

Spinner **A** – 6 equal sections

- 3 sections – muffin
- 1 section – cookie
- the rest of the sections – cracker

Spinner **B** – 8 equal sections

- 3 sections – cracker
- 4 sections – cookie
- the rest of the sections – muffin

⑩

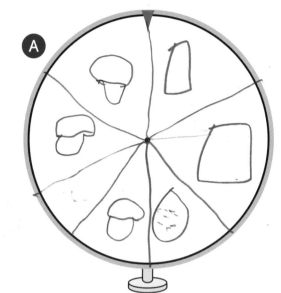

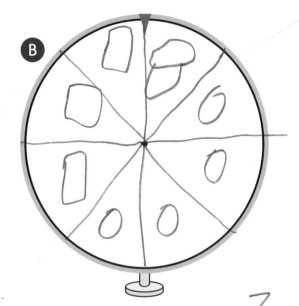

⑪ What is the probability that **A** will land on "cracker"?

$\frac{2}{6}$

⑫ What is the probability that **B** will land on "muffin"?

$\frac{1}{8}$

⑬

Which spinner should I choose to spin if I want to have a muffin? Why?

A because it has 3 muffins.

⑭

If the sections "cookie" and "cracker" on spinner A are replaced by "bone", what will be the probability of landing on "bone"?

$\frac{0}{6}$

MATHEMATICS
COMPLETE
Z 8

M = MULTIPLICATION
A = ADDITION
T = TRANSFORMATION
H = HEART
E = EXTREME
M = MARKS
A = ANGLES
T = TRIANGLES

I = INTELLIGENT
C = CREATIVE
S = SUBTRACTION

ENGLISH

European Microstates

Did you know that there are countries so small, many of us have never heard of them? Five of these smallest countries in the world are in Europe, commonly known as the five European microstates.

Andorra

This country is in the Pyrenees, the mountain range that separates France and Spain. It is a small principality, meaning it is ruled by a prince. It is about 470 square kilometres and has a population of about 78 000. Andorrans make up only about one-third of the population, almost half are Spanish, and the rest are Portuguese and French. The official language is Catalan.

Liechtenstein

Liechtenstein is also a principality. It is the fourth-smallest country in the world. Its area of 160 square kilometres is home to 36 000 people, most of whom speak German. There is great skiing to be found here.

San Marino

Founded in 301 CE, San Marino is one of the world's oldest republics. It is the third-smallest country in the world, with an area of 61 square kilometres and a population of about 32 000. Its people speak Italian and are in fact very much like Italians themselves. Tourism is the main industry, although banking, ceramics, clothing, wine, and cheese are also important to the country's economy.

Monaco

As the second-smallest country in the world, Monaco is located on the Mediterranean Sea along the coast of France, not far from the Italian border. It has a population of 35 000, which is not much until you learn that the country is only two square kilometres! It is the world's most densely populated country. Many wealthy people choose to live here, most of them being Monegasques, French, or Italians.

Vatican City

Known as the "headquarters" of the Roman Catholic Church, Vatican City is the world's smallest country, measuring only 0.44 square kilometres. It is located in Rome, the capital city of Italy. Although it is home to only about 800 citizens, 3000 people commute from Rome to work here every day. Millions of tourists visit each year to see its buildings and famous artwork.

A. Match the names with the descriptions.

1. San Marino   one of the world's oldest republics

2. Vatican City   official language of Andorra

3. Catalan   capital city of Italy

4. the Pyrenees   world's smallest country

5. Rome   a mountain range

B. Answer these questions.

1. What is a principality?

It is a place ruled by a prince,

x *The 4th smallest country located in Liechtenstein.*

2. Where is Monaco?

Its located on the Mediterranean Sea along the coast of France.

3. What can you say about Monaco in terms of its population density?

Monaco is so popular among wealthy people.

4.x Why do you think Monaco is so popular among wealthy people?

Many wealthy people choose to live here. It is a small country with an appealing,

5. The word "microstate" means "tiny state". Think of another word beginning with "micro" and tell what it means.

Microphone! For talking in School Assembly, 9nd *Church.*

Nouns

Nouns can fall into three groups. A **common noun** names any person, place, thing, or animal. A **proper noun** names a specific person, place, thing, or animal. It always begins with a capital letter. A **compound proper noun** is a proper noun with more than one word.

Examples: country (common)
Andorra (proper)
the Roman Catholic Church (compound proper)

C.   Write the underlined nouns in the correct groups.

Featured <u>Country</u>: **Monaco**

- second-smallest country in the world
- located on <u>the Mediterranean Sea</u>
- not far from the Italian <u>border</u>
- population: 35 000
- measures two square kilometres
- home to <u>Monegasques</u>, French, and Italians

1. Common:
    border

2. Proper:
    Monegasques

3. Compound Proper: *seg*
    the Mediteranean

D.   Rewrite these sentences by correcting the common and proper nouns.

1. Many tourists visit Vatican City for its Famous Architecture.

    _____✓_____

2. The Pyrenees is the Mountain Range between france and spain.

    The Pyrenees is the Mountain Range between France and Spain.

3. Besides Tourism, things like Banking, Ceramics, Clothing, Wine, and Cheese are also important to San marino's Economy.
    and Wine,

    Besides tourism, things like Banking, Ceramics, Clothing

    Cheese are also important to San Marinos Economy.

Verbs

Verbs can fall into two groups. A **transitive verb** must take an object. An **intransitive verb** does not need an object.

Examples: Most of the people in Liechtenstein <u>speak</u> German. (transitive)
Most of us <u>commute</u> every day. (intransitive)

E. Write the transitive verb and the object of each sentence.

	Verb	Object

1. Laurie measured the size of this <u>box</u>.   ~~Measured~~   Box

2. Bill chose Monaco to be his home.   ~~Monaco~~ *chose*   ~~Home~~ *monaco*

3. Bob <u>visits</u> Rome every two years.   ~~Rome~~ *visit*   Rome

4. Kara sees the Pyrenees far away.   ~~Pyrenees~~ *sees*   ~~Away~~ *the Pyrenees*

5. Cheryl learned German last year.   Learned   German

F. Underline each intransitive verb. Then write a sentence.

1. The more mistakes you make, the more you <u>learn</u>.

2. Marie <u>paints</u> every other weekend.

3. Walter always <u>listens</u> in class.

4. Thanks to the doctor, the blind man finally <u>sees</u>!

5. This parrot really <u>talks</u>.

6.
> *Some verbs can be both transitive and intransitive, like the word "see". Choose an intransitive verb from (F) and use it as a transitive verb in a sentence.*

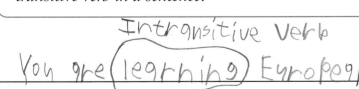

Intransitive Verb

You are (learning) European Microstates

Have you ever wondered about the ship on the Canadian dime? It is a schooner called *Bluenose*, Canada's most celebrated sailing vessel.

Bluenose was launched in March 1921 at Lunenburg, Nova Scotia. It was both a racing and cod-fishing vessel. In fact, "Bluenose" is a nickname for Nova Scotians, and has been so since around 1760. No one really knows why, but some say it is because of the purplish-blue potatoes that were once widely grown in the province.

Bluenose had the largest mainsail in the world. It was 49 metres long and weighed 258 tonnes. Its mainmast was 38 metres high with a sail area of a whopping 1036 square metres! Its crew comprised five officers, 12 deckhands, and a cook. The schooner was built in response to the fact that the United States had won the trophy in the annual International Fishermen's Race in 1920. The following year, our Bluenose won the trophy back and remained undefeated for 17 years!

Bluenose was a hard-working vessel. Besides its racing and fishing duties, it also served as a showboat, representing Canada at the World's Fair in Chicago in

Bluenose

1933. But later, new boat designs made fishing schooners obsolete. Despite attempts to keep the ship in Canada and preserved as a national institution, our Bluenose was sold to a company in the West Indies in 1938. It became a "tramp schooner" – a cargo vessel sailing the waters of the Caribbean Sea.

Despite some misfortunes over the course of its career – it sank in 1946 when it struck a reef off the coast of Haiti – Bluenose was depicted on a Canadian postage stamp and put on our dime in 1937, becoming a little bit of history in our pocket. Then in 1955, the schooner and its captain Angus Walters were inducted into the Canadian Sports Hall of Fame. In 1963, the beloved schooner was back as *Bluenose II*, an exact copy of the original. It now belongs to the government of Nova Scotia and acts as a goodwill ambassador, to remind us of Canada's greatest sailing vessel.

A. Fill in the information about Bluenose.

Information about Bluenose

Launch

Date: March _7927_

Place: Lunenburg, _Nova Scotia_

Size

Length: _49_ m

Weight: _258_ tonnes

Mainmast

Height: _38_ m

Sail Area: _1036_ m²

Crew

- 5 _years_
- 12 _deckhands_
- 1 _hare_

B. Answer these questions.

1. Why was Bluenose built?

It The ~~was~~ purplish blue potatoes that were once widely grown in the province.

2. What happened to Bluenose in 1938?

Bluenose was sold to a company in the West Indies.

3. How did Canadians preserve the memory of Bluenose before Bluenose II was built?

The beloved schooner was back at bluenose II.

Adjectives

An **adjective** describes a noun. Sometimes, a noun can also function as an adjective.

Examples: Bluenose is a <u>Canadian</u> vessel that was <u>hand-built</u>.
Bluenose has been depicted on a <u>postage</u> stamp.

"Postage" is a noun, but it describes "stamp", so it functions as an adjective in this sentence.

C. Underline each adjective and circle the noun that it describes.

1. Bluenose had a <u>large</u> (mainsail)

2. Bluenose is Canada's <u>national</u> (institution)

3. The game (room) is just right across from where we are.

4. Your (timing) was exact.

5. There were many crew (members) on board.

D. Complete this crossword puzzle with adjectives from the passage that describe Bluenose.

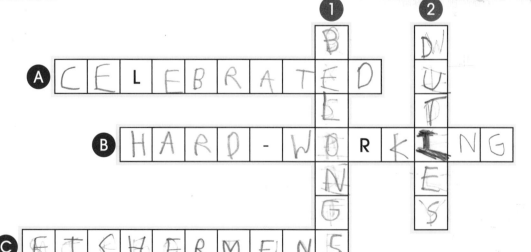

A. C E L E B R A T E D
1 (down) B E L O N G I N G
2 (down) D U T I E S
B. H A R D - W O R K I N G
C. F I S H E R M E N S

Adverbs

An **adverb** describes a verb. It often ends in "**ly**". Sometimes it is placed in front of the verb, and sometimes it is placed after.

Examples: Bluenose <u>easily</u> won the race.
Bluenose won the race <u>easily</u>.

E. Tell whether the underlined word is an adjective (ADJ) or adverb (ADV).

1. The province is full of <u>friendly</u> people.   ADJ

2. Purplish-blue potatoes were once <u>widely</u> grown here.   ADJ ✓

3. Bluenose II is <u>exactly</u> the same as the original.   ADV

4. What a <u>lovely</u> name this is!   ADJ

5. The schooner arrived <u>early</u>.   ADV

F. Rewrite each sentence by placing the adverb in a different spot.

1. We built the ships carefully.

   We carefully built the ships.

2. The ship calmly sails the sea.

   The ship sails the sea calmly.

3. The cook chopped the onions skilfully.

   The cook skilfully chopped the onions.

4. The crew greeted the kids cheerfully.

   The crew cheerfully greeted the kids.

Honeybees

Honey has made many a food and meal tasty and enjoyable to eat. Yet the busy bees that fly about us when we have our outdoor meals are most annoying!

There are two types of bees – the social bee and the solitary bee. Social bees, like the honeybee, live in communities or colonies and are divided into subgroups called castes. Solitary bees, like the carpenter bee, live alone or in very small groups.

As their name suggests, honeybees make honey. They live in a beehive made up of honeycombs, a structure made of wax produced by the bees. Each honeycomb has many six-sided holes called cubbyholes or cells. It is in these cells that the bees put their nectar and honey or lay eggs.

As a community, honeybees are divided into three subgroups or castes: the queen bee, the worker bee, and the drone. Each caste has a very definite and rigid role or job. The queen bee only lays eggs into the waxy cells. The drones' only job is to mate with the queen bee, after which they die. It is the worker bees that are the really busy bees: they build the hive, collect the food, and care for the young. In each hive, there are about 50 000 to 80 000 worker bees. These bees produce the honey we eat.

The farming of honey is called apiculture or beekeeping. The farmer builds a small artificial hive, which is a box hung with many trays of wax in wooden frames. The worker bees fill these trays with honey, and when the trays are full, the farmer takes them out and collects the honey. When the hive is overpopulated, the bees fly away in search of a new hive, usually an empty hive that the farmer has built in advance nearby.

The worker bees collect flower nectar with their long tongues and deposit it into a special "honey stomach". The nectar reacts with chemicals in the stomach to start the honey-making process. The worker bees then fly to their hives and deposit the nectar-chemical mixture into the cells and later, honey is formed.

Next time when you spread honey on toast or use it in your tea, remember where it came from.

A. Match the words with the meanings. Write the correct letters.

1. colonies _____C_____

2. cubbyholes _____A_____

3. castes _____H_____

4. rigid _____D_____

5. apiculture _____F_____

6. artificial _____B_____

7. deposit _____DG_____

8. process _____E_____

A six-sided holes in honeycombs

B not natural

C communities of bees

D not easily changed

E a series of actions

F farming of honey

G put

H subgroups

B. Circle "T" for the true sentences and "F" for the false ones.

1. Honeybees are social bees. (T) F

2. The carpenter bee lives in colonies. (T) F

3. Honeybees put nectar and honey in the cubbyholes. (T) F

4. The drones mate with the queen bee and help worker bees collect nectar. T (F)

5. An artificial hive consists of many trays of wax in wooden frames. (T) F

6. The bees die when a hive is overpopulated. T (F)

7. The worker bees collect flower nectar with their long antennae. (T) F

8. Chemicals in a bee's stomach are necessary in the honey-making process. (T) F

Easily Confused Adjectives and Adverbs (1)

Some adjectives and adverbs are often used incorrectly. We have to remember whether we are describing a noun or a verb when using them.

Examples: I'm doing <u>good</u>. (✘)   I'm doing <u>well</u>. (✔)
Were you hurt <u>bad</u>? (✘)   Were you hurt <u>badly</u>? (✔)
This candy is <u>real</u> good! (✘)   This candy is <u>really</u> good! (✔)
Your house is <u>nearly</u> mine. (✘) Your house is <u>near</u> mine. (✔)

C.   Circle the correct adjectives or adverbs.

1.   Kara needs to use the washroom really (bad) / badly .

2.   The library is   near / (nearly)   the swimming pool.

3.   This show turned out to be really (good) / well .

4.   It is always (good) / well   to think ahead.

5.   Bob is   near / (nearly)   seven feet tall.

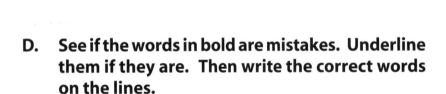

D.   See if the words in bold are mistakes. Underline them if they are. Then write the correct words on the lines.

My brother can get **real** distracted by the TV and does his homework **really bad**. He knows perfectly **good** that the TV often airs **badly** shows. That is why he only watches documentaries, which are stories about **real** people. But he can be **real** consumed by them. Maybe my brother should become a documentary filmmaker, so that his work will also be his play! That would be a **real** good idea!

1.   _really_   2.   _____   3.   _____

4.   _____   5.   _____   6.   _____

Easily Confused Adjectives and Adverbs (2)

Some words like "late" and "high" can be used as adjectives or adverbs. But their "ly" form, "lately" and "highly", are used as adverbs with different meanings.

Examples: Sue is <u>late</u>. (adjective)
Sue came <u>late</u>. (adverb)
Has Sue been to the park <u>lately</u>? (adverb meaning "recently")

E.   Fill in the blanks with the given words. Then identify each answer as an adjective (ADJ) or adverb (ADV).

hard   late   high   near

1.   That flag is flying ___high___ above the rooftop.   (ADV)

2.   This question on the test is very ___hard___ for me!   (ADJ)

3.   My cousin arrived ___late___ for the party.   (ADV)

4.   This is a very ___hard___ / late phone call since it is midnight!   (ADJ)

5.   Jim got a very ___high___ score on the test.   (ADJ)

6.   Ben is standing ___near___ the pole.   (ADV)

7.   You have to push the door ___hard___ to open it.   (ADV)

8.   Your birthday is ___late___ as it is already June.   (~~ADV~~)
                                                                      ADJ

F.   Use each of these adverbs to write a sentence.

1.   highly

   Angels are flying highly.

2.   hardly

   The test is very hard.

Jess "n" Jacki
Party Planners

In May, my friend Jess and I started looking for summer jobs. After a couple of weeks of looking for work in the retail and fast food industries, Jess and I decided we wanted to try something different. We decided to go into business for ourselves! We got the idea from something we did last year.

Jess and I both love to dance. We have been taking dance lessons for years. One day last fall, my aunt asked us to organize a birthday party for her daughter. She thought we could organize a girls' dance party, so we gave it a try. First, we did a short dance show for the girls. Then we taught them a few steps. We taught them some ballet basics and cowboy line dancing too. Because it was a girls' party, we also brought along nail polish and sticker tattoos. The girls really loved it! Everyone had a great time.

Jess and I thought of ways to make our parties bigger and better. We went to the library and borrowed books on magic tricks and Japanese paper folding. Jess's uncle knows how to make balloon animals and taught us how. Then he gave us three beanbag balls and a book that teaches you how to juggle. Jess loves to practise. She is better at juggling than I am.

Later, we were asked to do a party for Canada Day. We got everybody to dress up in red and white. Before long, we were busy several times a week doing birthday parties, bar mitzvahs, and keeping children entertained during large family summer barbecues. The people loved us! We even came up with the idea of offering to supply cakes and snacks because my aunt is a pastry chef.

Now we have our own website, and have decided to work throughout the year doing one party a week. We call our business Jess "n" Jacki Party Planners. We love being our own boss, and we enjoy working together to make our business better and better. We love what we do and are proud to be able to share our passion with our customers!

A. **Put these events in order for the website of Jess "n" Jacki Party Planners. Write 1 to 6.**

About Us: the Road to Our Sweet Success

2   We were looking for summer work.

6   We have our own website.

3   We borrowed books from the library.

5   We organized a Canada Day party.

1   We organized a dance party.

4   We learned how to juggle.

Jess "n" Jacki

B. **Quote a sentence from the passage to support each of the following sentences.**

1. Jess "n" Jacki Party Planners became more and more popular.

   Before long, we were busy several times a week doing birthday parties, bar mitzvas, and keeping children entertained during large family summer ____

2. Jess and Jacki can potentially be contacted by anyone in the world looking for party planners.

   Now we have our own website, and have decided to work throughout the year doing 1 party a week.

3. Even the relatives of Jess and Jacki became involved.

   Jesses uncle knows how to make balloon animals and taught us how.

Comparatives and Superlatives (1)

We use "**more**" (**comparative**) and "**most**" (**superlative**) with adjectives that have two or more syllables. We should never use them with adjectives that are already in the comparative or superlative form.

Examples: Their parties are the interestingest. (✗)
Their parties are the most interesting. (✔)
Jess is more better at juggling than Jacki. (✗)
Jess is better at juggling than Jacki. (✔)

C.   Write "more" or "most" in each sentence.

1.   This is the ___most___ delicious cake I have ever had!

2.   Jess and Jacki have a ___more___ organized party than Amy and Jill.

3.   This barbecue is the ___most___ enjoyable one this summer.

4.   The tricks this time are ___mre___ elaborate than the ones before.

D.   Rewrite each sentence by correcting the underlined words.

1.   This kid is <u>more smarter</u> when he is outside the classroom. Classroom

This kid is smarter when he is outside the

2.   Sally is <u>the most funniest</u> kid in class.

Sally is funniest kid in class.

3.   Lizzy is the <u>more beautiful</u> of all the daughters.

Lizzy is the beautiful of all the daughters.

4.   This story is <u>the most interesting</u> than the other one.

This story is interesting than the other 1.

Comparatives and Superlatives (2)

We should always use comparatives when comparing two things, and always use superlatives when comparing more than two things.

Examples: Of <u>all</u> the parties, this one is <u>better</u>. (✘)
Of <u>all</u> the parties, this one is <u>the best</u>. (✔)

E. Check the correct sentences. Put a cross for the wrong ones and rewrite them using the correct comparatives or superlatives.

1. [✓] In this year's list of movies, this one seems the least innovative.

_____

2. [✗] Of these two restaurants, this one is <u>the best</u>.
Of these 2 restaurants, this one is better.

3. [✗] Out of the whole class, Sarah <u>got less</u> juice.
Out of the whole class, Sarah got the less juice

4. [✓] This is the best job ever!

_____

5. [✓] Is that the bigger one of this bunch?

_____

_____

6. [✓] The kids built the smallest snowman today than yesterday.

_____

_____

The Superfoods

Everyone knows it is important to watch what we eat. We know we must not eat too much fast food or sugary and fatty food, and must eat more raw fruits and vegetables. More and more doctors are telling us that there are foods that can really help us live longer, healthier lives because they have certain nutrients that help our body regenerate and fight disease.

Based on studies of diets in places where people live relatively long and healthy lives – like the Mediterranean region and Okinawa, Japan – doctors advise that if we want the same for our own families, we should make the following list of food a regular part of our diet:

- beans and lentils
- broccoli and spinach
- oranges and pumpkins
- soy
- tomatoes
- walnuts

- blueberries and raspberries
- oats
- salmon
- tea (green or black)
- turkey
- yogourt

When you cook, use olive oil rather than vegetable oil or lard, and spice up your meals with onion, garlic, and ginger. Not only will these items make your food more flavourful, they also have special properties that help you stay healthy.

Don't like spinach, you say? Try it in a salad, mixed with sections of juicy orange and sprinkled with a handful of walnuts, a drop of olive oil, and a dash of balsamic vinegar. You will surely like it then. And instead of boring, old breakfast cereal, make your own morning parfait by layering granola oats, plain yogourt, berries, and honey. Healthful eating *is* delicious!

A. **Read the clues and complete the crossword puzzle with words from the passage.**

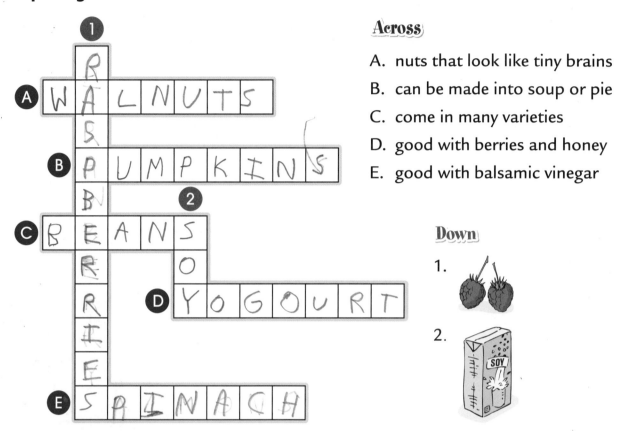

Across

A. nuts that look like tiny brains

B. can be made into soup or pie

C. come in many varieties

D. good with berries and honey

E. good with balsamic vinegar

Down

1.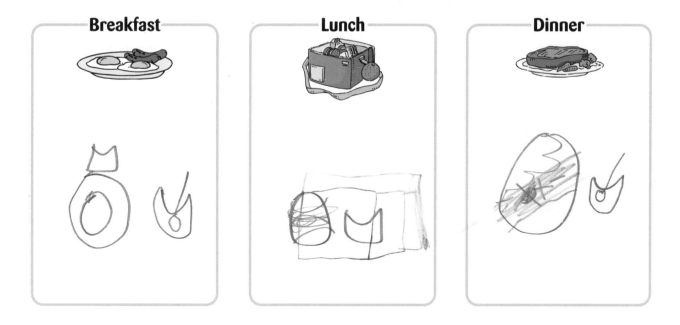

2.

Crossword answers:
- A. WALNUTS
- B. PUMPKINS
- C. BEANS
- D. YOGOURT
- E. SPINACH
- 1 Down: RASPBERRIES
- 2 Down: SOO

B. **Based on the information from the passage, plan a day of healthful meals.**

Breakfast	Lunch	Dinner

The Subject and the Predicate

The **subject** and the **predicate** are the two main parts of a sentence. The subject contains the noun or pronoun that performs an action. The predicate contains the verb and describes the action.

Example: The boy ate a salad with apples.
subject – the boy (the noun is "boy")
predicate – ate a salad with apples (the verb is "ate")

C.   Draw a line to separate the subject and the predicate in each sentence.

1.   Beth chews her food very carefully.

2.   Tom likes spinach.

3.   Kiwis contain a lot of vitamin C.

4.   The children ate a variety of vegetables.

5.   Sally added some walnuts to her tuna salad.

6.   Mom makes a very healthful breakfast for us every day.

D.   Unscramble the words of the predicate and write each sentence on the line.

1.   Sara (raw fruits vegetables every eats and day).

Sarah eats fruits and raw everyday.

2.   My father (milk bought soy containing).

My father bought milk containing soy.

3.   Yogourt (with becomes a when treat berries mixed).

Yogurt with berries becomes a treat when mixed

Compound Subjects and Compound Verbs

Sometimes we have **compound subjects** and **compound verbs**, which means we have two or more subjects, and two or more verbs.

Examples: <u>Yogourt and berries</u> go well together. (compound subject)
The kids <u>ate and chatted</u> in the den. (compound verb)

E.   Check the sentences that contain compound subjects.

1.   Broccoli and spinach are both dark green vegetables.   ✓

2.   Green tea and black tea are my favourite drinks.   ✓

3.   Balsamic vinegar is very good with bread.   ✗

4.   My picky mother needs to eat more fruits.   ✗

5.   Mom and Sally are making dinner together.   ✓

F.   Write a sentence with each compound verb. You may change the tense if necessary.

1.   sit and wait

Sit and wait for the haircut.

2.   cut and mash

Cut and mash the Apple.

3.   shake and bake

Shake and bake dinner

4.   sing and dance

The girls sing and dance.

ecember 6, 1917 is a date that all schoolchildren in Nova Scotia most likely know about. On this day in Halifax, a 3121-ton French freighter called *Mont-Blanc* was entering the city's lovely harbour. It was part of a convoy of ships that had come from New York City, and was on its way back to France. It was filled with munitions – over 2600 tonnes of highly explosive chemicals such as nitrocellulose, TNT, wet and dry picric acid, and benzol. It was the time of World War I.

A Norwegian vessel, *Imo*, was also in the harbour. It had been delayed from leaving the day before. Because a third ship was blocking the right channel, the captain of *Imo* decided to leave the harbour through the left channel, where *Mont-Blanc* was coming through. Despite attempts of both captains to avoid a collision, the two ships collided in the centre channel. The result was the largest artificial explosion before the atomic bomb in 1945. *Mont-Blanc* became a fireball that rose over a mile into the air. The ship vaporized. The force of the explosion caused a tsunami 18 metres high, throwing *Imo* onto the land. A wave of air pressure snapped trees and demolished buildings for kilometres.

Over 1000 people died instantly, another thousand died later, and 6000 people were seriously injured. Because many of the residents in Halifax had been looking at the harbour through their windows, they were blinded by flying glass when *Mont-Blanc* exploded. The entire north end of the city was destroyed and 1500 people were left homeless by the destruction. Even in Truro, which is many kilometres away, windows were shattered. Property damage was estimated to be over $30 million, which was a huge amount in 1917.

Ironically, the large number of eye injuries led to medical advances in the treatment of such injuries.

Even today, nearly a century later, what happened in Halifax Harbour on that fateful day in December ranks as one of the largest human-made, non-nuclear explosions ever to occur.

The Halifax Explosion

A. Match the five "W's" with the facts about the Halifax explosion.

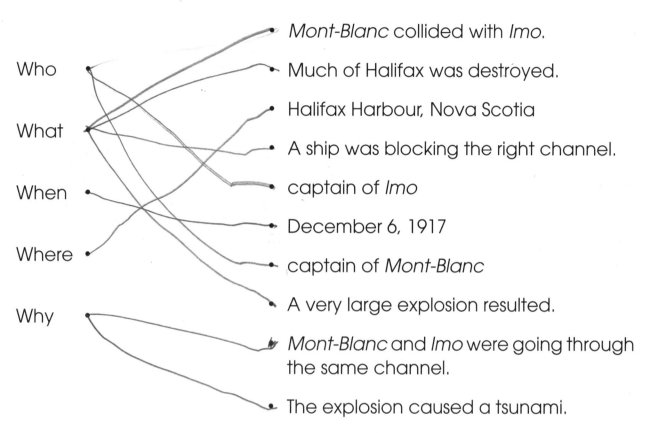

Who

What

When

Where

Why

Mont-Blanc collided with *Imo*.

Much of Halifax was destroyed.

Halifax Harbour, Nova Scotia

A ship was blocking the right channel.

captain of *Imo*

December 6, 1917

captain of *Mont-Blanc*

A very large explosion resulted.

Mont-Blanc and *Imo* were going through the same channel.

The explosion caused a tsunami.

B. Answer these questions.

1. What was going on in the world at the time of the tragedy?

   World where I was going on.

2. What happened to *Mont-Blanc* after the collision?

   It become a fire ball and vaporized.

3. What was the irony of the tragedy?

   It lid to medical advance in the treatment of insurace.

Subject-Verb Agreement

In a sentence, the subject and verb must **agree**. A single subject requires the singular form of the verb. A plural subject requires the plural form of the verb.

Examples: The ship <u>is</u> sailing ahead. (singular)
The two ships <u>are</u> sailing ahead. (plural)

C. Circle the correct form of the verb.

1. The freighter (has) / have over 2600 tonnes of explosives.

2. Another ship (is) / are also in the harbour.

3. Some people is / (are) blocking Mr. Shaw's view.

4. The two cars (collide) / collides in the intersection.

5. The sun rise / (rises) over on the other side.

D. Underline the verbs that do not agree with the subjects and correct them on the lines.

1. Everything vaporizes when the explosion <u>occur</u>. _____*O ccurs*_____

2. Sometimes, an explosion <u>cause</u> a tsunami that creates further damage. _____*Causes*_____

3. The ship becomes a fireball that <u>rise</u> into the air. *rises*

4. Aunt Meg <u>remain</u> very quiet and avoids talking about the event. _____*remained*_____

5. The students know about the tragedy and visits Halifax Harbour every year. _____

E. **Change the singular subjects to plural ones and the plural subjects to singular ones. Make sure the subjects and verbs agree.**

1. The captain attempts a different course.

   The captains attempts a different course.

2. A load of munitions is on board.

   A loads of munition is on board.

3. Numerous trees snap and many houses are demolished.

   Numerous tree snaps and many houses are demolished.

4. The families are devastated and refuse to believe it.

   The family is devasts and refuse to believe it.

F. **Write a sentence with each of these verbs. Make sure the verb agrees with the subject.**

1. happen

   What happened to the time of the tradegy.

2. leave

   Imo decided to leave the harbour.

3. find

   Find the people who died.

4. rank

   December ranks as 1 of the largest human made.

Cherry Blossom Time

Dear Sammy,

How are you? Is there still snow where you live? Where I live here in Japan, we get snow in the mountains in wintertime. But the snow is almost gone. Cherry trees are starting to flower now! I think there is nothing as pretty as a cherry tree in spring.

Each spring, we wait for the cherry blossoms to come out. There are four main islands of Japan: Kyushu, Shikoku, Honshu, and Hokkaido. Kyushu is in the farthest south, so cherry blossom time starts there and moves north. Announcers on the television news programs show us how the cherry blossom "front" is coming north, as if they are talking about some snowstorm. It is very exciting! When the cherry trees start to bloom, schoolchildren leave the classrooms and go to the parks. We sketch, paint, and have picnics under the cherry trees. Families and co-workers also take time to gather under the blossoms. We call this time *ohanami*. *O* means "honourable", *hana* means "flower", and *mi* means "to see".

When the cherry blossom front comes to the countryside around my town, it is like pale pink snow on the trees. After a while, the pink snow falls to the ground in the breeze. Cherry blossom time lasts such a short time – maybe that's why we love it so much.

I recently found out there are also many cherry trees in Vancouver and Washington, D.C. So they should have cherry blossom time, too. Do you have cherry blossom time where you live, Sammy? Why don't you come to Japan someday and see the beautiful blossoms with my family and me?

Your pen pal,

Kiyoka

A. **Fill in the blanks with words from the passage.**

1. Cherry trees start to flower in ___spring___ in Japan.

2. In Japan, there are four main ___islands___ .

3. The cherry blossom "front" starts ___north___ and then moves ___snowstorm___

4. In *ohanami, hana* means " ___flower___ ".

5. There are many cherry trees in ___vancouver___ and Washington, D.C.

B. **Fill in the blanks to complete these words from the passage. Then complete what Kiyoka says with the coloured letters.**

b __l__ __o__ s s __o__ m s

H __o__ n s __h__ u

H o k k __a__ i d o

H o __h__ __o__ __y__ r a b l e

m __o__ __y__ __h__ t __a__ i __h__ s

b l __o__ __o__ __m__

p __i__ c __h__ __i__ __c__ s

We call cherry blossom time __o__ __h__ __a__ __h__ __a__ __m__ __i__ !

Direct and Indirect Objects

The **direct object** is the noun that receives the action of the verb. The **indirect object** is the noun that the action is directed to.

Examples: Kiyoka drew a <u>picture</u> of the blossoms. (direct)
Kiyoka gave <u>Sammy</u> the picture. (indirect)

In this sentence, "picture" is the direct object because it receives the action of the verb "gave".

C. Tell whether the underlined object is "direct" or "indirect".

1. The teacher and the children left the <u>classroom</u>. _Direct_

2. A lady walked her <u>dog</u> in the beautiful park. _Indirect_

3. Sammy read her <u>dad</u> the letter before dinner. _Indirect_

4. A lot of children love <u>springtime</u> in Japan. _Direct_

5. The breeze blows the <u>blossoms</u> to the ground. _Direct_

6. Sammy sent <u>Kiyoka</u> a postcard. _Indirect_

D. Write the direct and indirect objects of each sentence.

	Direct	Indirect
1. Ann gave her sister a bracelet.	bracelet	Sister
2. Mom wrote Tom a little note.	note	Tom
3. Though it was late, I still told Bill a story.	story	Bill
4. Jill sent her cousin a parcel by sea.	Parcel	Jill
5. I mailed you a letter when I was vacationing in Japan.	Japan	You
6. Kelly showed Tom her project before heading home.	Project	Tom

E. Fill in the blanks with the correct objects to complete the sentences.

1. her painting / the audience

   The artist showed _____ audience _____
   _____ painting _____.

2. the customers / the menus

   The waiter handed _____ customers _____ menus _____.

3. the guests / a video

   My dad showed _____ guests _____ video _____ at our Christmas party.

4. Christmas cards / the children

   The teacher gave _____ children _____ cards _____ before sending them home for the holiday.

F. Use each name as the direct object in one sentence, and as the indirect object in another sentence.

1. **Sammy**

   Direct: _Sammy looked at Kyieas picture._
   Indirect: _Kiyoka gave Sammy the picture._

2. **Kiyoka**

   Direct: _Kiyoka drew a picture of the blossoms._
   Indirect: _Kiyoka gave Sammy the picture._

3. **Uncle Peter**

   Direct: _Uncle Peter watched the picture._
   Indirect: _Uncle Peter looked at Kiyokas picture._

Complete Canadian Curriculum • Grade 5   147

Winter Camp
at Lake Winnipeg

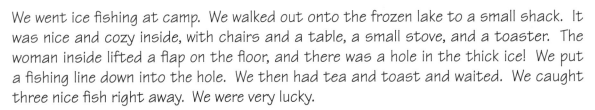

Dear Kiyoka,

Thank you for your letter. Springtime in Japan sounds fantastic. It is still winter here where I live. But I don't mind. I went to a winter camp last weekend. It was so much fun! The camp is on the shores of Lake Winnipeg. Lake Winnipeg is the world's tenth largest freshwater lake.

We went ice fishing at camp. We walked out onto the frozen lake to a small shack. It was nice and cozy inside, with chairs and a table, a small stove, and a toaster. The woman inside lifted a flap on the floor, and there was a hole in the thick ice! We put a fishing line down into the hole. We then had tea and toast and waited. We caught three nice fish right away. We were very lucky.

Then we went back to the lakeshore and cleared a space for building a campfire. Our camp leader taught us how to make a tasty meal. We chopped up some carrots and potatoes while she skinned the fish and cut it into fillets. We sprinkled on salt and pepper and some dried herbs, and then put everything inside pockets of aluminum foil. We let the campfire die down a bit; then we placed the pockets of foil inside the glowing sticks. We made hot chocolate while we waited for our meal to cook. Everything was delicious!

The next day, we learned how to do winter orienteering. It is like racing with snowshoes and a compass. It was very exciting! Maybe someday, you can come and spend the winter with my family.

Your pen pal,

Sammy

P.S. This is a picture of the ice fishing shack.

A. **Look at the clues and complete the crossword puzzle with words from the passage.**

This is a sport in which we have to find our way across rough terrain using a map and compass.

This word is used as a verb in Kiyoka's letter.

B. **Write a short letter to a friend about an experience you had this season.**

_____

_____

_____

_____

_____

_____

Pronouns (1)

A **pronoun** is a word used to refer to a noun. We use **subject pronouns** like "we" and "they" when referring to the subjects of sentences. We use **object pronouns** like "us" and "them" when referring to the objects. We use **possessive pronouns** like "ours" and "theirs" when expressing ownership.

Examples: The <u>fish</u> was caught. <u>It</u> was caught. (subject)
Amy thanked <u>Joey and me</u>. Amy thanked <u>us</u>. (object)
This is <u>our house</u>. This house is <u>ours</u>. (possessive)

C. **Write the stated pronoun in each case.**

1. **Subject pronoun**
    She went to winter camp with them.

    She

2. **Object pronoun**
    You are showing us such a good fishing trick!

    _us_

3. **Possessive pronoun**
    His fish is much bigger than ours.

    ours

4. **Possessive pronoun**
    Their fish is more unusual than his.

    this

D. **Rewrite each sentence by replacing the underlined words with a pronoun.**

1. We told <u>our camp leader Ben</u> that we wouldn't be long.

    We told him that it wouldnt be long ouydnt be long.

2. Look! All of these are <u>Monica's fish</u>!

    Look! All of those are her fish!

3. Although it is still winter in Winnipeg, <u>Sammy and her friends</u> don't mind the cold at all.

    Although it is still winter in winnipeg, me and her friends dont mind the cold at all

E. Fill in the blanks with the correct pronouns.

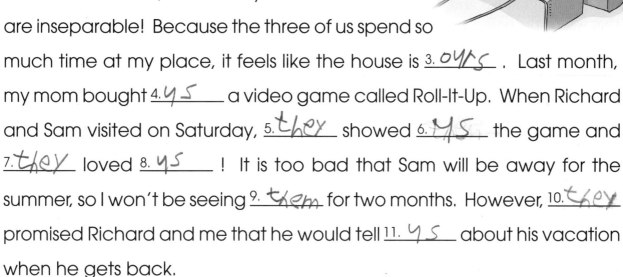

Richard, Sam, and I are great friends. 1. _we_ have known one another since kindergarten. Although I now go to a different school, my two buddies still visit 2. _us_ every weekend. We are inseparable! Because the three of us spend so much time at my place, it feels like the house is 3. _ours_ . Last month, my mom bought 4. _us_ a video game called Roll-It-Up. When Richard and Sam visited on Saturday, 5. _they_ showed 6. _us_ the game and 7. _they_ loved 8. _us_ ! It is too bad that Sam will be away for the summer, so I won't be seeing 9. _them_ for two months. However, 10. _they_ promised Richard and me that he would tell 11. _us_ about his vacation when he gets back.

F. Rewrite each sentence in different ways using a different pronoun each time.

1. Jenny wants my brother and me to go fishing with her.
    a. _He wants my brother and me to go fishing with her._
    b. _____

2. Uncle Max has always been good at ice fishing.
    a. _His uncle Max has always been good at ice fishing._
    b. _____

3. "You should've asked if that marker belonged to me," said May.
    a. _You should've asked if that marker belonged to me, he said_
    b. _____
    c. _____

Bethany Hamilton loves to surf. Growing up in Kauai, Hawaii, a place famous for its waves, Bethany had become a champion surfer by the time she was a teenager. Then on October 31, 2003, tragedy struck.

Bethany had gone surfing as usual with her friend Alana and Alana's father. It was a calm, clear day, and Bethany was relaxing on her board with her right arm on the board, and her left arm dangling in the water. Her friend was floating nearby. Suddenly, Bethany felt a clap of pressure and quick tugs at her arm. There was a flash of grey. The water around her was bright red. That was all the time it took.

Bethany says there was no pain at the time, and that she never panicked. She simply yelled to her friend that she had just been attacked by a shark, and started to make her way back to the shore. Alana's father used a surfboard leash to make a tourniquet for the stump of her upper arm, which saved her life. Her left arm was gone, bitten off by the three-metre tiger shark. The shark had also bitten off a chunk of Bethany's surfboard, 16 inches across and eight inches deep. The shark was later caught, though.

Bethany Hamilton
The Spirit of a Champion

Doctors say that Bethany's athletic training saved her life. Surprising everyone – except perhaps her parents – Bethany recovered and was back on her surfboard in less than a month! A few months later, Bethany competed at the 2004 National Scholastic Surfing Association Nationals Championships and took fifth place. Later that year, she secured a spot on the United States' National Surfing Team. The following year, Bethany came in first at the NSSA championships in the Explorer Women's Division. Bethany has won numerous awards, including the 2004 ESPY Award for "Comeback Athlete of the Year". She has written a book and often speaks about her experience, motivating others to overcome the obstacles in their lives.

Always with the spirit of a champion, Bethany says she is now interested in becoming a triathlete.

A. Use your dictionary to find the definitions of these words as they are used in the passage. Then use them in sentences of your own.

1. surf: Ride the crests of a wave towards the shore on a surfboard.

2. spirit: The essense of a persong the soul.

3. triathlete: Athlete who compees in 3 different sports.

4. tourniquet: Device to stop bleeding

B. Imagine you are Bethany Hamilton being interviewed by a student newspaper reporter. Write your responses to these questions.

1. What kept you from panicking after the shark attack?

My body gets cyt.

2. How were you able to remain positive with one arm gone?

To fix the arm.

3. What do you say to those who have encountered similar obstacles?

They surfa swim racea and float,

Pronouns (2)

When we ask questions, we can use **interrogative pronouns**: "what", "which", "who", "whose", and "whom". We can use them indirectly too. When we want to refer to a noun occurring earlier in a sentence, we use **relative pronouns**: "which", "who", "whose", "whom", and "that".

Examples: <u>Which</u> is the one you told me about? (interrogative)
The mall, <u>which</u> is in the city core, is still open. (relative)

C. **Tell what type of pronoun is used in each sentence. Write "interrogative" or "relative".**

1. The champion, who is a hero to the kids, is getting a lot of attention.

   relative

2. I asked Alana what she was going to do for her Science project.

   relative

3. "Sam, do you know whose this is?" Amy asked.

   Interrogative

4. Bethany, to whom the trophy was given, had a smile that stretched from ear to ear.

   relative

5. I asked Bethany what the secret to her success was.

   relative

6. My cousins love the guinea pig that I recently bought from the pet store.

   relative

D. Fill in the blanks with the correct pronouns.

1. The student, _who_ is new to the class, was shy at first but quickly warmed up to everyone.

2. The fly ball, _Whith_ Tony had wanted to give him a homerun, fell easily into my glove!

3. "To _Whom_ did you talk after school yesterday?" I asked.

4. Tell me _Which_ you want from this rack and I will get you the right size.

5. The little kid, _whose_ mother is away at work, mistakenly calls the babysitter "Mommy".

6. Ask your little cousin _who_ is making him so unhappy.

7. I have no idea _what_ Alice is going to do.

8. I wonder _who_ hid the little gift under my pillow.

E. Use each of these as an interrogative pronoun in one sentence, and as a relative pronoun in another.

1. what

   What is this?

   I wonder what is this.

2. whom

   Whom is this?

   I wonder whom is this.

The Inca

Before the Spanish built their own empire in South America around the 16th century, there was the Inca, an ancient civilization that once lived in the mountains in what is now a country called Peru.

The Inca were good fighters. Over the years, they built a large empire of 12 million people. They worshipped the sun, and believed their leader descended from it. Though they were defeated in 1533 by the Spanish, the ruins of one of their high mountain settlements still exist today at Machu Pichu.

To the Inca people, the llama was an important animal. The llama is sure-footed on the steep and rocky crags of mountains, much like the big-horn sheep and mountain goats that we can see – if we are lucky – when driving through the mountains of British Columbia. The llama provided the Inca with food and clothing, and was the main method of transport. Because of the importance of this animal to the Inca, it is found in many of their legends.

The Llamas and the Flood
– based on an Inca legend

Two Inca shepherds were resting on a rock high in the mountains when they noticed that their llamas were acting strangely. These llamas seemed to be staring at the sky. The two shepherds approached the llamas and asked them what was wrong. The llamas replied that the stars said it was soon going to rain, and that an enormous flood would overtake the land below.

The two shepherds, who were good and honest mountain people, loved their animals very much and believed their story. They went to get their families and moved further up the mountain to live in caves. Concerned about the people living below, they sent a message down to the people on the flat land about the ensuing flood. The people down at the bottom, who were not too kind or sensible, scoffed at the message and ignored the mountain dwellers. Not long after, the rain came and continued for four months.

Those living below the mountains died. The shepherds and their families repopulated the Earth, and the llamas were happy to live up high, close to the stars.

A. Fill in the blanks with words from the passage.

The Inca:

- were good 1. _fighters_
- was an 2. _ancient_ civilization
- 3. _worshipped_ the sun
- lived in what is now 4. _Peru_

The Llama:

- is 5. _rock_ on steep mountains
- was the Inca's main method of 6. _transport_
- provided the Inca with food and 7. _llamas_
- is found in many Inca 8. _civilization_

B. Answer these questions.

1. How big was the Inca empire?

   It was a large empire ior 1200000 people.

2. When did the Spanish build their empire in South America?

   It will build it around 16th century

3. In the legend, what disaster do the llamas say will overtake the land?

   They say that an enormous flood would overtake the land below.

4. If you were one of the shepherds in the legend, what would you have done after your message was ignored? Why?

   _The bricks ____ If ___ built all the bricks_
   then it will make an Inca civilization.

Pronouns (3)

When the subjects of sentences do things that turn back upon the subjects, we use **reflexive pronouns**: "myself", "yourself", "himself", "herself", "itself", "ourselves", "yourselves", and "themselves". When they do the same things, we use **reciprocal pronouns**: "each other" and "one another".

Examples: I'm so bored that I'm starting to talk to <u>myself</u>! (reflexive)
These <u>two</u> sisters always look out for <u>each other</u>. (reciprocal)
These <u>three</u> sisters always look out for <u>one another</u>. (reciprocal)

C. **Circle the correct reflexive pronouns.**

1. The children enjoyed (themselves) / ourselves tremendously at Benny's birthday party.

2. Marie said to us, "Look! I made this pumpkin pie herself / (myself) !"

3. Sara looked at itself / (herself) in the mirror before heading out the door.

4. All the cousins on my father's side of the family are very good at making (each other) / one another laugh.

5. Tim tried to correct myself / (himself) by coming up with a kinder remark about the restaurant's design.

6. "Don't worry. Emily and I will look after each other / (one another) at the camp," said Jenny to her mother.

7. The cat is blocking our view because it is cleaning ourselves / (itself) in front of the TV.

8. Mother said to us, "Remember to behave yourself / (yourselves) at Grandma's."

D. Fill in the blanks with the correct pronouns.

Paul and Sam are brothers who work as shepherds. They always keep watch for 1. *each other* when they are up in the mountains. They also love their herds of llamas very much. They do not always have to keep the llamas close, though, since these wise animals can look after 2. *one another*. One time, Sam said to the llamas as they were grazing, "We're very grateful that you can look after 3. *yourselves* up here." Having heard this, one of the llamas responded, "In fact, we can come up to the mountains 4. *herself*. We can also follow other shepherds when you're busy on the farm." Still, Paul and Sam insist on walking the beloved llamas 5. *himself* for fear the animals might lose their way in the journey. Because these animals provide the shepherds with food and clothing in return, the two groups – shepherds and llamas – depend on 6. *each other*.

E. Write a short paragraph using two reflexive pronouns and two reciprocal pronouns.

_____

_____

_____

_____

_____

_____

The Hummingbird – a Unique Flyer

Wing beats per second up to 200

Have you ever seen a tiny bird flitting from flower to flower? The wings move so fast that they appear to be just a blur. The bird appears not to be flying and seems to be hovering over the flowers. You hear a buzzing, humming noise. What kind of bird is it? You wonder. You have just seen a hummingbird!

Hummingbirds are the tiniest birds in the world. They are usually not more than 20 grams, though some can be as little as two grams! Their wings are quite long and pointy, which rotate rather than flap. This allows them to approach flowers in a way most other birds cannot. They move in this unique way to get very close to flowers for their food: besides feeding on insects like spiders, hummingbirds feed on nectar just like bees do.

This type of flying requires a lot of effort – the wings of a hummingbird beat up to 200 times per second! They can also fly up to 75 kilometres per hour. Because of this, hummingbirds need a lot of food each day to get their energy. They eat as much as half their body weight in nectar and insects every day! This is why the birds must spend most of their time flying around looking for food. Their feet are not well-developed as a result, since they are not for walking but for perching briefly on branches.

There are approximately 300 different types of hummingbirds, all inhabiting the western hemisphere from Canada down to Argentina. Canada and the United States are home to about 16 species, while the majority of hummingbirds live in the more tropical areas of Central and South America. Hummingbirds live for as long as five or six years in the wild, and many of them are migratory. For example, the ruby-throated hummingbird migrates across the Gulf of Mexico to take advantage of the warmer winter down south.

A. Find the words in the word search. Then write the correct words for the meanings.

rotate   hummingbird   tropical
hovering   western hemisphere   perching
nectar   ruby-throated   migratory

a	e	g	e	h	u	m	m	i	n	g	b	i	r	d	e	p	m	s
e	d	b	n	t	x	p	q		p	n	m	s	z	p	y	e	o	c
h	c	y	o	r	o	k	e	s	a	t	u	r	r	e	z	r	j	h
r	e	r	p	o	k	j	u	e	p	r	p	o	t	r	h	t	m	o
p	n	l		p	j	d	r	t	e	y	p	t	y	c	f	r	i	v
i	e	o	c	i	l	x	s	a	c	a	o	a		h	i	t	g	e
m	c	p	z	c	b	c	t	i	a	e	k	t	i	i	a	r	r	r
e	t	w	r	a	u	h	r	l	s	a	e	o	n	w		a	i
h	a	s	a	l	q	a	u	p	a	w	j	A	w	g	q	k	t	n
r	r	u	r	u	b	y	-	t	h	r	o	a	t	e	d	g	o	g
n	w	e	s	t	e	r	n		h	e	m	i	s	p	h	e	r	e
s	e	w	n	e	w	z	d	h	k	r	a	c	d	n	a	s	y	w

1. _Tropical_ : move in circles
2. _perching_ : resting or settling
3. _hummingbird_ : the world's smallest bird
4. _rotate_ : hanging suspended in the air
5. _western hemisphere_ : changing one's area of habitation with the seasons
6. _nectar_ : sweet substance produced by plants to attract pollinating insects

The Present Tense

When we want to talk about a habit or a simple truth, we use the **simple present tense**. When we want to talk about something that is going on or something that is planned for the future, we use the **present progressive tense**.

Examples: Hansel the Hummingbird <u>eats</u> a lot every day. (simple present)
Hansel <u>is perching</u> on a branch. (present progressive)
Hansel <u>is flying</u> south tomorrow. (present progressive)

B. **Complete each sentence with the simple present tense or the present progressive tense of the given verb.**

1. This hummingbird (weigh) __weighs__ only two grams!

2. The hummingbird's unique way of flying (consume) __consumes__ a lot of energy.

3. This ruby-throated hummingbird (leave) __leaves__ very soon for the warmer winter in the south.

4. Most of the world's hummingbirds (live) __living__ in Central and South America.

5. Just like bees, hummingbirds (feed) __feeds__ on nectar. But unlike bees, they do not use it to make honey.

6. I can see that Hansel the Hummingbird (approach) __approaches__ this beautiful flower with a lot of enthusiasm!

7. "Look! Hansel's wings (beat) __beating__ so fast they are a complete blur!" I say to Tom.

8. Considering how much hummingbirds have to eat, it is no surprise that they (spend) __spending__ most of their time looking for food.

C. Check the correct sentences. Put a cross for the wrong ones and rewrite them using the simple present tense or the present progressive tense.

1. ☒ Ben and Jill are giving their dog a bath once every three weeks.

   _____

   _____

2. ☒ Gwen is dashing to the park after school every day.

   _____

3. ☑ Janice is pondering what to say this very moment.

   _____

4. ☑ Henry is travelling to the North Pole this winter.

   _____

D. Use each of these verbs in the simple present tense in one sentence and in the present progressive tense in another.

1. flit

   The helicopter is flitting the hummingbird.

   _____

2. flap

   The hummingbird flaps his wings.

   _____

3. populate

   The hummingbird populates the nector.

   _____

A Letter from a **New Pen Pal**

Dear Samantha,

Hello! My name is Rakesh. I found your name and address from a Canadian magazine, which my aunt and uncle sent me from Toronto. They live there. In fact, they send me a magazine from Toronto every month. It's great, because I learn a lot about student life in Canada.

I speak Hindi – "Nah-mah-STAY" is how I say "hello" in my language – but I also speak and write English, as you can see. I'm an 11-year-old boy living in Mumbai, which used to be called Bombay. Can you guess what country I'm from? I'm from India! Perhaps you already knew that from the postmark on the envelope.

My family is not very big. I have a five-year-old sister named Kritika. My mom works for a magazine and my father is a computer programmer. We live in an apartment in the northern part of Mumbai. Mumbai is India's biggest city. Some say that there are 12 million people living here – but no one really knows for sure because many people here are homeless. Are there homeless people in your city? Sometimes when I take the train in Mumbai, I can see small shacks along the tracks. Families live in these shacks. It makes me sad.

I read in one magazine that the population of Canada is about 35 million. I think that's incredible! Your country is so big, and yet there are hardly any people compared to India. It's hard to imagine what it must be like to live in a place like that. My aunt and uncle said I can visit them in Toronto when I'm older. They said they would take me to Niagara Falls. My aunt sent me a postcard from there last year.

I hope you will write back to me, Samantha. I'm enclosing a photo of my sister and myself, and a bracelet made in Mumbai. I hope you like it. Write back soon and tell me more about your wonderful country!

Your friend in Mumbai,

Rakesh

A. **Help Samantha write about her new pen pal in her scrapbook.**

Name: 1. URakesh

Age: 2. 11

Home

Country: 3. India

City: 4. Mumbai

• used to be called 5. Blumbai

• population is about 6. 3500000

• the 7. Biggest city in the country

Family

• mother works 8. as a magazine

• father works 9. as a computer programmer

• has a 10. sister who is 11. 5 years old

• has 12. aunt and uncle who live in 13. Tronto canada

B. **Read what Samantha says and write a response.**

> *Why is it a good idea to have pen pals from other countries?*
> *Where would you want to find your new pen pal, and why?*

_____

_____

_____

_____

_____

The Past Tense

When we want to talk about something that happened habitually or at a particular time in the past, we use the **simple past tense**. When we want to talk about something that continued to happen before and after a particular time in the past, we use the **past progressive tense**.

Examples: Sara <u>spent</u> her summers in Halifax for three years. (simple past)
Greta <u>called</u> Louisa at five o'clock today. (simple past)
We <u>were having</u> dinner when a mouse ran across the kitchen! (past progressive)

C.   Underline the mistake in each sentence and correct it on the line.

1. Rakesh <u>was attending</u> English classes every Saturday last year.

   attended

2. When Leslie <u>was spotting</u> me in the crowd, she frantically waved.

   spotted

3. Martin <u>was practising</u> his dance steps every day last month.

   practised

4. Rakesh's mom <u>was admiring</u> the lovely tableware when the guest musicians were arriving.

   arrived

5. The kids <u>planted</u> flowers when their babysitter called them in for lunch.

   were planting

6. We were playing with the ponies when Mrs. Fields <u>was asking</u> us to feed these chicks.

   asked

7. Samantha's mom <u>was singing</u> along with the radio while her cat purred.

   singed

D. **Choose the correct verbs for each sentence and use them in the simple past tense or past progressive tense.**

~~watch~~ ~~bake~~ pour stay catch ~~begin~~ ~~leave~~ go recognize enjoy walk ring

1. Clara _bakes_ muffins for her party when the telephone _ring_ .

2. Robert and his brother _stays_ in Halifax two summers ago and _watches_ the seaside there.

3. Uncle Sam always _catched_ enough fish for a week when he _Poured_ fishing every weekend last summer.

4. The spectators _beggn_ the fireworks when it suddenly _going_ to rain and everyone _leaves_ .

5. Wendy _enjoys_ herself a cup of hot chocolate when a friend from kindergarten _recognizes_ her from afar and _walked_ over to say hello.

E. **Write about a memorable experience. Use two examples of simple past tense and two examples of past progressive tense.**

_____

_____

_____

_____

_____

Jeanne Mance
Angel of the Colony

Jeanne Mance was born in France in 1606. She came to North America in 1641 as a member of the mission of Paul Chomedey de Maisonneuve, who was sent to establish a settlement in New France. In addition to tending as a nurse to the soldiers who were in daily combat with the Iroquois of the area, Jeanne's role was to set up a hospital for the fledgling colony.

Jeanne provided basic medical care for both settlers and Aboriginal peoples. Later, in 1645, with funds that she had secured from French donors, she founded Hôtel-Dieu de Montréal, the oldest hospital in the city and one of the first in North America. Though Jeanne died in 1673, her hospital is still in operation today, with offshoots in other cities in Canada such as Québec City and Windsor.

Sometimes we use the term "founding father" to describe someone who establishes something, such as a town or an organization. Traditionally, women were not encouraged to do such things if they were not related to their church. But Jeanne Mance's dedication, courage, and skill certainly make her worthy of the term. Considered to be the first secular nurse of North America, Jeanne Mance is without doubt one of the "founding fathers" of New France.

Hymn to Jeanne Mance [1]
by Lady Amy Redpath Roddick

O brave Jeanne Mance whose fame is ours
As in a city's growth it flowers:
The seeds you humbly helped to sow
Give witness still and still they grow
Within tried hearts at mercy's call
In fanes and homes of Montreal,
In hospitals which hail you first
To soothe the sufferer, slack his thirst.

Heroic figure of the past
With Maisonneuve so staunchly classed,
Co-worker with ecstatic souls
Who showed the way to heavenly goals:
We have to-day a debt unpaid
Should we now fail where you have laid
Foundation on the rock of God
In turning thus our virgin sod.

[1] *From Library and Archives Canada*

A. Draw lines to match the descriptions with what is on the right.

1. those who establish something

2. colony of the French people in North America

3. natives of Canada

4. one of the first hospitals in North America

5. year that the oldest hospital in Montreal was founded

Hôtel-Dieu de Montréal

New France

founding fathers

Aboriginal peoples

1645

B. Find the words or lines from "Hymn to Jeanne Mance" that mean the following.

1. a. heroic: _brave_
   b. money owed: _debt_
   c. comfort: _suit_
   d. one who suffers: _sufferer_

2. We will owe Jeanne Mance a lot if we don't do a good job at running the hospital that she set up.

   We have to day a debt and pet. should we how fail where you have laid fail foundation on the rock of god.

3. Jeanne Mance's fame blossoms just like the growth of the city that she helped found.

   O brave jeanne mance whose fame is ours as in a city growth it flowers; the seeds are humbly helped to sow Give witness still and still they grow will be hosting.

The Future Tense

When we want to talk about something that will happen, we use the **simple future tense**. When we want to talk about something that will happen over a period of time, we use the **future progressive tense**.

Examples: Susan <u>will visit</u> us again next year. (simple future)
The music <u>will be playing</u> for the evening. (future progressive)

C. Circle the correct future tense in each sentence.

1. Our neighbours (will host) / will be hosting the summer barbecue for the next two years.

2. When Jeanne returns, she (will show) / will be showing you the directions to the station.

3. The boat (will turn) / will be turning around once it gets close to the waterfalls.

4. "Oh dear," sighed Mr. Graham. "The skunk has made a home and (will share) / will be sharing the backyard with us for the summer.

5. Since it (will snow) / will be snowing for the rest of the day, Marianne (will read) / will be reading a book by the fireplace instead.

6. My cousin Kevin (will arrive) / will be arriving from Charlottetown tomorrow. I'm very excited since he (will stay) / will be staying with us for the entire Christmas holiday!

D. **Help these people finish what they say. Write the correct letters.**

(A) they'll be begging me for hours to buy them candy

(B) they'll beg me to buy them a tub of ice cream

(C) we'll have to make sure we leave nothing behind

(D) we'll watch a hockey game at the Air Canada Centre

1.

I'm at the grocery store with my kids, and I know that __B__ .

2.

I'll be spending the whole day at the fairground with my kids, where __A__ .

3.

We're leaving in a few minutes for Toronto, so __C__ .

4.

In two days, we're taking our kids to Toronto, where __D__ .

E. **Write down some of your plans for the future. Use the simple future tense or the future progressive tense.**

1. Tomorrow, _is swimming._ _____

   _____ .

2. This summer, _is canada day._ _____

   _____ .

3. When I grow up, _I will be a Pro._ _____

   _____ .

Canadian Sports

Canadians love sports. Did you know that many of our most loved sports were invented by Canadians or developed in Canada?

Five-pin bowling was developed in Canada by Thomas Ryan in 1909. It is no surprise that the bowling pin resetter was invented in the same country in 1956.

Basketball, a major spectator sport in the United States, was actually invented in 1891 by a Canadian physical education instructor named James Naismith, who wanted to keep his students active indoors over the winter.

Ringette, invented as a sister game for hockey so that girls could also play, was the creation of Sam Jacks, the Director of Parks and Recreation for the City of North Bay. The first game was played – with sticks and rubber rings – in Ontario in 1963, and is now played around the world.

Wheelchair rugby was invented in Winnipeg in the 1970s. It was a demonstration event in 1996 at the Paralympic Games in Atlanta, and became a full medal sport at the Sydney Paralympic Games in 2000.

Canadian football is different than American football. The ball is bigger, the field is wider and longer, and the end zone is deeper. There are twelve players instead of eleven, and three downs instead of four.

Besides hockey, **lacrosse** is Canada's other national sport, invented by the Aboriginals of North America. It is like field hockey, but the ball is passed in the air to and from net-like rackets. It is becoming more and more popular around the world.

Synchronized swimming, a form of water ballet, was invented in Canada. It was once an Olympic sport. For that reason, some call it a Summer Games equivalent of figure skating.

Can you think of any other sports that were first developed in Canada?

A. Read the clues and complete the crossword puzzle with words from the passage.

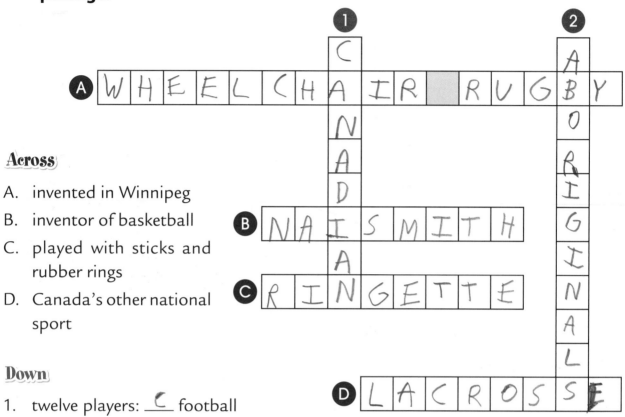

Across

A. invented in Winnipeg
B. inventor of basketball
C. played with sticks and rubber rings
D. Canada's other national sport

Down

1. twelve players: __C__ football
2. inventors of lacrosse

B. Circle "T" for the true sentences and "F" for the false ones.

1. Basketball was invented to keep kids active indoors over winter.   T (F)

2. Although five-pin bowling was invented by a Canadian, the bowling pin resetter was invented by an American.   (T) F

3. Synchronized swimming can be considered the Summer Games equivalent of figure skating.   T (F)

4. The end zone of Canadian football is deeper than the one in American football.   T (F)

5. The first game of ringette was played in Quebec.   (T) F

Active Voice and Passive Voice

When we want to focus on the performer of the action in a sentence, we use the **active voice**. When we want to focus on the receiver of the action, we use the **passive voice**.

Examples: <u>Willie</u> spotted a hare in the backyard yesterday. (active)
A <u>hare</u> was spotted by Willie in the backyard yesterday. (passive)

C. **Complete each sentence using the active or passive voice. Focus on the part of the sentence that is in italics.**

1. performer: *Mrs. Maple* (verb: bake)
   receiver: a pumpkin pie

   Last Saturday morning, _Mrs. Maple baked a pumpkin pie._

2. performer: the nature-loving Aboriginal girl (verb: explore)
   receiver: *the ravine*

   Because of its beauty, _The nature loving Aboriginal girl explores the ravine._

3. performers: the basketball players (verb: patron)
   receiver: *the diner around the corner*

   The basketball players patron the diner around the corner after practice.

4. performers: *Vikki and her teammates* (verb: swim)
   receivers: many lengths of the pool

   Vikki and her teammates swim many lengths of the pool to build up stamina.

D. **Classify the underlined sentences into the active voice or passive voice and answer the questions.**

Have you ever been amazed by something called *aurora borealis*? It is the northern lights. <u>They are seen more often by people who live near the Arctic.</u> These diffused lights can be pink and orange, or yellow and white. <u>The colours create a spectacular light show.</u> Sometimes, they even look like giant curtains! <u>The curtains appear to be shielding the Earth.</u> They may last for hours once they appear. <u>But the occurrence of northern lights cannot be predicted.</u> Maybe that is what makes these lights so special.

1. Sentences in the active voice:

    a. The colours create a spetocular light show.

    b. But the occurrence of northern lights cannot be predicted.

2. Sentences in the passive voice:

    hear the are K.

    a. They are seen more often by people who live

    b. The curtains appear to be shelding the earth.

3. Rewrite 1b and 2a in the other voice.

    be Predicted.

    The occurence of Northern lights but cannot

    more.

    People who live near the arctic and they are seen

4. The sentences in 1b and 2a work better in their original voice for the paragraph. Why?

    So active is 1st then passive is 2nd.

My Best Friend

Dear Diary,

I had a bad day at school. Tonetta was acting strangely toward me – AGAIN! She was playing with Bernice, the new girl, during recess, and when I came over to join them, Tonetta grabbed Bernice and they went running away! I watched them go, and then they both turned around and made faces at me. I decided to go to the library after that. I don't know why Tonetta is doing this to me. She used to be my best friend. I'm really sad.

Dear Diary,

Mom asked me what was wrong today. I finally told her what Tonetta has been doing. As soon as I started telling her, I began to cry! Mom listened while I talked and cried. When I was finished, Mom said it was not good. I thought she was going to tell me to just put up with it, but she didn't. She said that Tonetta was acting like a kind of bully, and that I needed to stand up for myself. Mom and I practised what I'm going to say next time Tonetta is rude to me. I'm going to ask her if it makes her feel good to hurt her old friend.

Mom says the reason why Tonetta is doing this may have to do with how she feels about herself, not how she feels about me. We both hope that Tonetta will understand this someday. But for now, I think I'll just be friends with my other classmates.

Dear Diary,

Mom left this note under my pillow today:

Dear Evelyn,

When I was about your age, I also had a friend who suddenly became a problem for me at school. I told my granny about it, who said that I should think of myself as my own best friend. I have always remembered her advice, and I hope that you will remember it as well, my darling daughter.

Love,
Your other Best Friend,
Mom

A. **Use your dictionary to find the definition of "bullying". Then make a web of examples.**

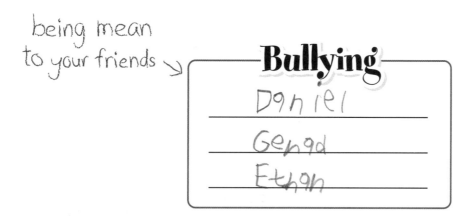

being mean
to your friends

Bullying

Daniel

Genad

Ethan

B. **Give your opinions.**

1. Do you think Evelyn is being bullied by Tonetta? Why or why not?

   Yes because they sticked their tongue out.

2. Why do you think Tonetta is being rude to Evelyn?

   They are not being nice.

3. Do you like the advice that we should think of ourselves as our own best friend? Why or why not?

   Yes because everyone in my class is being very nice.

The Present Perfect Tense

When we want to talk about something that happened at a particular time in the past, we use the simple past tense. But when we want to talk about something from the past that is linked to the present (indicated by words like "finally", "yet", and "so far"), we use the **present perfect tense**.

Examples: I <u>saw</u> the rainbow yesterday. (simple past)
I <u>have seen</u> a rainbow before. (present perfect)

C. **Complete the sentences with the simple past tense or the present perfect tense of the given verbs.**

> sing   ring   hear   think

1. The parents ___have___ never ___heard___ this song from the choir.

2. " ___Have___ you ___rung___ the doorbell yet?" Ben asks Tom.

3. Our dog Sonic, ever so excitable, started wagging his tail as soon as he ___has heard___ the doorbell.

4. Janice ___has/sung___ this song many times before.

5. During choir practice last Tuesday, we ___sung___ a new song.

6. "When I didn't hear from you last week, I ___has thought___ you had lost my phone number," said Kate to Jill.

7. "Do you think Tonetta ___has___ ever ___thought___ about the way she is behaving?" Evelyn asks Amy.

8. I forgot my key and ___rung___ the doorbell many times before my brother opened the door for me.

D. Check the correct sentences. Put a cross for the wrong ones and rewrite them using the correct tense.

1. ☑ Evelyn has finally told her mother about Tonetta.

   _____

2. ☒ Little Tim has finished his homework at six o'clock today.

   _____

3. ☒ The teachers did not notice anything wrong so far.

   _____

4. ☑ My mother has not come home from dance class yet.

   _____

5. ☒ My brother has thrown one of his slippers out of the window a minute ago but luckily it didn't land on anyone's head!

   _____

   _____

6. ☑ Evelyn's mother slipped a note under her daughter's pillow when she was sound asleep.

   _____

   _____

   _____

E. Think of a verb. Use it in the simple past tense in one sentence and in the present perfect tense in another.

_____

_____

The Skeleton Coast

Have you ever heard of the Skeleton Coast? It sounds like a scary place, but it is really one of the most awesome landscapes on the planet.

The Skeleton Coast is a stretch of coastline in a country called Namibia, located in southwestern Africa. It is a place where barren dunes of desert sand rise up along the Atlantic Ocean in peaks as high as 500 metres. These dunes are a part of the Namib Desert, which takes up most of the area of Namibia. The place seems spooky and desolate, especially when the fog rolls, as it often does.

The coastline is often shrouded in fog, because a current of cold water – called the Benguela Current – passes through the waters of the coast, making the sea breezes cold too. These cold sea winds blow towards the land, which is hotter. The air mixes along the coast, producing a thick fog, which is unusual for desert areas.

The frequent fogs are the reason why this stretch of coastline is called the Skeleton Coast. There have been hundreds of shipwrecks in these waters over the years. Stories abound of shipwrecked sailors washing ashore into the desert, desperate with thirst, only to perish in the dunes. If you are there, you will see the remains of many ships that have been washed up on the shore, looking in many ways like the skeletons of old ships.

But the fog which has brought death to countless sailors over the centuries is what brings life to this unique desert land. Areas of low green desert bushes, fed by the moisture-laden winds, can be found in the canyons of the area. Animals like the desert elephant, springbok, brown hyena, and spiral-horned oryx antelope make this desert their home. And at Cape Cross, there are even seal colonies and an assortment of birds including the flamingo, pelican, and rare tern.

As much as it became a place of doomed sailors and ship remains, this seemingly scary coast is actually a land of fascinating wildlife, and a fine example of how even a harsh environment can be home to abundant life.

A. Circle the correct answers.

1. In which continent is the Skeleton Coast located?

    A. Asia   B. Africa   C. Antarctica

2. Much of Namibia is _C_ .

    A. wet soil   B. mountains   C. desert

3. An unusual characteristic of the Skeleton Coast is its _B_ .

    A. skeletons   B. thick fog   C. hot air on land

4. The winds of the Skeleton Coast are _B_ .

    A. non-existent   B. very dry   C. full of moisture

5. In southwestern Africa, there are _C_ and _C_ .

    A. sheep; cows   B. seals; penguins   C. pelicans; elephants

6. The Skeleton Coast got its name partly from _A_ .

    A. being the site of shipwrecks and deaths of sailors in the past
    B. being a land of desolation and extinct wildlife
    C. being in the most remote region of Africa

B. Write about an imaginary place similar to the Skeleton Coast. Include these words in your paragraph.

barren   spooky   desolate   life   unique

_____

_____

_____

_____

_____

Punctuation (1)

For a complete sentence, we use the **period** (.), the **question mark** (?), or the **exclamation mark** (!). If a sentence is borrowed (e.g. from a book) or in direct speech, we use **quotation marks** (" "). To show a pause in a sentence, we use the **comma** (,). We also use the comma instead of the period when ending a sentence in certain instances of direct speech.

Examples: The Skeleton Coast is in Namibia.
Have you ever heard of the Skeleton Coast?
"Look out for the rising sand, Camille!" Adrian exclaimed.
"This place is home to many animals," Kevin said.

C.   Write the missing punctuation mark(s) in each sentence.

1. The sand dunes of the Skeleton Coast can rise as high as 500 metres,

2. The frequent fogs are the reason why this stretch of coastline is called the Skeleton Coast, Samuel quoted from his reading.

3. Of the elephant, springbok, brown hyena, and spiral-horned oryx antelope which one would you want to see the most?

4. Where do you want to visit next? my father asked me.

5. Do you think the Skeleton Coast is really all that spooky ?

6. "Yes, seal colonies can be found in Africa" said Tom matter-of-factly.

7. "What a wonderful example of life in extreme environments" our teacher exclaimed in wonder.

8. Oh dear Look at all these ship remains!

9. "You won't believe what my friend has done" Amy said in anger.

10. "Sara look at those seals over there," her mother said.

D. Circle the wrong punctuation mark in each sentence. Then put the correct one above it where necessary.

1. When cold air mixes with hot air, moisture is produced ? , creating fog.

2. "I seem to hear voices speaking to me as the fog rolls , " Anna whispered to me.

3. " The cold Benguela Current causes the sea breezes to be cold as well. "

4. "From the shores of northwest Africa, can I see the Atlantic Ocean , " ? Bob asked.

5. "Maybe there were not that many sailors who perished here!" Marie tried to make her sister feel better in her calm voice.

6. "I can't take this anymore , " Fran called out in exasperation.

E. Put the missing punctuation marks in this paragraph.

Lizzie and Paula go swimming every weekend. Lizzie is training to be a competitive swimmer, while Paula swims for fun. Someday, Lizzie tells Paula, I'm going to be an Olympic silver medalist! A bit puzzled, Paula asks A silver medalist. Why don't you want to be a gold medalist? Sounding matter-of-factly. Lizzie answers, Silver is my favourite colour. Gold is a little too shiny for me. When I'm up on the podium, I want to be wearing my favourite colour! Finding Lizzie's aspirations a little unusual, Paula is quiet and thinks to herself. Sounds like Lizzie Always making unpredictable choices.

The Story of K'iid K'iyass

Canada is a country famous for its trees. Perhaps the most famous tree of all was the giant golden Sitka spruce. Its home was Port Clements, on Queen Charlotte Islands in British Columbia. What happened to it is a sad story, though.

This tree was at least 300 years old. It stood on the banks of the Yakoun River, in one of the last stands of virgin coastal forest of the Pacific Northwest. It was a popular site of ecotourism and moreover, was sacred to the Haida, the Aboriginal people of the area. They called the tree K'iid K'iyass – "Old Tree" – and it had been a part of their local oral history for generations.

Golden Sitka spruces are rare. This tree was not green – it was gold! It had a golden colour because of a lack of chlorophyll, which is the green substance needed for photosynthesis. Yet, K'iid K'iyass was able to thrive, because of the area's misty climate, or because the sunlight reached the tree by reflecting off the water of the river next to it. Even among rare trees, however, K'iid K'iyass was special: it was very tall, over 40 metres high and more than two metres in diameter at its base. Unlike most Sitka spruces, which branch out haphazardly, it was uniformly conical. K'iid K'iyass stood like a perfect, shining golden Christmas tree in a forest of green. It stood as a monument that united people who were loggers and people who were against lumber companies' methods, like clear-cutting. All agreed that K'iid K'iyass was never to be cut down.

Then on the night of January 20 in 1997, a man crept into the forest and cut deeply into K'iid K'iyass with a chainsaw. He had once been a logger and knew how to damage the tree. When he was done, he sent letters to newspapers and the logging company leasing the land, saying what he had done was a protest against the destruction of the forests taking place all around K'iid K'iyass. Despite attempts to save the tree, K'iid K'iyass fell a few days later. The misguided protester was charged with criminal mischief and illegal cutting of timber. Strangely, while on his way by kayak to a court hearing, he disappeared and has not been found since. Though the wreckage of his kayak was later washed up in Alaska, many in the community suspect that he faked his death to escape his trial.

Fortunately, a branch from the dying Old Tree was rescued, and a baby golden Sitka spruce is growing in Port Clements today in protective custody. With golden needles shining under the sun, this spruce will one day become a rare giant in the forest.

A. **Fill in the blanks with words from the passage.**

1. My teacher is a supporter of ___ecotysiom___ . "Not only do tourists get to explore exotic places of the natural environment," he says, "they also get to support conservation efforts."

2. The ___low 990 9ts___ in the community are going on strike because the company they work for will not give up clear-cutting methods.

3. "This ancient statue was carved many years ago as a gift for god," our teacher explained to us the ___scqred___ nature of an artifact in the museum.

4. For the Aboriginal peoples of Canada, much of the knowledge from one generation to the next is not handed down in the form of books, but by means of ___oral___ history.

5. From what her best friend told me, Bernice appeared to have made a hasty and ___misgqidqnce___ decision when she dropped out of school to travel around the country.

6. The tipi is the traditional dwelling of Canada's Plains Aboriginal peoples. It is ___cohci9l___ in shape, built with poles and cloth or animal hide.

7. "___united___ we stand, divided we fall!" Little Timmy recites a line from a song written in 1768, to the surprise of his elder brother and sister.

Punctuation (2)

When we want to introduce a list, or give an explanation for something, we can use the **colon** (**:**). When we want to show possession, or indicate where the missing letters are in a contraction, we use the **apostrophe** (').

Examples: We need three vegetables: lettuce, celery, and onions. (list)
It's easy to prepare: just toss everything together. (explanation)
This salad is Joey's creation. (possession)
I'd love to try this salad! (contraction of "I would")

B. **Tell how the colon or apostrophe is used in each sentence. Write the correct letter.**

Baby Golden Sitka Spruce

A to introduce a list

B to give an explanation

C to show possession

D to indicate missing letters

1. Here are some examples of trees in Canada: spruce, cedar, birch, and maple. _C_

2. Despite a lack of chlorophyll, Old Tree thrived in the forest possibly because of the area's misty climate. _A_

3. Old Tree stood as a monument that united people who were loggers and people who were against clear-cutting: it was a tree that everyone agreed not to cut. _C_

4. "The man cared about the forests in the province and had good intentions," Dad explained, "but he didn't have to damage a rare tree to make his point." _A_

5. Old Tree was special even among rare trees: it was very tall and uniformly conical. _C_

6. A baby Sitka spruce is growing in British Columbia's Queen Charlotte Islands. _A_

C. **Write the missing colons and apostrophes in the paragraph.**

Canada has produced some very talented people writer: Alice Munro; scientist: David Suzuki; dancer: Rex Harrington, and retired hockey player: Mario Lemieux. A prolific writer, Munro's short stories always deal with the fascinating complexities of the human heart, winning international acclaim. Suzuki's charm and knack for public speaking make him a scholar and a great communicator his show *The Nature of Things* draws the public's attention to the importance of protecting our environment. Harrington makes his ballet performances look so easy from his natural flare, you wouldn't have guessed how much hard work is required behind the scenes. Finally, Lemieux – whose name means "the best" in French – captained Team Canada into a gold medal at the 2002 Winter Olympic Games. Despite cancer and back pains, Lemieux never fails to play a good game, and is one of the NHL's greatest hockey players in history.

D. **Write your own paragraph containing the uses of the colon and the apostrophe.**

_____

_____

_____

_____

_____

_____

_____

As one of Canada's most memorable poems, "In Flanders Fields" was written as a tribute to soldiers everywhere. Its author John McCrae, who was a Canadian soldier and doctor in World War I, wrote the poem after his friend was killed on May 2, 1915 in Ypres, Belgium. (McCrae himself died of pneumonia in 1918 while on duty.) But when the poem was finished, McCrae tossed it away in the field. Were it not for a fellow soldier who picked up the poem and sent it to England, we would probably not be reading it today. The poem was first published in *Punch Magazine* in December of 1915.

In Flanders Fields
– *a Poem of Remembrance*

In Flanders Fields

In Flanders fields the poppies blow
Between the crosses, row on row,
That mark our place; and in the sky
The larks, still bravely singing, fly
Scarce heard amid the guns below.

We are the Dead. Short days ago
We lived, felt dawn, saw sunset glow,
Loved, and were loved, and now we lie
In Flanders fields.

Take up our quarrel with the foe:
To you from failing hands we throw
The torch; be yours to hold it high.
If ye break faith with us who die
We shall not sleep, though poppies grow
In Flanders fields.

If you visit Flanders Fields in Belgium, you will still see the poppies waving among the crosses. Each year in November, we wear the bright red poppy over our hearts to remind ourselves of the soldiers that died in battle and the ones that have survived. We should try to imagine the lives that the fallen soldiers may have had, to think of the sacrifices that they made, and realize the futility of war.

A. **Use your dictionary to find the definitions of these words. Then use them in sentences of your own.**

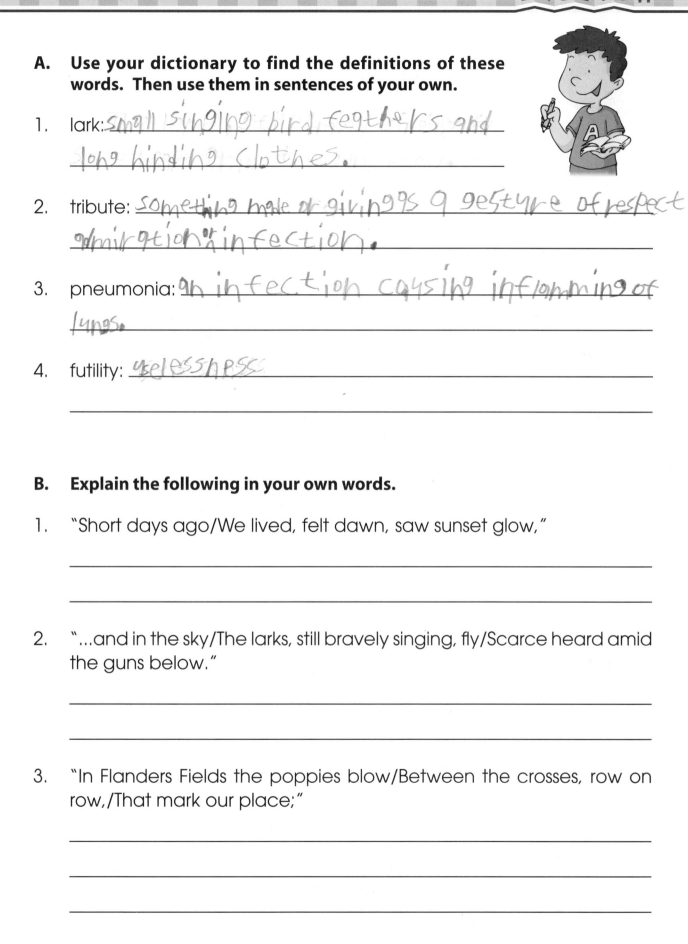

1. lark: <u>small singing bird feathers and</u> <u>long hinding clothes.</u>

2. tribute: <u>something made of givings a gesture of respect</u> <u>admiration, infection.</u>

3. pneumonia: <u>an infection causing inflamming of</u> <u>lungs.</u>

4. futility: <u>uselessness</u>

B. **Explain the following in your own words.**

1. "Short days ago/We lived, felt dawn, saw sunset glow,"

2. "...and in the sky/The larks, still bravely singing, fly/Scarce heard amid the guns below."

3. "In Flanders Fields the poppies blow/Between the crosses, row on row,/That mark our place;"

Prefixes and Suffixes

A **prefix** is a group of letters placed at the beginning of a word – called the base word or root word – to change its meaning. A **suffix** is also a group of letters that changes the meaning of a word, but is placed at the end.

Examples: The prefix "re" in "rewrite" changes the meaning of "write" to "write again".
The suffix "able" in "memorable" changes the meaning of "memory" to "easily remembered".

C.   Form new words with the prefixes.

un   re   im   in

1. place   _replace_

2. possible   _impossible_

3. complete   _incomplete_

4. willing   _unwilling_

5. generate   _regenerate_

6. precise   _imprecise_

7. formal   _informal_

8. discrete   _undiscrete_

D.   Circle the words that have a prefix, a suffix, or both. Then write their base words on the lines.

exaggerate   _un_   lampost   _in_

present   _re_   bounty   _un_

careful   _be_   (re)late   _un_

(in)security _to_   fulfill   _re_

sincerity   _un_   thoughtful   _re_

(re)unification _____   perform   _im_

E. **Complete each sentence by rewriting the base word with the correct suffix.**

ial   able   ation   ance

1. "Be careful with that ornament. It's (break) _breakable_ ," my dad said.

2. The trillium is the (province) _provincial_ flower of Ontario.

3. Many of us wear a poppy on (Remember) _remembrance_ Day.

4. The United Nations has put out another (public) _publication_ on world peace.

F. **Look at each base word and its changed meaning to write the correct prefix. Then make a sentence with the base word and a sentence with the new word.**

re   mis   de   in   dis

1. **view** ➔ view again: _re_ view

   We review our works

2. **cover** ➔ find out: _dis_ cover

   We discover our places

3. **place** ➔ put in the wrong spot: _re_ place

   We replace our papers

4. **organized** ➔ chaotic: _re_ organized

   we reorganized our objects

The Seven Wonders
of the Modern World

What are the most wondrous things of the modern world? It is difficult to say, but a group of civil engineers have tried to answer this question.

Civil engineers are people who build big things such as airports, hydroelectric dams, and impressive buildings. The American Society of Civil Engineers wanted to compile a list of engineering achievements to honour our ability to create things that seem almost impossible to build. So in 1994, the organization asked people around the world to tell them what they felt were the seven wonders of the modern world. Here is the resulting list of the greatest civil engineering feats of the 20th century:

Channel Tunnel
This underwater tunnel measures 50 kilometres and connects the United Kingdom with France in continental Europe.

CN Tower
As one of the world's tallest free-standing structures, this tower measures over 500 metres and weighs as much as 232 214 elephants!

Empire State Building
Built in 1930 in New York City, this building was the tallest in the world for 40 years.

Golden Gate Bridge
This is one of the world's most photographed bridges. Built in 1937, it was the world's longest and tallest suspension bridge for almost 30 years.

Itaipu Dam
At 8 km wide, this hydroelectric dam spans the Parana River between Brazil and Paraguay. It provides almost 75% of Paraguay's energy needs and 28% of southern Brazil's electric energy.

Netherlands North Sea Protection Works
Without this system of dams, floodgates, and storm surge barriers which make up the Netherlands' tidal defences, much of the country would be in the sea.

Panama Canal
Digging this canal through the Isthmus of Panama would have been the same as moving enough earth to open a five-metre-wide tunnel to the centre of the Earth!

A. **Read the clues and complete this crossword puzzle with words from the passage.**

Across

A. country below sea level: The _N_

B. free-standing structure

C. built in 1937: _G_ _G_ Bridge

D. _P_ Canal

E. in New York:
   _E_ _S_ Building

Down

1. Itaipu _D_

2. connects France and the United Kingdom

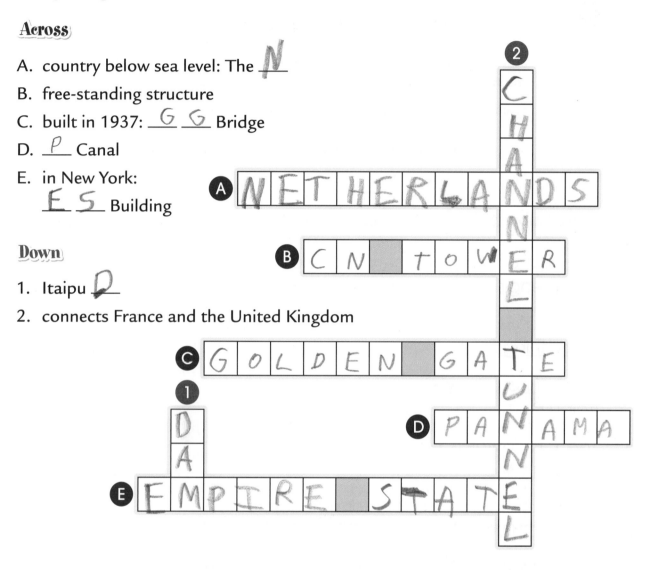

B. **Imagine yourself to be a civil engineer. Which one of the seven wonders would you wish to have built? Why?**

_____

_____

_____

_____

_____

_____

Noun Phrases

A phrase is a group of words that can take the same spot in a sentence as a single word. A **noun phrase** contains a noun and other words such as articles and adjectives, and functions like a noun or pronoun. It may be the **subject**, **object**, or the **complement** in a sentence.

Examples: <u>This city's buildings</u> are very tall. (subject)
I can give you <u>my own list of wonders</u>. (object)
The CN Tower is <u>one of the seven wonders</u>. (complement)

C. Write "subject", "object", or "complement" for each underlined noun phrase.

1. <u>A group of civil engineers</u> compiled a list of seven engineering achievements.

   subject

2. The list of wonders honours <u>our ability to build great things</u>.

   complement

3. <u>Most of Paraguay's energy</u> is provided by the Itaipu Dam.

   subject

4. The CN Tower is <u>one of the world's tallest free-standing structures</u>.

   complement

5. <u>France and the United Kingdom</u> are connected by the Channel Tunnel.

   subject

6. The Netherlands' tidal defences are <u>a system of dams, floodgates, and storm surge barriers</u>.

   complement

D. Complete these sentences with noun phrases of your own.

1. _____ *CN Tower* _____ is my favourite wonder on the list.

2. I really want to photograph _____ *myself* _____ .

3. The place I want to see most is _____ *CN Tower* _____ .

4. _____ *I* _____ opened my eyes to the world!

Verbals: Gerunds and Participles

A **verbal** is a verb form that does not function like a verb in a sentence, such as gerunds and participles. A **gerund** is a verbal that functions like a noun. A **present** or **past participle** is a verbal that functions like an adjective.

Examples: <u>Engineering</u> involves both math and design. (gerund)
The <u>painting</u> class takes place every Sunday. (present participle)
The <u>painted</u> door is a work of art. (past participle)

E. Fill in the blanks with the given words. Then circle the correct answers to tell their functions in the sentences.

> moving   free-standing   digging
> photographed   resulting

1. The Golden Gate Bridge is one of the world's most
    Photographed bridges.

    verb
    adjective (circled)

2. As one of the world's tallest _freestanding_
    structures, the CN Tower is also a landmark of Toronto.

    verb
    adjective (circled)

3. _Digging_ the Panama Canal would have
    been the same as _moving_ enough
    earth to open a five-metre-wide tunnel to the centre
    of the Earth!

    noun (circled)
    verb

4. A squirrel was _digging_ a hole just now.

    noun
    verb (circled)

5. "Here is the _resulting_ list of the greatest
    civil engineering feats of the 20th century,"
    announced Michael.

    noun
    adjective (circled)

6. The plates on Earth are in fact constantly
    moving , though at a very slow rate,
    which we cannot detect.

    noun
    verb (circled)

The Seven Natural Wonders of the World

In addition to a list of modern wonders, a list of natural wonders has also been made. They are places that have been sources of awe and wonder ever since people walked the Earth. As we are now much more familiar with the geography of our planet than before, these natural wonders have become places that we strive to protect.

Mount Everest in the Himalayan Mountain Range that borders Nepal and Tibet is the highest mountain on Earth.

The **Great Barrier Reef** in the Pacific Ocean off the northeast coast of Australia is the world's largest coral reef.

The **Grand Canyon** around the Colorado River in the state of Arizona in the United States is the largest canyon in the world.

Victoria Falls is a majestic 100-metre waterfall in Africa, where the Zambezi River falls into a two-kilometre-wide chasm to the Batoka Gorge.

The **Harbour of Rio de Janeiro** in Brazil is one of the most striking in the world, where tall mountains loom up from the water, and the city hugs the hillsides around the crowded beaches.

Paricutin is perhaps the world's youngest volcano. It erupted out of a cornfield west of Mexico in 1943! In the first year it grew 336 m high. Now it is 424 m high.

The **northern lights** are the natural phenomenon that appears in the night sky at high latitudes. At their best, they look like purple and green streaks dancing across the sky, a result of particles reacting with the Earth's magnetic field.

Some may think that these natural wonders are even more wonderful than our list of human-made wonders. What do you think?

A.   Draw lines to match the natural wonders with the locations.

1.   Mount Everest

2.   Paricutin

3.   The northern lights

4.   The Grand Canyon

5.   The Great Barrier Reef

6.   Victoria Falls

7.   The Harbour
     of Rio de Janeiro

Australia

Brazil

Africa

near Mexico

Nepal and Tibet

The United States

high latitudes

B.   Give your opinions.

1.   What do you think are the
     criteria for something to be
     a natural wonder?

     _____

     _____

     _____

2.   Why is it important to protect our natural wonders?

     _____

     _____

3.   What other things or places do you think we should protect?

     _____

     _____

Adjective and Adverb Phrases

An **adjective phrase** contains an adjective and functions like an adjective in a sentence. An **adverb phrase** contains an adverb and functions like an adverb in a sentence.

Examples: Laura is <u>very happy</u> today. (adjective phrase)
Laura ran <u>very quickly</u> to the park. (adverb phrase)

C. **Write "adjective" or "adverb" for each underlined phrase.**

1. We are now <u>much more familiar</u> with our planet than before.

   Adjective

2. Laura finishes her lunch <u>quite fast</u>.

   Adjective

3. Laura's sister is <u>quietly excited</u> about the Christmas holiday.

   Adverb

4. Ted is doing his homework <u>unusually well</u>.

   Adverb

5. "Nobody sings this song <u>more wonderfully</u> than you do, Carol," says Bernice.

   Adverb

6. The northern lights dance <u>so beautifully</u> in the night sky.

   Adverb

7. "What can be <u>even more wonderful</u> than my list of seven wonders?" my little brother asks.

   Adjective

8. "Is there a list of <u>forgotten ancient</u> wonders?" asks my little cousin.

   Adjective

9. Bob is walking <u>very slowly</u> along the hillsides.

   Adverb

10. "Can I help you?" someone asks Tommy. "You look <u>completely lost</u>."

    Adverb

D. **Underline the adjective phrases and circle the adverb phrases in this paragraph.**

For adventure seekers looking for mountains to climb, Mount Everest is a very popular choice. With its summit at 8850 metres, it is incredibly high. To reach the summit of Everest is to reach the top of the world because it is the highest mountain on Earth. To some climbers, it is like conquering the impossible. But failing to reach the top does not necessarily mean failure. There are really persistent climbers who so desperately want to keep going, but whose bodies simply cannot withstand the lack of oxygen at extremely high altitudes. Knowing only too well that there have been deaths on this mountain in the past, these people have no choice but to turn back. In their case, nothing is more sensible than walking back down, which can save their lives.

E. **Write a paragraph containing two adjective phrases and two adverb phrases using these words.**

more	most	very	quite

_____

_____

_____

_____

_____

_____

A Letter from Sammy

Dear Mom, Dad, Hugh, and Choco,

I'm so excited to be here in Japan that I don't even know what to start telling you about! First, the flight to Tokyo was a lot of fun. The flight attendants were all very kind to me. On the flight to Vancouver, Debra, the Chief Purser, introduced me to the lady sitting beside me. Her name was Mrs. Ward, and she was going to visit her son, who is teaching English in Japan.

At the stop in Vancouver, Debra took me to a special place to wait for my next flight. She called it a transit lounge. Then another flight attendant took me to my next plane, and Mrs. Ward was waiting for me there. When we arrived in Japan, an airline employee met me at the airplane door and took me through customs. I felt special. I had been scared to travel alone at first, but there was actually nothing to worry about.

Kiyoka and her parents were waiting for me in the arrivals hall. Kiyoka shouted out my name as I came through the doors. She grabbed my hand and I could feel it shaking. She was so excited — and so was I! Her parents said Kon-ni-chi-wa ("Hello") and Ha-ji-me-ma-shi-te ("Nice to meet you"). We got on a bus and travelled through Tokyo to a big station to take a train. Before long, I found myself in a Japanese home in the mountains, drinking green tea with Kiyoka and her grandparents. We can't talk much but we laugh a lot together. Kiyoka is good at translating what her grandparents say.

Already I have eaten sushi, I have slept on the floor on tatami mats, and I have learned to compliment Kiyoka's mother for her good cooking. I say Go-chisou-sama-deshita, which means something like: thank you for the meal. I helped Kiyoka pick some persimmons off their tree for dessert — it's called kaki in Japan.
I know I've only been here for a day but I love Japan already!
There is a small temple down the street, and Kiyoka will take me there tomorrow.

Love,

Sammy

A.   Put these entries in order for Kiyoka's vacation diary.

[4] travelled through Tokyo on a bus

[1] met a kind lady named Mrs. Ward

[6] had green tea with Kiyoka and her grandparents

[3] was greeted by Kiyoka and her parents at the airport

[5] took a train to Kiyoka's house

[7] picked persimmons for dessert

[2] boarded another plane in Vancouver

B.   Quote a sentence from Sammy's letter to support each of the following.

1.   Sammy has only been in Japan for a very short time, but she has done many things already.

Already I have eaten sushi. I had slept on the floor on totemy mats, and I have learned to complement kiyokas mother for her good cooking.

2.   The train ride to Kiyoka's home did not feel long at all.

Before long I found myself in japanese home in the mountains, drinking green tea.

3.   There are many languages in the world, but a smile speaks them all.

We cant talk much but we laughed a lot tose ther.

Conjunctions

When we want to join ideas together, we use **conjunctions**, which are also called **connecting words**.

Examples: I'm so excited <u>that</u> I don't know where to start.
We got on a bus <u>and</u> travelled through Tokyo.

C.   Circle the conjunction in each sentence.

1. Kiyoka taught me some useful Japanese words, so I used them (to) compliment her mother for her cooking.

2. Someone met me at the airplane door (when) I arrived in Japan.

3. I had been scared to travel alone (but) there was in fact nothing to worry about.

4. Kiyoka shouted out my name (as) I came through the doors.

5. There is a small temple nearby (and) Kiyoka will take me there tomorrow.

6. I found myself in a Japanese home (before) I had time to take in the scenery along the train ride.

7. Debra took me to a place (where) I waited for my next flight.

8. Although I have only been in Japan for a day, I love this place already!

9. We stayed up (until) midnight!

10. If I had a longer summer holiday, I would stay longer in Japan.

D. Fill in the blanks with the correct conjunctions.

| unless | since | whenever | where | while |

1. Kiyoka acts as translator _unless_ her grandparents want to talk to Sammy.

2. "Canada is the country _where_ I come from," said Sammy.

3. The girls picked persimmons outside _whenever_ the others prepared dinner inside.

4. They can go to the temple any time _while_ it is just down the street.

5. Kiyoka's grandparents do not eat fish _since_ it is fresh.

E. Choose five conjunctions from (C) to write your own sentences.

1. _____

_____

2. _____

_____

3. _____

_____

4. _____

_____

5. _____

_____

How Hurricanes Get Their Names

Have you ever wondered how hurricanes get their names? Many of the hurricanes we hear about in Canada are those that originate in the Atlantic Ocean. For some time since 1953, it was the U.S. National Hurricane Center that had been responsible for naming these hurricanes. But today, the lists of hurricanes around the world are maintained and updated by a specialized agency of the United Nations called the World Meteorological Organization.

The history of naming hurricanes is fascinating. Early on in the West Indies, for instance, names of saints were used. For example, if a hurricane occurred on February 3, it would be called Hurricane Blaise because, by the Christian calendar, February 3 is Saint Blaise's Day. (Every day is named after a saint in the Christian calendar. You probably know that March 17 is Saint Patrick's Day.)

Later, women's names started to be used to identify storms that resembled hurricanes. Some believe the practice began in Australia in the late 19th century. It became more common during World War II when the United States also adopted this method. Over time, however, people recognized that it was wrong to name hurricanes only after women. In 1978, both men's and women's names started to be used in alternate fashion – first on the Eastern North Pacific Storm lists and, a year later, on the lists for the Atlantic and the Gulf of Mexico.

There are over a dozen lists of names for the various regions around the world. For the Atlantic region, there is a list of 21 designated hurricane names for each year, which follows the alphabet, though there are no names beginning with the letters Q, U, X, Y, or Z. Each list is recycled every six years. If there are more than 21 hurricanes that year, later storms will be named after the letters of the Greek alphabet.

A name is retired if the hurricane is especially catastrophic. This is done as a mark of respect for the victims of that hurricane, who do not wish to be reminded of the event six years later. Since 2010, four names have been retired: Igor, Tomas, Irene, and Sandy.

A. Answer these questions.

1. Who maintains the lists of hurricanes around the world?

   The world metroligical organization.

2. How were hurricanes named in the West Indies in earlier days?

   They were named after saint in 02 03 is saint day. _Moises_

3. What is special about the Christian calendar?

   Everyday is name after a saint.

4. What was changed in the practice of naming hurricanes in 1978?

   Instance of using only womens names started to be used in alternate fashion.

5. What happens to the name of an especially catastrophic hurricane?

   It is retired.

B. Read what John says. Then write a short response and make up some hurricane names.

> *Why do you think there are no hurricane names beginning with Q, U, X, Y, or Z? Can you think of any names beginning with these letters?*

Q _____

U _____

X _____

Y _____

Z _____

Clauses

A **clause** is a group of words that has the same structure as a sentence (containing a subject and a verb) but is part of a larger sentence. An **independent clause** can stand alone. A **dependent clause** cannot, and needs to be supported by an independent clause.

Examples: <u>The whole class laughed</u> when Mrs. Kemp told a joke.
(independent)

"We can go <u>wherever you like</u>," said Jan to Alice.
(dependent)

C. Underline the stated type of clause for each group of sentences.

Independent

1. A hurricane <u>name is retired</u> if the hurricane is especially catastrophic.

2. <u>Names of saints had been used</u> to name hurricanes before men's and women's names were used.

3. "<u>I won't go</u> out to the backyard unless that skunk leaves the deck," my sister says.

4. "<u>I'm not coming out of my room</u> until it's dinnertime!" my little sister pouts.

Dependent

5. We began using both men's and women's names for hurricanes <u>after we recognized</u> how wrong it was to use only women's names.

6. The practice of naming hurricanes with women's names became more common <u>during World War II</u> when the United States also adopted this method.

7. Whenever there is <u>a squirrel in the backyard</u>, my sister goes out to say hello.

8. "Why don't you help me wash <u>the lettuce</u> while I cut the carrots?" my mother asks.

D. Check the sentences that have a dependent clause. Then underline each dependent clause.

1. There were hurricanes whose names have been retired. ☑

2. The four names are Igor, Tomas, Irene, and Sandy. ☑

3. Did you see Teddy this morning? ☑

4. This is the place that Charlotte does not want to remember. ☑

5. The history of naming hurricanes is fascinating. ☑

6. It is fascinating only because you like storms. ☑

7. There are over a dozen lists of names for the various regions around the world. ☑

8. If there are more than 21 hurricanes in a given year, the additional storms will be named after the letters of the Greek alphabet. ☑

9. Ben thought of another way of naming hurricanes while he was doing his math homework. ☑

E. Complete each sentence by adding an independent clause.

1. As we were walking to the park,

_____

_____.

2. Since we played well during our game, _____

_____.

3. Even though Ann did not win the race, _____

_____.

Strange Names
Strange Places?

If you ever thought that Moose Jaw in Saskatchewan and Medicine Hat in Alberta were strange Canadian place names, you haven't actually seen really strange place names yet. It's always fun to discover a new, weird place name to add to the list. Here's a sampling for you.

There are street names you would never expect to find. If you ever find yourself in Bandra, which is a neighbourhood in Mumbai, India, you might find yourself at Wit's End, a dead-end street. And if you are touring Hong Kong, don't be surprised if you come across Rednaxela Terrace. This strange name was created when the sign painter painted the letters backward!

In the United States, you'll find a street in Massachusetts called Goah Way. And in Ohio, you'll find a road called Needmore Road. If you go to a place called Salt Lick in Kentucky – whose name is odd enough in itself – you'll probably find yourself driving down Mudlick Road. But that's not all. There is also Psycho Path in Michigan and Divorce Court in Pennsylvania.

The United States is full of quaint towns with strange names. You would probably have a great summer road trip just visiting the following places: Peculiar, Missouri; Embarrass, Wisconsin; Dull, Ohio; Unthanks, Virginia; Stinking Bay, Arkansas; Last Chance, Colorado, and Boring, Maryland (though you might want to avoid Accident in that same state). If you love to eat, then check out these towns: Goodfood and Hot Coffee, both in Mississippi; Buttermilk, Kansas; Tea, South Dakota; Oatmeal, Texas; Cheesequake, New Jersey, and Two Egg, Florida.

Have you ever wanted to visit a small town that has a big name? Head over to Wales in the United Kingdom, and ask someone to point you in the direction of – take a very deep breath – Llanfairpwllgwyngyllgogerychwyrndrobwllllantysiliogogogoch. The name translates into this: St. Mary's Church in the hollow of white hazel near a rapid whirlpool and the Church of St. Tysilio near the red cave. Most people call it "Llanfairpwllgwyngyll" or simply "Llanfair PG". But even this is not the longest place name in the world. There is in fact a town in Thailand with 168 letters in its name:

Krung Thep Mahanakhon Amon Rattanakosin Mahinthara Ayuthaya Mahadilok Phop Noppharat Ratchathani Burirom Udomratchaniwet Mahasathan Amon Piman Awatan Sathit Sakkathattiya Witsanukam Prasit

Strange – and long – indeed!

A. Read the riddles and complete the crossword puzzle with the strange names from the passage.

Across

A. "Mind if I pour myself another cup?"
B. "This place is certainly odd."
C. "This is part of a complete breakfast!"
D. "I've just about had it!"
E. "There's a missing 's'."
F. "Out of my way!"

3 HO

4 NEEDMORE ROAD

Ⓐ T E A

Ⓑ P E C U L I A R

COFFEE

2 B
Ⓒ O A T M E A L

1 L A S T
Ⓓ W I T S END
CORN
IN

Ⓔ T W O E G G

C H A N C E

Ⓕ G O A H W A Y

Down

1. "We'd better get there fast!"
2. "There's nothing to do here."
3. "This place should go well with doughnuts."
4. "It's a little too short, this road."

Sentences

A **sentence** is a group of words that contains a subject and a verb. If the sentence has two or more independent clauses, it is a **compound sentence**. If it has one independent clause plus one or more dependent clauses, it is a **complex sentence**.

Examples: This is a quaint town and it has a strange name. (compound)
Don't be surprised if you come across Rednaxela Terrace. (complex)

B. Read each sentence and write "compound" or "complex".

If there is a dependent clause, then the sentence is complex. Every dependent clause begins with a conjunction.

1. There is Psycho Path in Michigan and there is Divorce Court in Pennsylvania.

    Compound

2. Michelle wants to visit Goodfood but Richard wants to visit Hot Coffee.

    Compound

3. I'll take you to Buttermilk if you take me to Tea.

    Complex

4. "Rednaxela" was created when the sign painter painted the letters backwards!

    Compound

5. Although you would want to avoid Accident, you might want to visit Boring since it's in the same state.

    Complex

6. "We could visit Dull, or we could head down to Stinking Bay," I tell Gabriel.

    Compound

7. My mom won't go to Cheesequake with my dad unless he takes her to Oatmeal.

    Complex

C. **Read this paragraph. Identify the underlined sentences as compound or complex.**

Has it ever occurred to you that the doughnut has multiple personalities? <u>It comes in many flavours and it comes in a variety of shapes.</u> <u>There is the Dutchie which looks like a pillow.</u> There is the cruller with its fun-loving twist. There is the fritter which is shapely and cute. And there is the classic "O", which is the shape that gave this dessert its name. <u>The shape looks like a ring but it also resembles a nut.</u> <u>Since this treat is made of dough, we decided to call it "doughnut".</u>

1. Compound Sentences:

a. *It comes in many flavours and it comes in a variety of shapes.*

b. *The shape looks like a ring but it also resembles a nut.*

2. Complex Sentences:

a. *There is the duchie which looks like a pillow.*

b. *Since this treat is made of dough, we decided to call it doughnut.*

D. **Write a short paragraph containing one compound sentence and one complex sentence.**

_____

_____

_____

_____

_____

_____

Farewell, *Kiribati*

Kiribati ("Ki-ri-bas") is a small country in the South Pacific. It is only 719 square kilometres in land area, comprised of one island and 32 atolls, which are ring-shaped coral reefs above the ocean surface, enclosing a body of water. Though individually small, these atolls spread across the Pacific Ocean in an area as large as the continental United States, looking like pale aqua gems dotting the deep blue sea. When viewed from atop, they are a lovely sight.

The population of Kiribati is 100 000. A third of its population lives in the capital city of Tarawa. Tourism, coconut-processing, and fishing are the main industries. On December 31, 1999, people around the world suddenly became familiar with this country: being the closest country to the International Date Line, Kiribati was the first to celebrate our entry into the new millennium. For those who were glued to their television sets that day, it was exciting to see the people of Kiribati dance and sing their welcome to the first sunrise of year 2000.

But Kiribati may not exist much longer. According to scientists worldwide, sea levels may rise up to 69 centimetres in the next 100 years, due to melting polar ice caps and glaciers from global warming. Soon, this low-lying country will be inundated by the sea. Salt water intrusion has already affected the drinking water supply in some parts of the country. Some habitats of marine life in Kiribati have begun to suffer as well. According to Greenpeace, two small atolls are already submerged. That is why New Zealand is accepting about 700 environmental refugees from Kiribati and the neighbouring country of Tuvalu every year.

But it is not just these South Pacific atoll nations that will be destroyed by rising sea levels. Equally at risk are the Maldives in the Indian Ocean and the millions of people who inhabit the coastal plains around the world. Over in the United States, the city New Orleans was damaged by Hurricane Katrina in 2005, and new buildings must be built on platforms that are close to one metre high. Rising sea levels will continue to affect many countries – long after we have bade farewell to Kiribati.

A.   Match the words with the meanings.   Write the letters.

1.   gems _____D_____

2.   atolls _____F_____

3.   glaciers _____C_____

4.   habitats _____B_____

5.   inundated _____A_____

6.   environmental
      refugees _____E_____

7.   millennium _____G_____

A   people who need to move
    due to natural disasters or other
    environmental causes

B   coral reefs in the shape of rings
    surrounding a body of water in
    the ocean

C   slow-moving masses of ice in
    very cold regions of the Earth

D   precious stones

E   1000 years

F   flooded

G   homes

B.   Complete these sentences.

1.   The land of Kiribati is only 719 square kilometres,
     but the country covers an area as large as the
     United States because _it has attolls which are_
     ribbon shaped coral reefs above the ocean surface.

2.   The main industries in Kiribati are _Tourism, coconut pressing, and fishing._
     _____ .

3.   The world suddenly became familiar with Kiribati in December of
     1999 because _it was the first to enter the new millennium,_
     being the closet country to the International date
     line.

4.   Kiribati may not exist much longer because _it is a low lying country will be_
     flooded by the raising sea level from glowing warming.

Words about Quantity

We often make mistakes when it comes to words that have to do with **quantity**. In order to use these words correctly, we need to know how many things we are talking about. We also need to know whether or not what we are talking about is countable.

C. **Read about each pair of words and fill in the blanks with the correct words.**

1. **Between vs. Among**

When we are talking about only two things, we use "between". When we are talking about more than two things, we use "among".

a. This is the biggest one _among_ all the atolls.

b. _between_ Kiribati and Tuvalu, which country do you want to see?

c. There are nine kilometres _between_ these two atolls.

d. There is worry _among_ the people who live along coastal plains.

2. **Fewer vs. Less**

We use "fewer" when referring to things that can be counted individually. We use "less" when referring to something that cannot be counted.

a. In Canada, there is _less_ daylight in winter than in summer.

b. No _fewer_ than four names of hurricanes have been retired since 2010.

c. "I see _less_ water in that tank now," says Anne.

d. This year, there are _fewer_ than 700 refugees from Kiribati and Tuvalu to New Zealand.

3. **Number vs. Amount**

"Number" is used when referring to things that can be counted individually. "Amount" is used when referring to something that cannot be counted, such as money and milk.

a. Can you tell me the _Amount_ of atolls there are in Kiribati?

b. The _Amount_ of places that will be inundated by the sea is rather alarming.

c. "You will never guess the _Amount_ of wealth that some people have!" says Grace.

d. "50.5 kilograms is a bigger _Number_ than 5.05 kilograms," Bill tells his little sister as he helps her with decimal numbers.

D. **Fill in the blanks with words from (C).**

Tom and Alan have just been given their allowance. Off they go to the candy shop. 1. _Among_ all the treats on the shelves, the one that catches their attention is a giant bag of marble candies! The two boys fish their pockets and look at the 2. _Amount_ of coins they have: they don't have enough to pay. A little disappointed, Tom says, "That's okay, we wouldn't be able to eat the whole bag 3. _Between_ the two of us anyway." As they head out, the shopkeeper says, "I see you really want that bag of goodies. I can actually sell it to you for 4. _Less_ ." Surprised and delighted, Tom and Alan put together their money to pay for it at the counter. Each of them eats no 5. _Fewer_ than ten pieces before they even get home!

Going Camping with a Rock Star

My dad is a geologist. My mom calls him her "Rock Star". I like going with him on camping trips to the Canadian Shield, which is a huge landmass that stretches across half of Canada. It touches parts of the Northwest Territories, Saskatchewan, and Alberta; covers half of Manitoba, most of Ontario, Quebec, and Nunavut, and spans all of Labrador. It even reaches Greenland! The rock of the Canadian Shield goes back a very long time: anywhere between 350 million and 4.5 billion years old.

We always take our fishing rods – there are abundant lakes and rivers in the Canadian Shield – and a small pickaxe. I like looking for nice stones. Once, my dad took me to Ontario to look for amethyst, which is my mom's birthstone. Amethyst is a semi-precious stone that is violet in colour, but I like plain old rocks too. I love the way granite glints in the sun and comes in multiple colours. Sometimes I'm able to find granite stones that have other kinds of stones threaded through them. These ones are very colourful. There is a lot of granite in the Canadian Shield.

I also like finding mica. It is not very colourful, but I like the way it can break into tiny sheets. My dad explained that different rocks break – or cleave – in different ways. For example, mica cleaves into sheets and galena cleaves into cubes.

Sometimes it rains on our camping trips, so my dad and I would take out our cards or chess set to play, which we usually bring along. We also talk a lot. We talk about life, about how I'm doing in school, and about how he is doing at his job.

Sometimes we make lists of famous rocks. On our last camping trip, we tried to think of as many as we could. This is the list we came up with:

- Perce Rock, Canada
- Plymouth Rock, United States
- Stonehenge, United Kingdom
- Rock of Gibraltar, Gibraltar
- Blarney Stone, United Kingdom
- Devils Tower, United States
- Table Mountain, South Africa
- Mt. Rushmore, United States
- Ayers Rock, Australia (the rock is also called "Uluru")
- Hope Diamond (it's in a museum in the United States)
- Brighton Rock, United Kingdom
- Giant's Causeway, United Kingdom
- Rosetta Stone (it's in a museum in England, but belongs to Egypt)

And more will be made on future camping trips!

A. **Use point form to complete this chart with information from the passage.**

Stone	Colour	Other Information
Amethyst	Violet	Amethyst ~~stone~~ is a semi precios stone.
Granite	All	Granite stones have other kinds or stones.
Mica	None	The way it can break into tiny sheets.

B. **How does camping foster relationships? Write a response and support it with examples from the narrator's camping trips.**

_____

_____

_____

_____

_____

_____

_____

Descriptive Writing

We use **descriptive writing** when we want to create a vivid picture of a person, thing, or an event in the reader's mind. One way of doing this is by using adjectives and adverbs to give detail. Another way is by replacing the existing words of a given sentence with more effective ones.

Examples: Naomi uses her pickaxe to find stones.
Naomi uses her pickaxe <u>delicately</u> to find stones.

There are many lakes and rivers in the Canadian Shield.
There are <u>abundant</u> lakes and rivers in the Canadian Shield.

C.   Fill in the blanks with the given adjectives and adverbs to make the sentences more descriptive.

massive
anxiously   easily   steadily   fun-loving
slowly   carefully   always   hilarious   broad

1.   Sara is very excited about her fishing trip.
She is ___carefully___ getting her fishing gear.

2.   Polly loves the woods. She ___easily___ finds her way around.

3.   David does not hurry when looking for stones. He ___hilarious___
searches ___slowly___ for nice ones.

4.   Alan is very persistent. He ___always___ but ___broad___ knits
a scarf for his grandmother.

5.   Shelley likes ___steadily___ paintings and has a habit of painting
very ___massive___ strokes.

6.   My ___anxiously___ little brother likes to make ___fun-loving___
sounds to make all of us laugh.

D. **Underline the words that are different in each pair of sentences. Then explain why the second one is more descriptive than the first.**

1. The Canadian Shield makes up half of Canada.
   The Canadian Shield stretches <u>across</u> half of Canada.

   <u>Across is Descriptive.</u>

2. Amethyst is a semi-precious stone.
   Amethyst is a semi-precious stone that is <u>violet</u> in colour.

   <u>Violet is Descriptive.</u>

3. I love the way granite looks in the sun.
   I love the way granite <u>glints</u> in the sun.

   <u>Glint is Descriptive.</u>

4. Different rocks break in different ways.
   Different rocks <u>cleave</u> in different ways.

   <u>Cleave is Descriptive.</u>

E. **Write a descriptive paragraph on one of these topics.**

My Best Friend   My First Trip   My Room

_____

_____

_____

_____

_____

_____

_____

_____

Most people think that extreme sports are a relatively new invention in the sporting world, but a surprising number of extreme sports are not new at all; they are just adaptations of centuries-old, traditional games and rituals. Let's look at the examples of surfing and bungee-jumping.

The Long History of
Extreme Sports

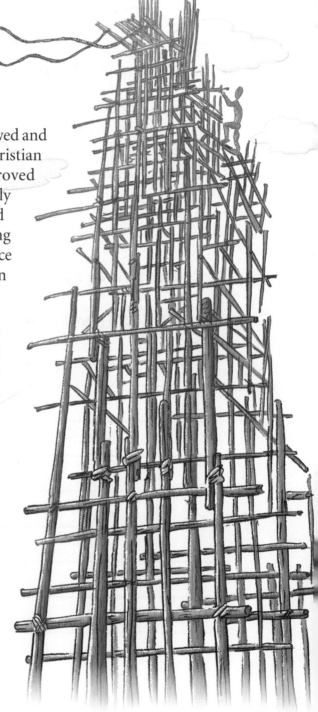

Surfing was invented in Hawaii centuries ago. It was called *he'e nalu* ("wave sliding"). Surfboards were first made from lumber and came in all shapes and sizes: from about one to four metres in length. Historically, all Hawaiian islanders could ride the waves, but it was mainly royalty who had the time to perfect the skills, which involved learning how to read the waves as much as knowing how to stay upright on the board.

The first western explorers who came to Hawaii were awed and impressed by the sight of wave sliding. However, Christian missionaries who came to the island later disapproved of the sport and banned it. It was not until the early 20th century that surfing was introduced to the world by Duke Kahanamoku, the Hawaiian-born swimming medalist at the 1912 and 1920 Olympic Games. Since then, the sport of surfing has developed into an important part of the beach culture.

Bungee-jumping was also invented by a group of people living in the Pacific Ocean, on the island of Pentecost in Vanuatu. Legend has it that the first person to ever jump was a woman named Tamalie. These days, however, the jump is performed only by men, who tie vines to their feet and jump from scaffolds. In addition to being a manhood ceremony, the jump is done to ensure a bountiful yam harvest. In 1979, a group of students from the Oxford University Dangerous Sport Club – who had seen a film about the vine jumpers of Pentecost – jumped from the Clifton Suspension Bridge in Bristol, England, and then later from the Golden Gate Bridge in San Francisco, *dressed in tuxedos and top hats!* Before long, bungee-jumping became the popular extreme sport that it is today.

A. Circle "T" for the true sentences and "F" for the false ones.

1. Some extreme sports are adaptations of traditional games and rituals.

T (F)

2. Surfing was invented in Hawaii.

(T) F

3. Christian missionaries were impressed by the sight of wave sliding.

(T) F

4. Surfing was introduced to the world in the early 20th century.

T (F)

5. Bungee-jumping originated on an island in the Pacific Ocean.

T (F)

6. Bungee-jumping was introduced to the world by a group of British university students.

(T) F

7. Bungee-jumping was traditionally performed to ward off evil spirits.

T (F)

8. These days, only men would go bungee-jumping for fun on the island of Pentecost in Vanuatu.

T (F)

B. Between surfing and bungee-jumping, which extreme sport would you try? Why? Think of another extreme sport you might want to try and explain why.

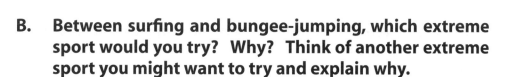

_____

_____

_____

_____

_____

_____

Narrative Writing

We use **narrative writing** when we want to tell a story. This type of writing often involves telling about events in **chronological order**: the order that the events happen in time. A narrative may include vivid descriptions, and may be one or several paragraphs in length.

C. Read the order of narration. Then use the given sentences to finish the narrative paragraph about surfing.

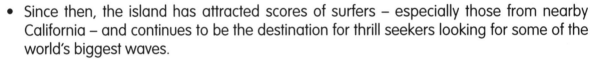

Order of Narration:

1. *Tell when surfing made its comeback.*
2. *Tell why surfing made its comeback.*
3. *Tell who played an important role in its comeback and what they did.*
4. *Tell what happened as a result.*

- Since then, the island has attracted scores of surfers – especially those from nearby California – and continues to be the destination for thrill seekers looking for some of the world's biggest waves.
- Along came a Hawaiian teenager named Duke Kahanamoku, who spent his days riding the waves.
- The missionaries' influence over the island had begun to decline by this time, which allowed the sport to regain its popularity.
- He and his buddies even created their own surfing club called "The Club of the Waves" and gave surfing a rebirth in Hawaii.

The comeback of surfing in Hawaii can be traced to the beginning

of the 20th century. _____

_____

_____

_____

_____

_____

_____

D. **Write a narrative paragraph on one of these topics.**

My Day at School   My Baseball Practice
My Club Meeting   My Summer Vacation

Topic: *My Summer vacation*

Order of Narration:
1. Milton Sport center
2. Cornation Park
3. Swimming
4. Mohawk Jump
5. Basket Ball

Witch's Brew –
or, "EEEEeeeeew!"

Ruth is the name of a witch I once knew,
Who loved to make soup she called "Witch's Brew".
(The soup was quite gooey – it was more like a stew.)
And let me tell you how she made it, too.

She took some soot from the roof
And some water from the pool.
She took some stuff from the chicken coop
And thought, "This will be lovely soup!"

She stirred it with a broom
(She'd forgotten her spoon.)
Adding roots, shoots, a boot,
And the juice of a prune.
She dug into her suitcase
And found two huge scoops of – *Gasp!* – food?
(No clue what it was, but it smelled really rude!)

Then she threw in some noodles
And a spoonful of glue.
Then a scoop of something gooey.
It was red, white, and bluey.
(I knew it was toothpaste! She put in some toothpaste!)
And – What do you know? – she threw in the tube too.

Her friend, the ghoul, took a spoonful,
A big scoop of her brew.
He sniffed it and snoofed it
And started to chew.

Next thing I knew, the dude flew from the room.
He tripped over the Hoover as he started to spew!
EEEEeeeeew!
Wouldn't you?

A. **Find all the words in the poem that rhyme with "stew".**

Brew — Eww

Threw — Few

Root — Too

Coop — Soup

Root — Shoot

Boot — Type

B. **Answer these questions.**

1. What do you think is the nastiest ingredient? Why?

_____

_____

2. Write your favourite rhyming lines from the poem. Why do you like them?

_____

_____

_____

_____

3. Lines within parentheses are used in several places throughout the poem. What is their use?

_____

_____

4. Writers and poets are allowed to use made-up words in their work because they have "poetic licence". What are the made-up words in this poem?

_____

_____

Writing Poetry

It is fun to write poems with rhyming words. When a pair of lines contains rhyming words in the end, they are called **rhyming couplets**.

Example: Ruth is the name of a witch I once knew,
Who loved to make soup she called "Witch's Brew".

C. **Write a word that rhymes with each of these.**

1. spell _____bell_____

2. vision _____mission_____

3. hour _____sour_____

4. jumpy _____grumpy_____

5. gold _____hold_____

6. tricks _____bricks_____

7. conceal _____monceal_____

8. treasure _____pleasure_____

D. **Brainstorm some rhyming words related to the topic of "Elf". Then use them to write the rhyming couplets in this short poem.**

tricks – sticks

Elf

Ralph is the name of an elf who _____lives in the snow._____
Who _____lives in the snow._____ .
He took some yarn and _____some are barn._____
And some _____are barn._____ .
He turned on his spinning wheel _____then he spinned heel._____
Then _____he spinned heel._____ .

E. Think of a topic to write a poem about. Brainstorm some rhyming words
    related to the topic. Then write a poem about it using rhyming couplets.

Gaming

_____

_____

_____

_____

_____

_____

_____

_____

_____

_____

_____

_____

Folk Music
Brings the World Together

As we visit other countries and become more familiar with them, we also become more interested in the traditional folk music of cultures around the world. Though the music is different from culture to culture, the meaning and reason behind the music are the same.

Work songs and chants are a major type of traditional folk music. Whether the work was fishing, planting rice, harvesting grain, picking fruit, coal mining, logging, weaving, railway building, or even sponge diving, people sang songs to cheer themselves up and to get them through their long, hard day. Below are three well-known examples.

The Shanty-man's Life
(an American lumberjack song)
A shanty-man's life is a wearisome life, although some think it void of care.
Swinging an axe from morning till night in the midst of the forests so drear.
Lying in the shanty bleak and cold while the cold stormy wintry winds blow.
And as soon as the daylight doth appear, to the wild woods we must go.

Railway Song
(an American railroad song)
I've been working on the railroad all the livelong day
I've been working on the railroad just to pass the time away
Can't you hear the whistle blowing, rise up so early in the morn
Can't you hear the captain shouting: Dinah, blow your horn

The Banana Boat Song
(a Jamaican work chant)
Day-o, day-ay-ay-o! Daylight come and me wanna go home.
Day! Me say day, me say day, me say day-o.
Daylight come and me wanna go home.
Come, Mr. Tally Mon, tally my bananas.
Daylight come and me wanna go home.
Come, Mr. Tally Mon, tally my bananas.
Daylight come and me wanna go home.

A shanty-man's life...

A. Use your dictionary to find the meaning of each word. Think of a synonym for it. Then write a sentence with each word and a sentence with its synonym.

1. wearisome   synonym: _life_

A shanty mans wearisome life.
life is a

2. drear   synonym: _forest_

Swinging an axe from morning till night in the midths of the forests so drear.

3. bleak   synonym: _cold_

lying in the shanty bleak and cold while the cold stormy wintry winds blow

B. Pretend you are having a "long, hard day". Make up your own work song to help you get through the day.

_____

_____

_____

_____

_____

_____

_____

_____

_____

Writing Letters (1)

Letters can be **formal** or **informal**. An informal letter may or may not have a purpose, and may use casual sentence structure. We often write informal letters when writing notes, e-mails, or greeting cards, where space is limited.

Example: Hey Kiyoka!

Back in Canada now. Will be starting school tomorrow and so I have some butterflies in my stomach...but I'm also excited because I'll be seeing my old friends and meeting new ones!

Hope you're doing well.

Sammy

C. Write a postcard using informal writing.

You are on a trip and have just bought a postcard for a friend.

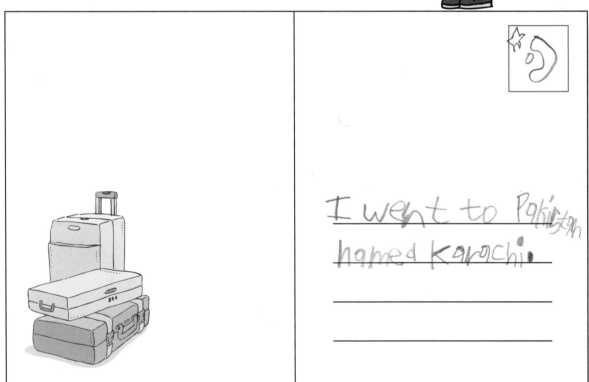

I went to Pakistan named Karachi

Writing Letters (2)

A formal letter – or business letter – has a specific purpose. It begins with a formal salutation and ends with a closing and your name.

It usually contains three paragraphs:

Paragraph 1 states the purpose of your letter.
Paragraph 2 gives details about the subject of your letter.
Paragraph 3 suggests a course of action and/or solution and asks for a follow-up.

D. Write a formal letter.

The city wants to build a high-rise condominium in your neighbourhood, which involves tearing down old but historically important buildings. You want to voice your concern to the mayor of the city.

Dear _____ :

_____

_____

_____

_____

_____

_____

_____

_____

_____

_____

_____

Sincerely,

_____

ENGLISH

COMPLETE

☑ ENGLISH

E = ENTRY

N = NARRATIVE

G = GUARD

L = LIST

I = INDENTIFY

S. = SYNONYM

H = HOMOPHONE

SOCIAL STUDIES

Indigenous Peoples (1)

Canada's Indigenous Peoples include the First Nations, Inuit, and Métis. First Nations and Inuit peoples were living in present-day Canada before European settlers arrived. The Métis are the descendants of the first marriages between Indigenous women and European men. There are more than 600 First Peoples groups in Canada, each with their own customs, languages, systems of governance, and traditional territories.

A. Circle the correct words.

Algonquin

My ancestors migrated to places with good **(air)** / food supply. They lived in a type of hut called a wigwam. They were excellent hunters, like my dad and grandpa today! Some of the animals they hunted were deer, moose, and **(beavers)** / **penguins**. They also fished and planted. Wild rice, seed, and berries were supplements to their diet. They travelled by birchbark canoes in water. In winter, they travelled in toboggans and **(snowshoes)** / **skates**. The women planted and the men hunted but it's different today. Men were leaders of the family. My grandma has taught me a lot about the beliefs she learned from her parents and grandparents. For us, everything has a spirit and we have to respect all living things.

Cayuga

My ancestors lived year round in **(longhouses)** / **igloos**. We still gather in this structure today to see friends and family and practise our customs. Like my auntie Carla today, my ancestors were excellent farmers. Their main source of food came from crops like the Three Sisters which are corn, beans, and **(coconuts)** / **squash**. They also fished and hunted deer, moose, and caribou. At that time, the men hunted and the women planted but everyone helps one another today. Each longhouse is still headed by a **man** / **(woman)**, called clan mother, who looks after her extended family or clan. We have ceremonies and festivals to honour the spirits who change the seasons and provide good crops and **animals** / **(minerals)**.

B.   Using the information from (A), compare the two First Peoples.

	Algonquin	Cayuga
 **Dwelling**	Air	Longhouses
 **Food**	Beavers	Coconuts
 **Roles of Men and Women**	Snowshoes	Woman
 **Beliefs**		Minerals

C.   Use the information in (A) to answer the questions.

1.   What specific skills did the Algonquins develop because of their frequent migration?

_____

_____

2.   How did agriculture affect the daily activities of the Cayugas?

_____

_____

Indigenous Peoples (2)

The daily lives of various First Peoples were very different in part because of where they lived and the resources available to them.

A. Label the Anishinaabe nations on the map and list the Haudenosaunee nations in the box. Then answer the questions.

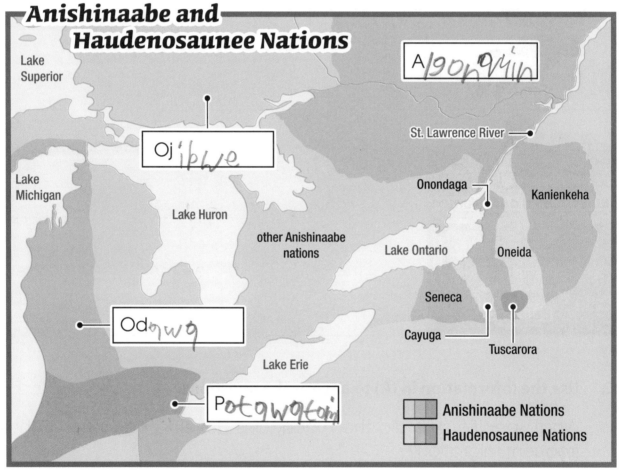

Anishinaabe and Haudenosaunee Nations

Lake Superior

Algonquin

Oj ibwe

St. Lawrence River

Lake Michigan

Onondaga

Kanienkeha

Lake Huron

other Anishinaabe nations

Lake Ontario

Oneida

Odawa

Seneca

Cayuga

Tuscarora

Lake Erie

Potawatomi

Anishinaabe Nations
Haudenosaunee Nations

This map only shows the approximate areas of the nations.

1. **┌Anishinaabe Nations┐**

Odawa

Ojibwe

Potawatomi

Algonquin

2. **┌Haudenosaunee Nations┐**

Onondaga

Cayuga

Tuscarora

Oneida

Seneca

Kanienka

3. Check the region that was not occupied by the Anishinaabe nations.

   Ⓐ the north of Lake Ontario

   Ⓑ ✓ the east of Lake Ontario

   Ⓒ the north of Lake Huron

4. Check the region that the Haudenosaunee nations occupied.

   Ⓐ ✓ by Lake Huron in Western Ontario

   Ⓑ ✔ by Lake Ontario in Eastern Ontario

   Ⓒ ✓ in Newfoundland and Eastern Quebec

5. Name the bodies of water that the Haudenosaunee nations had access to for their water source.

   Lake Hurong Lake Ontgrio7 Lake Michiggh7 Lake Enie7 lake superior,

6. How did the locations of the Haudenosaunee nations benefit them in agricultural activities?

   They were located negh water and they easy increace to water benefit infarming

7. What caused the Anishinaabe nations to move from place to place?

   They shorted of animals after hunting caused the anishinggbe nation of magr it

8.
   > My ancestors' government system had a different structure from the Haudenosaunee nations. How did their frequent migration contribute to this?

   An Algonquin

   _____

   _____

Haudenosaunee Confederacy

The Haudenosaunee Confederacy was founded with the intention of uniting the nations and allowing them to live in harmony. It has a structured government system led by chiefs from all nations.

A. Fill in the blanks. Then answer the questions.

peaceful   Haudenosaunee   Longhouse   Tuscarora

The **Haudenosaunee Confederacy**, meaning "the People of the
1. _Longhouse_ ", was referred to by the Europeans as the Iroquois
Confederacy. It was formed to unite various 2. _Haudenosaunee_ nations.
Its purpose was, and continues to be, to allow the nations within it to
make 3. _peaceful_ decisions together. The nations that first joined
the confederacy were the Kanienkeha, Oneida, Onondaga, Cayuga,
and Seneca. In the early 1720s, the 4. _Tuscarora_ , a nation located
between the Oneida and Onondaga, also joined the Confederacy.

5.

Haudenosaunee Confederacy

Nations:

- Cayuga
- Kanienkeha
- Oneida
- Onondaga
- Seneca
- Tuscaroro

6.

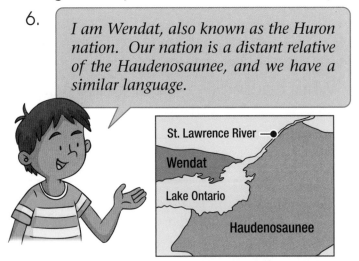

I am Wendat, also known as the Huron nation. Our nation is a distant relative of the Haudenosaunee, and we have a similar language.

St. Lawrence River
Wendat
Lake Ontario
Haudenosaunee

Why didn't the Wendat join the confederacy? (You may have to do some research.)

The _____ have _____

_____

B. **Trading among the nations became easier after the formation of the confederacy. Match the pictures of the traded goods with the descriptions.**

Traded Goods

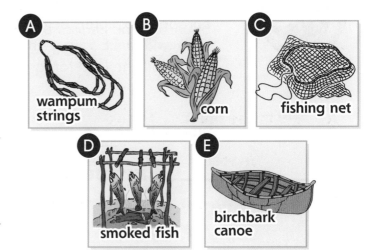

(D) used for travelling in water

(B) a kind of preserved food

(A) shell beads used as money

(C) used for fishing

(E) the main source of their diet

A wampum strings

B corn

C fishing net

D smoked fish

E birchbark canoe

C. **Study the diagram about the Haudenosaunee Confederacy's government system. Then fill in the blanks.**

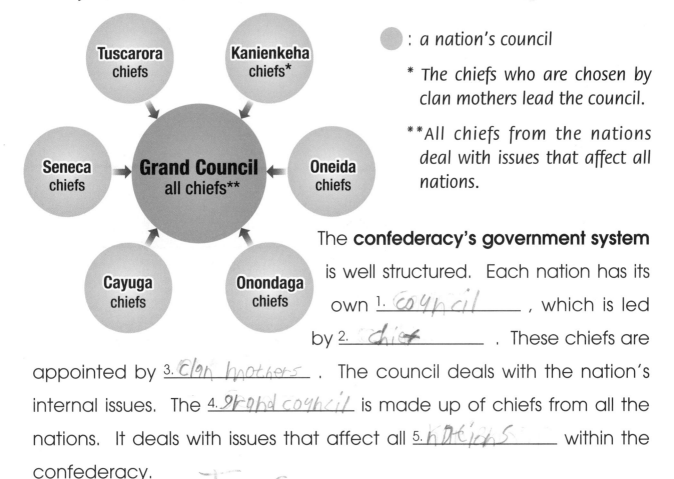

Tuscarora chiefs

Kanienkeha chiefs*

Seneca chiefs

Grand Council all chiefs**

Oneida chiefs

Cayuga chiefs

Onondaga chiefs

● : *a nation's council*

* *The chiefs who are chosen by clan mothers lead the council.*

***All chiefs from the nations deal with issues that affect all nations.*

The **confederacy's government system** is well structured. Each nation has its own 1. _council_ , which is led by 2. _chief_ . These chiefs are appointed by 3. _clan mothers_ . The council deals with the nation's internal issues. The 4. _grand council_ is made up of chiefs from all the nations. It deals with issues that affect all 5. _nations_ within the confederacy.

Tuscarora

Early European Explorers

European explorers began arriving in the land we now call Canada as early as 800 CE. Since then, more Europeans arrived and continued to exploit the land for its riches and resources.

A. **Trace the routes with the correct colours. Then answer the question.**

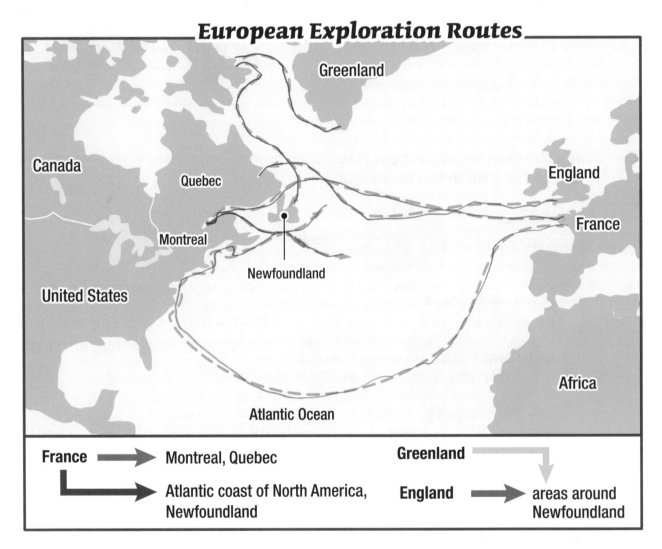

European Exploration Routes

Greenland

Canada

Quebec

England

France

Montreal

Newfoundland

United States

Africa

Atlantic Ocean

France ➡ Montreal, Quebec
➡ Atlantic coast of North America, Newfoundland

Greenland
England ➡ areas around Newfoundland

Of all regions in Canada, why was Newfoundland the first place the Europeans found and explored?

Newfoundland was the first destination of europeans explodes rich because it is the part of North america that is nearest to europe.

B. **Look at the timeline of the early European explorations. Fill in the blanks.**

European Exploration Timeline

Quebec City   overcrowding   Vikings   Newfoundland
King Francis I   Jacques Cartier   King Henry VII
North America   Asia   Atlantic   St. Lawrence River

900 ← European explorers began to arrive in Canada.

1000 ← The Norse, who are known as the 1. _Vikings_ , were Scandinavians who travelled by sea regularly to explore and trade in waters and lands outside Scandinavia. They left Scandinavia because of 2. _overcrowding_ and political unrest. Leif Erikson led his crew to 3. _North America_ and landed in what is now Newfoundland.

1497   John Cabot, an English explorer, was hired by 4. _King Henry VII_ of England to discover new lands and a route to Asia. In one
1499   of his voyages, he landed in what is now 5. _Newfoundland_.

1524   Giovanni de Verrazano was sent by 6. _King Francis I_ of France to explore the east coast of North America and find a route to 7. _Asia_ . Verrazano did not find a route to Asia but explored the 8. _Atlantic_ coast of North America and
1528   Newfoundland.

1534   9. _Jacques Cartier_, another French explorer, was sent by King Francis I to continue finding a route to Asia and claim the Newfoundland area for France. He travelled inland in North America and sailed up to the 10. _St. Lawrence River_ and visited Stadacona and Hochelaga, which are now 11. _Quebec City_
1542   and Montreal respectively.

First Contact

The first encounters between Europeans and the Indigenous nations living on these lands would lead to enormous changes. The European and Indigenous worldviews were vastly different. They struggled to make sense of each other's way of life.

A. **Identify the challenges faced by the Indigenous nations, European explorers, or both. Write the letters in the correct spaces.**

Challenges Faced by the Indigenous Nations and European Explorers

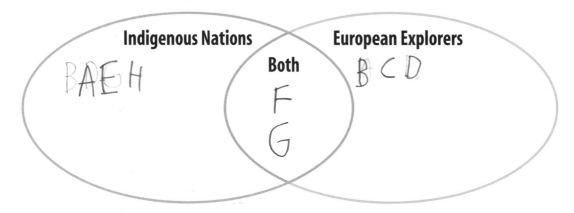

Indigenous Nations **Both** **European Explorers**

BAEH   F G   B C D

A facing threat of explorers taking over their land

B adjusting to a new lifestyle

C getting used to the cold climate and settling in

D starting a different way of life away from their families and friends

E worrying about the explorers imposing their ways and religion onto their people

F dealing with life threatening diseases they had never encountered

G interacting and communicating with people who spoke a different language and had a completely different culture

H being concerned about their food supply as animals were killed not just for subsistence but for sale of their furs

B. **Read the passage. Then answer the questions.**

European Survival Depended on Indigenous Know-how

Regardless of the potential threats the European explorers posed, Indigenous Peoples believed all people must be treated respectfully. Many assisted the Europeans with their basic necessities and helped them adapt to the new lands. To help the explorers get adjusted to the harsh climate, their Indigenous hosts provided them with warm clothing and traditional nutritious foods like pemmican (a mixture of fat and protein). The Indigenous nations the explorers encountered also helped them treat a disease called scurvy, which was caused by the lack of vitamin C. To supplement the diet of the patients, the Indigenous Peoples gave the explorers fish and venison. They also taught them to make a herbal drink to treat the disease.

1. Describe how the Indigenous Peoples helped the explorers... Pemmican
    a. adjust to the harsh climate: <u>They provided them with warm clothing and tradrional nutritious food like</u>
    b. treat scurvy: <u>They give them fish and vension.</u>

2. Why were the Indigenous Peoples being kind to the Europeans even though they presented the Indigenous Peoples with challenges?

    <u>The indigenous Peoples believed all people must be treated respectfully.</u>

3. In your opinion, what actions of the Indigenous Peoples were of the greatest significance to the Europeans? Why?

    _____

    _____

Impacts of Contact

During the first contact between the Europeans and Indigenous Peoples, knowledge, traditions, and cultures were exchanged. Goods were also shared.

A. Write the letters in the arrows to show the trade between the Indigenous Peoples and the Europeans.

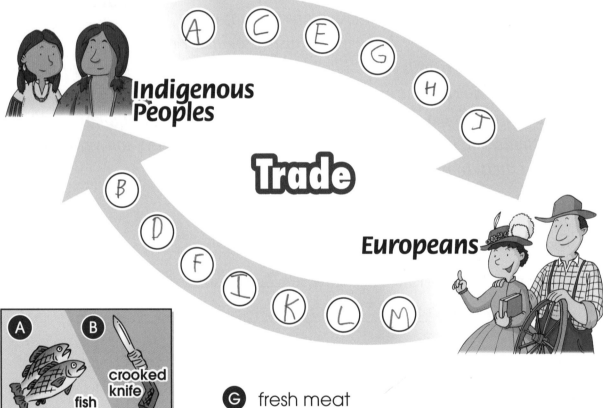

Indigenous Peoples

Trade

Europeans

A C E G H J

B D F I K L M

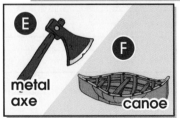

A fish **B** crooked knife

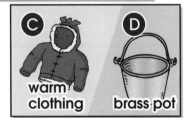

C warm clothing **D** brass pot

E metal axe **F** canoe

G fresh meat

H herbal medicine

I wool blankets

J beaver pelts

K alcohol and tobacco

L European-style pipes

M powder horns (containers for gunpowder)

B. Fill in the blanks. Then answer the question.

Things That Were Introduced to the...

Indigenous Peoples:

farm   metal   travel
grains   hunt

- 1. _metal_ tools:
  making their lives easier

- lightweight firearms:
  able to 2. _hunt_ more
  successfully

- horses:
  able to 3. _travel_ faster
  and greater distances

- 4. _farm_ animals:
  (e.g. chickens, cows, pigs)
  providing stable food sources

- 5. _grains_ :
  (e.g. wheat and barley)
  an alternative food source

Europeans:

survival   plants
warm   lands

- new ways of life:
  including methods of travel
  and 6. _survival_

- medicinal 7. _plants_ :
  enhancing their survival skills

- new 8. _lands_ :
  able to search for more furs

- sewing 9. _warm_ clothing:
  keeping themselves warm
  throughout harsh winters

10. Some Indigenous women married European men. What were the
    benefits of these unions?

    They unions strenthed the ties between the
    2 groups and lessoned the chanced or confederonce.

Negative Impacts on First Peoples

The presence of the Europeans influenced the Indigenous cultures and traditions and threatened their health and way of life.

A. Fill in the blanks.

Although the interactions between the First Peoples and the Europeans may have benefited both groups in different ways, the Europeans' presence had a very negative impact on First Peoples in different aspects.

decrease	waterways	British	decreased	parenting
pelts	cleared	Wendats	alcohol	Catholic
		conflicts	influenza	culture

Overhunting

Prior to the arrival of the Europeans, the First Peoples hunted and fished sustainably so there was always enough for food and basic needs. The European presence upset this balance. Beavers were overhunted for 1. _Pelts_ to satisfy the Europeans' demand for furs. The introduction to guns made hunting a lot easier but this, together with the increased demand for fur, led to a drastic 2. _decrease_ in the beavers' population.

Land Exploitation

Forests were 3. _cleared_ and even crops were burned so that the Europeans could take over the lands near 4. _waterways_, which were the First Peoples' prime locations for food sources.

Warfare

The French fought alongside the 5. _Wendat_ against the Haudenosaunee nations who sided with the 6. _british_. The use of guns made 7. _conflicts_ more deadly. Many people from the Indigenous nations died during wars.

The First Peoples were exposed to diseases from which they had no immunity, such as 8. _influenza_ , tuberculosis, smallpox, scarlet fever, and measles. Their population drastically 9. _decreased_ after several outbreaks. The Europeans also introduced 10. _alcohol_ to the First Peoples, contributing to the challenges they already faced from disease, starvation, and poverty.

Trade was tied to religion. The French appointed 11. _catholic_ missionaries to change the First Peoples' way of life. Before trading took place, conversations around Christian practices of 12. _culture_ , marriage, and burial of the dead were imposed. This led to the diminishing of the First Peoples' traditional 13. _parenting_ and identity.

B. **Read the quotes. Match to show whether each quote is from an Indigenous person or a European.**

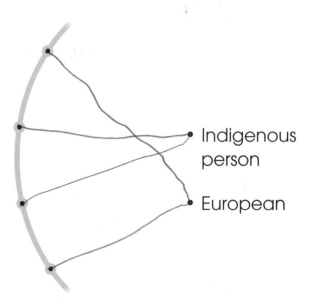

"They are sharing valuable beaver pelts with us for cheap axes."

"The animals have been overhunted for their furs so there is not enough food for us to survive."

"There is so much money to be made from the riches on this land!"

"They are taking the best lands where we fish and hunt."

Indigenous person

European

New Home

New France

During the 1600s, the king of France encouraged his people to migrate to the new colony that had been named "New France".

A. Circle the correct words.

Seigneurial System

The French colonists wanted to make New France like their homeland. King Louis XIII introduced a method of land ownership known as the seigneurial system for the French emigrants.

King

- **borrower /** **(owner)** of all lands
- allocated large areas to different **(noblemen) / soldiers** called seigneurs

Seigneurs (noblemen)

- kept a **small /** **(large)** portion of land for themselves and their families
- divided up the rest of the land among **(farmers) / kings** called habitants
- built a small **(church) / temple** for worship
- built a **silo /** **(mill)** for the habitants to grind wheat

king

seigneur

habitant

Habitants (farmers)

- paid rent to the **(seigneur) / king**
- gave the seigneur a portion of their **(harvest) / land**
- worked for the seigneur for a certain number of days each year, usually building **(roads) / parks** and bridges

B.   Read the paragraph. Check the correct diagram and answer the question.

The lands given to seigneurs were usually beside a waterway, which was used for transportation and irrigation. Seigneurs would divide the land into strips for the habitants so that they could all have access to water.

1.   Check the diagram that shows how the land was divided.
      (S – seigneur, H – habitants)

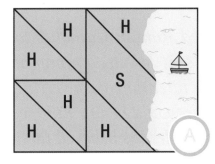

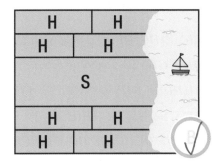

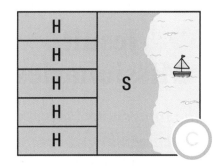

2.   If you were a seigneur, would you divide the land the same way?
      Explain.

      Yes becquse I divide the land like division 9nd I give 9ll man99ers the land c9rd.

C.   Look at the map. Then answer the questions.

1.   The Europeans settled in the ___eastern___ part of Canada.
      eastern/western

2.   Circle the three European settlements that were close to the St. Lawrence River.

3.   How did the location of the European settlements benefit them in trades?

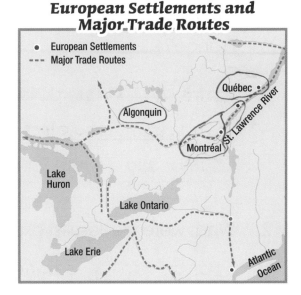

European Settlements and Major Trade Routes

Goods were trahsported by canoes settling close to waterways benefit by europeghr in trades.

New Home

Jesuit Missionaries

One of the first groups to emigrate from Europe to Canada was the Jesuit missionaries. Their presence had significant negative impacts on Indigenous culture and religion, as well as their families, communities, and ways of life.

A. Read the paragraph. Answer the questions.

Jesuit Missionaries

The king of France encouraged Roman Catholics to emigrate to New France. He sent Jesuits, a group of Catholic missionaries, with the intention of converting the Indigenous Peoples to Christianity so that New France would be like Europe, which would give him better control of his new colony. The Jesuits believed their beliefs were superior. They saw it as their obligation to save the Indigenous Peoples, whom they wrongly believed were "lost souls". They learned their languages and kept close contact with them. Some Jesuits were welcomed, some were not, and they largely had a difficult time convincing the Indigenous Peoples to adopt their Christian beliefs.

a Jesuit

1. Why did the king send the Jesuits to New France?

The king wanted to convert the indigenous peoples to christianity so that new france would be like europe.

2. What were the Jesuits' experiences with the Indigenous Peoples like?

The jesuits learned their languages but they kept close contact with them. Some jesuits were welcomed, some were not, and they largely had a difficult time convincing the indigenous peoples.

B. Fill in the blanks to describe the missions and roles of the Jesuit missionaries. Then answer the questions.

Missions and Roles of Jesuit Missionaries

maps   king
priests   traditions
Sainte Marie

Mission

- build a community called __Sainte Marie__ with the purpose of establishing power and control in New France, creating a base for missionary work and the spread of European values, and establishing representatives of the king for economic goals.

- set up parishes where people can train to become 2. __priests__

- write about the 3. __traditions__ of the Indigenous Peoples and draw 4. __maps__ of these Indigenous groups, which would help in controlling them

- submit reports to the 5. __king__ who sends money and people to support the Jesuits

Role

- manage all the 6. __trades__ between the Europeans and the Indigenous Peoples

convert
trades
Christianity

- 7. __convert__ the Indigenous Peoples to 8. __Christianity__ through the frequent contact in trades

9. Why did the Jesuits who arrived in New France start learning the native languages?

   They wanted to bland into their culture so they could convert the indigenous peoples more sucessfully

10. Why did the king of France assign the Jesuits to trade with the Indigenous Peoples?

   by having the jesuits trade with the indigenous peoples increase their change of converting by indigenous peoples.

New Home

Filles du roi

Filles du roi, also known as the King's Daughters, refers to a group of young European women who emigrated to New France with the sponsorship from the king.

A. **Read the paragraph. Then circle the correct words and answer the question.**

Filles du roi

In the 17th century, the number of single European men far outnumbered single European women in New France. To increase the French population and dominate the colony, the king selected approximately 800 single women who were called *filles du roi, or King's Daughters, and sponsored their passage to New France. Once a couple married and had children, the family would be paid a good pension.*

1. I will **gain** / **lose** control of my colony with the increasing French population. It means that the Indigenous Peoples will have **less** / **more** control over this land.

king

2. I am selected to be a **fille du roi** / **slave**, so I can start a new life in the new country. The expense of the journey is covered by **the king** / **myself**.

fille du roi

3. Why would a French couple in New France be paid a good pension if they had children?

The king wanted to increase the French population by encouraging the french couples have the children.

B.   Read the passage. Then answer the questions.

*Filles du roi were from different parts of France including Paris and Normandy.
Some of them were from other countries including Germany, England, and
Portugal. They were mostly between the ages of 16 and 25. They were all very
poor and vulnerable. Most of them were orphans while some were "spares" from
very large families and they had very low levels of literacy skills.
To be selected, the girls had to be physically fit enough to survive
the hard work and be able to support their future husbands in
New France. The time it took them to find husbands varied but it
was between a few months and three years. Marriage ceremonies
were held at church parishes and administered by priests.*

1.   **Filles du roi**

    a. where they came from: <u>different parts of france including</u>
 <u>Paris and normandy other countries including Germany, English</u>
<u>and portugal.</u>

    b. ages: <u>between the ages of 16 and 25.</u>

    c. background: <u>very poor and vulnerable most were orphans while some</u>
<u>were spares from very large families.</u>

    d. requirements: <u>physically fit enough and people to support their fut</u>
<u>family.</u>

2.   Describe the marriage ceremony.

    <u>Many ceremonies were held at church purchase and administrad</u>
<u>by priests.</u>

3.   Why was it important to choose girls who were physically fit as filles
du roi?

    <u>They needed to able to hard work and support their future husbands. in new france</u>

People in the Fur Trade

The Europeans were very interested in the First Peoples' animal pelts, hunted and prepared by the First Peoples, because they could be sold in Europe for a lot of money. In exchange for furs, the Europeans offered metal tools and other items to the First Peoples. Soon, the fur trade began.

A. Write the words in bold in the correct boxes. Then answer the question.

*The Europeans and the First Peoples started trading and, very soon, the **fur trade** expanded and covered large areas of Canada. **Trading posts** were set up at various locations, usually near waterways. The **coureurs des bois** were French settlers who illegally traded fur and who could navigate the interior lands of Canada very well. The First Peoples shared their knowledge of the hunt with the coureurs des bois, and they participated with the First Peoples in hunting beavers, even in deep forested areas. Another group of French people, called **voyageurs**, were hired to navigate canoes briskly along some dangerous sections of waterways and deliver furs to trading posts.*

1. a. Trading posts : small stores set up in remote places for trading

   b. fur trade : an important activity of buying and selling animal pelts between the Europeans and the First Peoples

   c. voyageurs : boatmen who transported goods to and from trading posts by canoes

   d. coureurs des bois : Frenchmen who made illegal trading agreements and collected furs; they were skilled at wilderness travel

2. How did the fur trade change the First Peoples' purpose of hunting?

   Before the fur trade their purpose of hunting was food Since the fur trade begins theyhunted alot more for animal pelts.

B. Fill in the blanks and do the matching.

Indigenous Women in the Fur Trade

The voyageurs travelled to Canada every 1. _Spring_ to
<small>spring/winter</small>

trade 2. _furs_ . After the trading was over, some of them
<small>herbs/furs</small>

3. _stayed_ in the Indigenous communities with whom they had
<small>left/stayed</small>

developed a relationship. Very often, these voyageurs 4. _married_
<small>met/married</small>

Indigenous women. These marriages were often 5. _encouraged_ as it
<small>encouraged/discouraged</small>

was a good strategy, for both sides, to 6. _strengthen_ the relationship
<small>strengthen/weaken</small>

between the First Peoples and the voyageurs. For example, voyageurs

benefited from the 7. _survival_ skills of Indigenous women,
<small>survival/entertainment</small>

especially the ones they shared along the journeys between trading posts.

8.

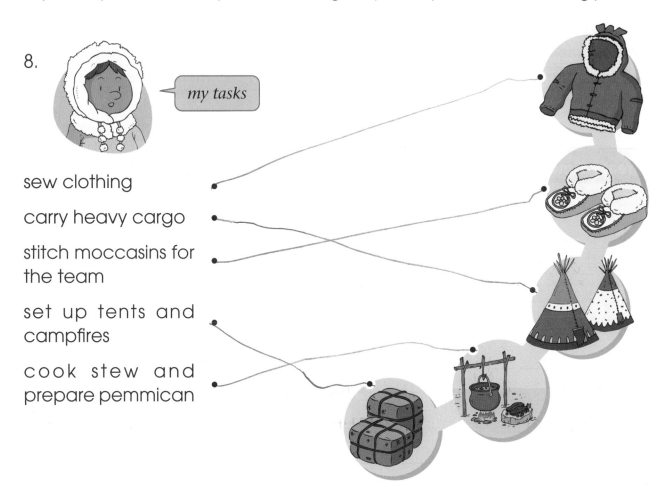

my tasks

sew clothing

carry heavy cargo

stitch moccasins for
the team

set up tents and
campfires

cook stew and
prepare pemmican

12

Treaties and Land Claims

More and more Europeans arrived and occupied First Peoples' lands. The First Peoples advocated for their rights, which led to the writing of treaties and land claims.

A.   Read the paragraph. Then complete the timeline.

Treaty

A treaty is an agreement negotiated between two or more nations that gives valid rights to each party.

In 1764, the Niagara Treaty was signed. It was the first treaty signed between the British and the First Peoples. It was intended to establish a relationship of peace and respect between the two parties. In 1787, they signed another treaty called the Gunshot Treaty.
It stated the British had the right to the land and its resources within a large area stretching from Lake Ontario to north of the Great Lakes. It was a blank contract that was to be filled later. In return, the First Peoples were offered some money, reserve lands, and annual gifts. Between 1871 and 1921, 11 treaties called the Numbered Treaties took place. They were signed between the federal government and various First Nations. In these treaties, the First Peoples received reserve lands and various forms of government assistance by giving up their rights to large tracts of land and the resources within them.

| Treaty Timeline | *1764* | *1787* | *1871 to 1921* |

The __Niagra__ **Treaty**

Parties: __British__ and
__First Peoples__

Purpose:
to establish a
relationship of peace
and respect between
the 2 parties.

The __Gunshot__ **Treaty**

Parties: __British__ and
__First peoples__

For the First Peoples:
were offered some
money, reserve lands
and various form
and government
assistance.

The __Numbered__ **Treaties**
(11 treaties)

Parties: __British__ and
__First__

For the First Peoples:

_____

_____

_____

_____

B. Fill in the years in which the land claims took place.

Land claim is a grievance filed by a nation in response to a violation of their rights, from which the issue may be settled with land or financial compensation. Below are some of the land claims in Canada.

1978 in Quebec
James Bay and Northern Quebec Agreement

1992 in Eastern Yukon
Gwich'in Comprehensive Land Claim Agreement

1993 in Nunavut
Nunavut Land Claims Agreement

1994 in Northern Northwest Territories
Sahtu Dene and Métis Comprehensive Land Claim Agreement

2000 in Northwestern British Columbia
Nisga'a Final Agreement

2005 in Eastern Northwest Territories
Tlicho Agreement

2005 in Newfoundland and Labrador
Labrador Inuit Land Claims Agreement

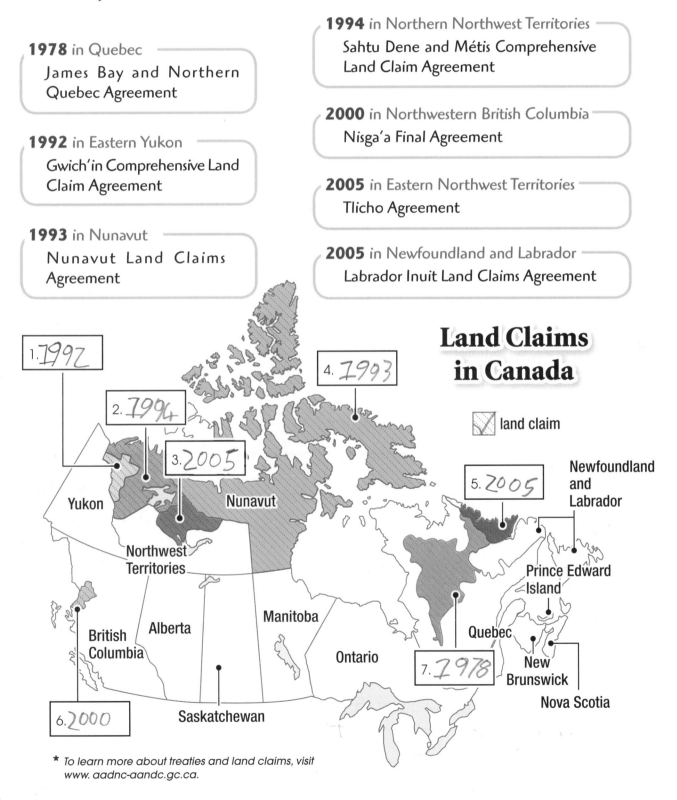

Land Claims in Canada

☑ land claim

1. 1992
2. 1994
3. 2005
4. 1993
5. 2005
6. 2000
7. 1978

Yukon

Nunavut

Northwest Territories

British Columbia

Alberta

Saskatchewan

Manitoba

Ontario

Quebec

Newfoundland and Labrador

Prince Edward Island

New Brunswick

Nova Scotia

* *To learn more about treaties and land claims, visit www.aadnc-aandc.gc.ca.*

Aboriginal Self-Government

In addition to the three levels of government, Canada also has a form of government called the Aboriginal self-government. Indigenous Peoples had to fight to win back their right to their traditional self-governance.

A. **Circle the correct words. Put "+" for pros and "-" for cons. Then answer the question.**

Aboriginal self-government is a form of government that was acknowledged by the (federal) / municipal government as a response toward Indigenous communities' fight for the (right) / permission to govern themselves once more. It (gives) / denies the First Peoples authority over decisions that (affect) / hinder their lives including health, education, and social and economic development. The First Peoples believe that they have an inherent right to self-governance, meaning to govern according to their customary traditions and, for some, according to what the Creator intends.

Pros and Cons from the Perspective of the First Peoples

> Before the status was acknowledged, there was a lot of debate within the Indigenous communities on its pros and cons.

(−) lack of access to foreign resources

(+) adequate resources and training to establish our own institutions

(+) have control of our land and freedom to make decisions ourselves

(−) First Peoples' needs no longer recognized by provincial and federal governments

5. If you were a member of the First Peoples, would you vote for or against the status? Explain.

    Vote for because I vote for everything.

B. Determine whether the roles below fall under federal jurisdiction (F) or Aboriginal self-government (A). Circle the correct letters.

1. determining the tax rate on goods and services ⓕ A

2. setting fishing and hunting laws F Ⓐ

3. setting guidelines for the First Nations Child and Family Services Program F Ⓐ

4. managing import and export activities in the territory Ⓕ A

5. licensing health and wellness programs F Ⓐ

6. overseeing international transportation Ⓕ A

C. Read the quote and answer the questions.

Cultural revival among aboriginal people is just one step toward regaining what has been lost. Self-government is the other key to the future of native people. When they are permitted to gain influence over the central institutions in their communities — the schools, the justice system, the child welfare system – Indian and Métis people have already demonstrated that they can repair the damage caused by centuries of racism and neglect.

Geoffrey York
Author of *The Dispossessed: Life and Death in Native Canada*

1. Why is Aboriginal self-government necessary according to Geoffrey York?

   Aboriginal self government would
   allow Ist peoples to regain were
   they had lost after the european arrived.

2. What does Geoffrey York mean when he says "centuries of racism and neglect"?

   Indian and Metis people have already demonstrated
   that they can repair the damage caused by centuries of
   racism and neglect.

Traditional Ecological Knowledge

Traditional Ecological Knowledge (TEK) is a complex body of knowledge built up by the First Peoples and their close connection to nature. TEK is passed down from generation to generation, and is an asset to their survival.

A. Fill in the blanks. Then check the correct sentence in each pair.

Traditional Ecological Knowledge (TEK) is gained through human interaction with 1. _nature_ . The First Peoples use it on a daily basis and it has been built up over a long period of time. TEK is a necessary tool for their 2. _survival_ , and it has allowed them to live sustainably using natural resources. Even today, some First Peoples communities living on reserves still live a life lacking 3. _electricity_ and running water. TEK continues to be an essential part of First Peoples' lives. Now, environmentalists are looking to the First Peoples to find ways to live 4. _sustainably_.

electricity
survival
nature
sustainably

How the First Peoples Connect Themselves to Nature

- (A) Mother Earth is a gift that can be used as one pleases.
- (B) ✓ Mother Earth needs to be respected and used responsibly.

- (A) Everyone needs to take care of only his or her own affairs.
- (B) ✓ Sacrificing one's needs for the betterment of the community might be necessary.

- (A) ✓ Every plant or animal, big or small, is connected in the circle of life.
- (B) In the community, the rule of reciprocity can be ignored.

B. **Study the case below to see how TEK can help us understand more about nature. Complete the chart and answer the questions.**

An Example of the Use of TEK:

The Bowhead Whale Census

The Inuit elders had been observing for years that a large number of bowhead whales did not migrate within visual sighting distance from where the observations were being carried out by scientists in 1977. The scientists were studying the bowhead whale population along the Beaufort Sea. They estimated the population to be about 1500 by observing the migration in open waters. However, through TEK, the elders estimated that the population should be a lot more. This information made the scientists

include the whales migrating offshore and under the ice. Their findings, with the whale population estimated to be about 7000, confirmed the elders' observations.

1. Population of the Bowhead Whale in 1977

TEK	The Inuit	a. Scientist
Method	b. TEK	scientific analysis
Areas Observed	c. open water off shore and under the ice	d. open waters
Population	e. about 7000	f. about 1500

2. Whose estimation in 1977 was more accurate?   The inuit

3. From this example, do you agree that TEK is a valuable resource to scientists on environmental studies? Explain.

   Yes because TEK has scientists on the chart.

Rights and Responsibilities of a Canadian Citizen

Canada is a democratic country that provides many rights to its citizens. As a Canadian citizen, you have rights, but you also have to take on responsibilities.

A. Identify the rights.

Legal
Language
Democratic
Equality
Freedom
Mobility

The Canadian Charter of Rights and Freedoms

describes rights and freedoms that are guaranteed to every Canadian citizen.

1. **Legal Rights**

right to life; right not to receive cruel or unusual punishments

2. **Language Rights**

right to speak with the government in English or French

3. **Mobility Rights**

right to enter and leave Canada

4. **Equality Rights**

right to be treated and protected equally by laws

5. **Freedom of Religion**

right to worship the religion of our choice

6. **Democratic Rights**

right to vote and join political activities

B. **Check the statements that identify the responsibilities of a good citizen.**

The Responsibilities of a Good Citizen

(A) to ignore environmental responsibilities

(B) to disrespect people from other cultures

(C) ✓ to follow rules in schools, in institutions, on roads, etc.

(D) ✓ to advocate more assistance to the homeless and the less fortunate

To call for emergency when something is wrong, e.g. medical emergency, fire, or theft. ✓

Every citizen should help make Canada the best country to live in.

C. **Study and analyze the cases. Identify the rights that are violated and give reasons.**

Case 1

A store has refused to hire Peter as a cashier because he has a history of reckless driving.

Violation: _Eaugity Rights_

Reason: _The job does not driving petro is not treades eavgally as other._

Case 2

Farida is hired to work at a store with the condition that she removes her head scarf during work hours.

Violation: _Freedom of Religion_

Reason: _Farida is discrimented against prackising her religion and its forced to abandont her religion to get employed._

Levels of Government in Canada

There are three levels of government in Canada: Federal, Provincial/Territorial, and Municipal. Each level has its own responsibilities but they are all connected to almost everything that we do.

A. **Identify each level of government and circle the correct words. Fill in the blanks to show its responsibilities.**

The Three Levels of Government

Federal Government

Provincial/Territorial Government

Municipal Government

1. **Federal** Government

- is headed by the Governor General of Canada on the advice of the
  Queen / **(Prime Minister)**

- looks after the entire country and **minor** / **(international)** issues that affect Canada

- makes decisions that affect **(all)** / **certain** parts of Canada

- is responsible for immigration, taxes, **(national defence)** / **policing** , and criminal laws

- Prime Minister of Canada:
  Justin Trudeau

Parliament Hill in Ottawa

Some of its Responsibilities

- setting a. **food** safety regulations
  food/park

- setting the minimum b. **age** for a Canadian soldier
  weight/age

- determining the criteria for the eligibility for c. **employment** insurance
  life/employment

2. **Provincial** /Territorial Government

- is given authorities by the (federal) / **municipal** government
- is responsible for health care, education, and **office** /(road) regulations
- premier or commissioner of ___24t___ : ___Doug Ford___
  your area   name

Some of its Responsibilities

(✓) A   issuing driver and vehicle licences

( ) B   providing national defence

(✓)   providing health care services

( ) D   setting school curriculum

Legislative Building in Ontario

3. **Municipal** Government

- governs cities, towns, and **provinces** /(districts)
- is responsible for libraries, parks, and local **airports** /(police)
- mayor of ___24___ : ___Doug ford___
  your area   name

Some of its Responsibilities

(✓) A   arranging garbage disposals

( ) B   passing marriage laws

(✓) C   building city parks

(✓) D   providing water and sewage services

City Hall in Toronto

A law was passed to make a two-dollar coin. Which level of government was responsible for making this decision? Do some research to find out when the Toonie was introduced.

4. ┌─────────────┐
   │ Federal   │
   └─ **government**

5. ┌─────────────┐
   │ 1860   │
   └─**year**

Health Care

Canada's health care system provides services on the basis of need rather than the ability to pay. Through taxes, the values of fairness and equity are demonstrated through sharing health care resources.

A. Fill in the blanks to complete the paragraph. Then put the letters in the circles under the correct levels of government.

The three levels of government work together to provide health care services for citizens. Most of the responsibility of providing health care services rests with the p_rovincial_ government. The f_ederal_ government is responsible for delivering services to certain groups of people including the First Peoples. The m_unicipal_ government shares responsibility in the areas of public health, sanitation, infectious diseases, and related education.

Health Care Services

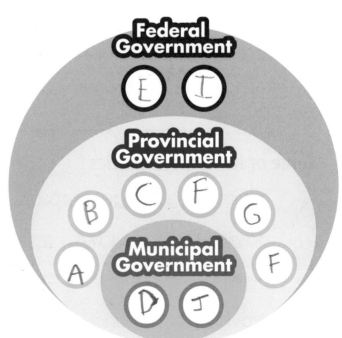

A operating hospitals

B supplying prescription drugs

C providing emergency services

D keeping immunization records

E funding health research

F managing medical clinics

G providing long-term homes for the elderly

H providing rehabilitation services for those in need

I providing health care services for Canadian Forces, veterans, and refugees

J publishing brochures on prevention and treatment of common diseases and injuries

B. **Study the graphs about Canada's population and spending on health care. Then answer the questions.**

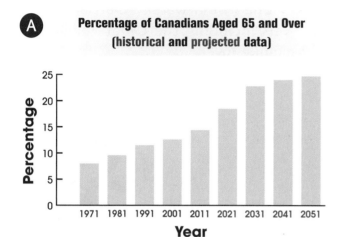

A **Percentage of Canadians Aged 65 and Over (historical and projected data)**

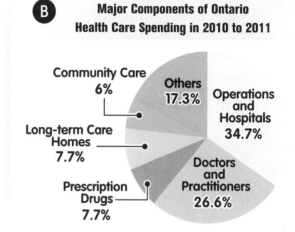

B **Major Components of Ontario Health Care Spending in 2010 to 2011**

Community Care 6%
Long-term Care Homes 7.7%
Prescription Drugs 7.7%
Others 17.3%
Operations and Hospitals 34.7%
Doctors and Practitioners 26.6%

Graph A

1. Describe the trend for Canadians aged 65 and over.

   The elderly population has been increasing and his predicted an increase in the cost to whole

2. How does this trend impact the spending on health care?

   The expense to long tynpcare homes and community care will go up the cost to uprgde hospital will also increase.

3. On which two categories does Ontario spend most?

   Ontario spend most on Operations and Hospital and Doctors and Practitioners.

Graph B

4. As the Canadian population ages, how will this category be affected? Explain.

   As the population ages more help problems will racen to support the increasing demand more doctors need to hired and more hospitals and medical centers need to be built.

5. *Make two suggestions to the government that support the health care needs for the aging population.*

   2010 and 2011.

Water Management

Canada is home to 7% of the globe's fresh water. Our landscape is defined by our lakes and rivers including the Great Lakes, the St. Lawrence River, and the Mackenzie River.

A. Fill in the blanks.

The responsibility for the provision of water and sanitation services is shared by the federal, provincial, and municipal governments. They jointly work to deliver clean water and resolve issues that would affect water quality.

Federal Government

- 1. _conserves_ and protects water resources
- deals with water 2. _boundaries_ shared with the U.S.
- leads 3. _scientific_ research
- allocates funds to the provincial and 4. _municipal_ governments
- monitors 5. _fisheries_ and navigation

conserves
scientific
boundaries
fisheries
municipal

Provincial Government

- governs water 6. _quality_ and sanitation
- takes action to resolve 7. _ecosystem_ issues
- regulates 8. _costs_ and service quality

costs
ecosystems
quality

Municipal Government

- 9. _delivers_ safe drinking water
- collects and treats 10. _wastes_
- conducts water 11. _quality_ tests

quality
waste water
delivers

B. **Study this bill that was presented to the Parliament of Canada. Then answer the questions.**

Canada Water Preservation Act

Introductions:

first read to Parliament in September 2011 and again in March 2012

Description:

stating that Canada must protect the integrity of its ecosystems from the harmful impact of a large-scale removal of fresh water from the nation's major drainage basin

> *Before a bill becomes a law, it must get a majority vote in Parliament. Here are the arguments from each party.*

1. Rate the arguments.

   1 – most convincing
   4 – least convincing

     NDP ✓

    Green Party ✓

   ✓ Liberal   Conservative ✓

2. If you were a Parliament member, would you vote for or against the bill? Explain.

   vote for because I vote for everything.

   _____

3. Did the bill become a law?
   (Do some research.)

    Yes / (No)

NDP

I have seen other precious resources in our ground mined and exported with too little regard for Canadian priorities and needs. That must not happen with our water. We must pass this law to protect our waters from being exported to the U.S.

Liberal

The U.S. is at a crisis. They have 6% of the world's fresh water, but their population is nine times ours. At a conference, a U.S. government official was heard to say: "We don't have to worry about this (water shortage) because we'll just get the water from Canada." We need to protect our natural resource.

green
PARTY OF ONTARIO

This bill prohibits massive transfers of water. This bill needs to be legislated. We think we are a water-rich nation, but the reality is that we only have 9% of the world's renewable water. The U.S. has 6%. We are roughly in the same territory. If we allow a single transaction of the shipment of water in bulk from one drainage basin to another, we will have turned on the tap to impossible trade agreements with the U.S.

Conservative

The responsibility to manage natural resources has traditionally been at the provincial level. The federal government shares the responsibility when needed. Our provinces have put in place laws, regulations, or policies that prevent the transfer of water between basins or outside their boundaries. This bill does not need to become a law because it is duplicative.

Recycling and Waste Management

The responsibility for recycling and waste management is shared among the three levels of government. Their roles include imposing regulations and policies, collecting and transporting waste, and encouraging sustainable waste management practices.

A. **Fill in the blanks to learn the responsibilities of the three levels of government. Then identify and write the level of government that is responsible for each role.**

word bank:
waste
recycles
homes
monitoring
manages
international

Federal Government

responsible for services on federal lands and resources; involved with interprovincial and 1. _international_ transport of 2. _waste_ materials

Provincial Government

3. _manages_ and sets policies for waste management including approving, licensing, and 4. _monitoring_ of services

Municipal Government

collects, 5. _recycles_, and disposes of waste and recycle materials from 6. _homes_, businesses, construction sites, and schools

7. collecting waste materials from construction sites   _Municipal_

8. performing research and creating programs and practices that help reduce waste   _Federal_

9. passing legislation that defines hazardous materials   _Provincial_

B. **The graph displays how Ontarians' waste is managed, either disposed or diverted. Answer the questions about the graph.**

Every day, Ontario generates more than 33 000 tonnes of waste. This adds up to more than 12 million tonnes a year! Most of the waste is disposed in landfills while some of it is diverted (recycled, reused, or reduced).

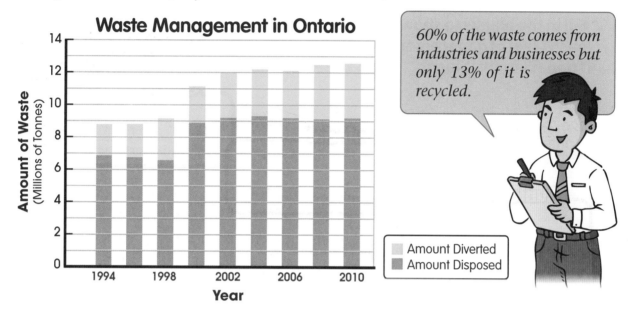

60% of the waste comes from industries and businesses but only 13% of it is recycled.

1. In 2010, about how much

    a. waste was disposed of?

    ___9.7M___

    b. waste was diverted?

    ___3.4M___

2. Describe the trend of the

    a. amount of total waste:

    ___increasing___

    b. amount of diverted waste:

    ___increasing___

3. Even though the amount of waste has stayed quite steady over the past decade, Ontarians are still generating a large amount of waste. What environmental problems will this cause?

    ___Landfields will even trully run out and burning garbage adds to greenhouse guesses.___

4. Suggest two solutions to the problem.

    ___Reduce weste and Recycle materials.___

Transportation

Transportation is a joint responsibility of all three levels of government. Traffic congestion is one of the major problems in big cities like Toronto.

A. **Fill in the blanks to show the responsibility of each level of government on transportation. Then fill in the blanks.**

Transportation in Canada

urban   intra-provincial
interprovincial

Federal
interprovind
Transportation

Provincial
intr 9-provin
Transportation

Municipal
urban
Transportation

Over the last two decades, the federal government has been transferring some of its roles to private sectors and non-profit organizations.

Commercializing the Transportation System

more   expenditure   control   public
fewer   costs   benefits   investment

Advantages

- providing opportunities for company 1._investment_

- transportation users have 2. _more_ say

- reducing government 3. _expenditure_

- 4. _fewer_ hurdles (e.g. getting consensus from the public to begin work)

Disadvantages

- higher 5._costs_ to the public (e.g. more toll roads)

- fewer government jobs and 6. _benefits_

- government has less 7. _control_ over developments

- may not meet the needs of the 8. _public_

B.   Look at the graphs and answer the questions.

Roundtrip Commute Time
(in Toronto, Vancouver, Canada)

272

Average Time (min): 80, 75, 70, 65, 60, 0

Toronto   Vancouver   Canada

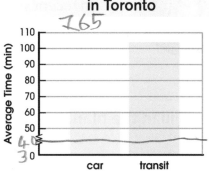

Roundtrip Commute Time
in Toronto

765

Average Time (min): 110, 100, 90, 80, 70, 60, 50, 40, 30, 0

car   transit

1.   Compare the average commute time in Toronto with

is longer.

a. that of Vancouver.

Toronto advantage community is longer,

b. that of the whole country.

Toronto advantage community

2.   Compare the average commute time in Toronto between those who use cars and those who use transit.

The average commute time of those who travel by transit is double that of those who drive.

3.   Write two things indicated in the graphs about Toronto's transportation.

which commute time compared to other cities in canada the transport system need to be improved.

4.   Make two suggestions to help Sally lower her transportation costs but still minimize the time she spends on the road.

> *I live in Toronto and drive on Highway 407 for about 40 mins to go to work in Brampton. I pay $600 a month on toll. If I don't drive on the toll route, it will take me over 2 hours.*

*   *live home earlier to avoid traffic on toll free road live closer to her work place.*

*   _____

    _____

Homelessness

In recent years, homelessness has become one of the major social issues in Canada, especially in cities such as Toronto and Vancouver. All three levels of government are looking for ways to solve this problem.

A. Fill in the blanks.

There are different reasons for homelessness, but the inability to pay for living expenses is the main cause. The federal government is trying to reduce the homeless problem by funding different social programs and services. The provincial and municipal governments are responsible for the implementation of the programs.

Causes of Homelessness

- mental disorders
- inability to pay 1. _rent_
- escaping from 2. _conflicts_ or abuse
- alcohol or 3. _drug_ use problems
- exiting foster care or 4. _hospitalization_
- low social assistance from the 5. _government_

conflicts
drug
hospitalization
government
rent

federal   housing
affordable

Solutions from the Government

- In 1999, the National Homeless Initiative was created to fund 6. _affordable_ housing and support a range of services for the homeless.

- In 2007, the 7. _federal_ government decided to spend $270 million between 2007 and 2009 to address homeless issues.

- In 2008, the Government of Canada announced that it would set aside $387.9 million per year for the next five years for 8. _housing_ and homelessness programs.

B. Study the chart and answer the questions.

1. Describe the changes in the population of people living

   Homeless Population in Toronto

	2006	2013
Living Outdoors	735	447
Living in Shelters	3649	3970

   a. outdoors:

   discreased

   b. in shelters:

   increased

2. According to the data, do you think the government funding towards alleviating homelessness is effective?

   Yes!

3. The demand for permanent housing among the homeless increased from 86% to 93% between 2006 and 2013. Check the possible solutions to help meet the demand. Then suggest one solution.

   (A✓) provide funds for those in need of a home

   (B) build more affordable housing

   (C) shut down shelters to force the homeless to find housing

   (D✓) subsidize rent based on income

   (✓) _86－93_

4. Solving the homeless problem helps build a better society. Check the positive outcomes it would bring about.

   (A✓) lower crime rates

   (B✓) reduced demand for health care services

   (C) higher demand for police services

   (D✓) improved overall make-up of the city

Taxation and Spending

All the services provided by the Canadian government come from taxation. There are many types of tax a taxpayer pays. In return, he or she can enjoy the public services the government provides.

A. Look at the chart. Fill in the blanks and answer the questions.

use   parks   value
facilities   sale   tax

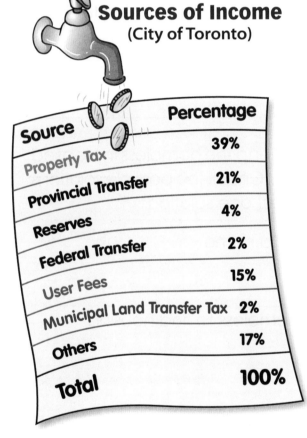

Sources of Income
(City of Toronto)

Source	Percentage
Property Tax	39%
Provincial Transfer	21%
Reserves	4%
Federal Transfer	2%
User Fees	15%
Municipal Land Transfer Tax	2%
Others	17%
Total	100%

Property Tax

amount of 1. _tax_ is based on the value of land and its 2. _use_ (i.e. business or residential); the value is determined using market 3. _value_ standard

User Fees

payments for 4. _facilities_ including pools, skating rinks, and 5. _parks_

Municipal Land Transfer Tax

one-time payment on 6. _sale_ price of property (since 2006)

7. What are the three major sources of income?

   Property tax, User fees, and Municipal land transfer tax.

8. If house prices increase, which two sources of income would change? Explain how.

   Municipal land transfer tax and Property tax because tax is a money.

B. **Answer the questions by using the information from the graph.**

Expenditure of City of Toronto

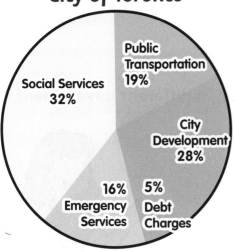

Social Services 32%

Public Transportation 19%

City Development 28%

16% Emergency Services

5% Debt Charges

Toronto Transit Commission (TTC): 16%
Transportation Services: 3%

Public Libraries: 2%   Parks, Forestry, and Recreation: 4%
City Planning: 0.5%   Municipal Licensing and Standards: 1%
Economic Development and Culture: 0.5%   Others: 20%

Police Services: 10%   Fire Services: 4%
Medical Emergency Services: 2%

Shelter, Support, and Housing Administration: 9%
Children's Services: 4%   Long-term Care Homes: 2%
Public Health: 2%   Employment and Social Services: 15%

1. Rank the types of expenditure of the City of Toronto (1 – least, 5 – most). Then identify the item in each type that incurs the most expenses.

(A) Public Transportation: _19 8_

(B) City Development: _28 8_

(C) Emergency Services: _16 8_

(D) Social Services: _32 8_

(E) Debt Charges: N/A _5 8_

2. Below are some ways to reduce Toronto's debt. Pick one of them and describe what negative consequences it could bring to the city.

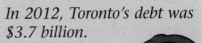

In 2012, Toronto's debt was $3.7 billion.

- increasing class size in schools
- charging fees for using libraries
- reducing government expenditure on police services

reducing government expenditure on
police services.

Public Opinion

Canada has a democratic government system. As Canadian citizens, we have the means to work with the government in making the country the best it can be.

A. Fill in the blanks to show a citizen's participation in different government needs.

> In Canada, the general public elect the politicians who they think will represent them in their best interest. After elections, the public still have ways to share their opinions with government officials.

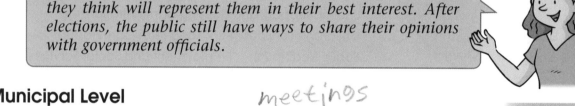

Municipal Level

meetings

- public can attend 1. _council_ to share concerns about their communities

- government makes decisions at 2. _town hall meetings_

- public elect 3. _local council_ _ors_ from their ward (area) to represent them at these meetings

local councillors

town hall meetings

council meetings

Provincial Level

- public can attend the 4. _leglislathre_ and hear the proceedings _Parliament_

- government makes decisions at the 5. _Provincial_

- public elect a Member of the 6. _Provincial_ _legislative_ (MPP) to represent them at the Legislative Assembly

Provincial Legislative

Provincial Parliament

legislature

Federal Level

- government makes decisions in the 7. _Parliament_ in Ottawa

- public elect a Member of the 8. _Houses of Commons_ (MP) to represent them at the House of Commons

House of Commons

Parliament

B. Circle the correct words to complete the report of the royal commission.

*A **royal commission** is a public inquiry that is conducted by a team of experts appointed by the Governor General. Their goal is to make a detailed investigation into a national problem. A significant part of its research comes from public opinion. The reports would be sent to the Government of Canada for appropriate action.*

A Royal Commission Report: Future of Health Care in Canada

Roy Romanow
appointed to manage the Royal Commission on the Future of Health Care in Canada in 2001

less   equal   status   transparent
medical   healthiest   health care

Observations

- We support the values of the health care system – _status_ and timely access to medical services for all citizens, regardless of _less ~~Ethiest~~_ and wealth.

- The federal government contributes _transport_ to health care than it did before the 1990s.

- There are inefficiencies between supply and demand, which have led to unacceptable wait times for some _health care_ procedures.

Recommendations

- We need to pay closer attention to where the _equal_ funding is going.

- We need a _medical_ health care system where information is shared with Canadians.

- We need to have a prevention and wellness strategy so that Canadians are the world's _healthiest_ people.

Result In 2004, the Government of Canada granted a transfer of an additional $41 billion over the next 10 years to support the health care system.

Public Activism

Canadian citizens can take an active role in addressing environmental and social issues in their community. These actions are called public activism, which plays an important role in the government's decision-making.

A. Match each form of public activism with its description.

Public Activism is the use of direct actions in an effort to show one's opposition to a change or support of a cause.

> *Over the last decade, using the Internet to initiate activism to address one's political concern has become increasingly popular.*

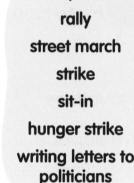

boycott

rally

street march

strike

sit-in

hunger strike

writing letters to politicians

1. **sitin**

the most peaceful form of activism

2. **street march**

a mass group walking from one designated point to another

3. **hunger strike**

withdrawal from commercial or social relations as a protest

4. **strike**

a group of participants fasts as an act of protest

Forms of Public Activism

5. **writing letters with politicians**

withdrawal of workers' services for the approval of workers' demands or in protest against terms imposed by an employer

6. **rally**

a large gathering of people for a protest or showing support for a cause

7. **boycott**

one or more people occupying an area for a protest

B. **Study the case below to see how public activism could make an impact. Do the matching and fill in the blanks.**

The Oak Ridge's Moraine is a largely undeveloped belt of hills, forests, and streams across the northern edge of Toronto. It acts as a natural filter for rainwater and snow melt, which flow to rivers and streams and into the lakes. In the late 1980s, public awareness was brought to conserve the moraine as land developers wanted to develop the area. Many people were opposing the idea of construction because they wanted to conserve the moraine.

Stakeholders' Views and Actions

Views

Local Residents

Naturalists

- **A** It adds greenery.
- **B** It is inhabited by many species.
- **C** Developing it eases crowding in Toronto.
- **D** It serves to purify groundwater.
- **E** It is a diverse plant and animal habitat.

Actions

Biologists

Hydrologists

Land Developers

- **A** made a case against the threat to groundwater quality
- **B** hired scientists to argue that construction could be done without damaging the area
- **C** wrote to politicians to voice their concerns
- **D** made a case to protect over 900 species inhabiting the area
- **E** gathered 450 scientists to petition against developing the area

Outcome (Do some research.)

In 2001, a conservation plan was released. According to the plan, the moraine was to be divided into ____225____ zones with increasingly stringent controls on development in each. It limited the development to no more than __450__% of the land mass of the moraine.

SOCIAL STUDIES COMPLETE

Photo Credits:

Unit 16 p. 264 – Parliament Hill in Ottawa

"Centre Block - Parliament Hill" by Saffron Blaze - Own work. Licensed under Creative Commons Attribution-Share Alike 3.0 via Wikimedia Commons - http://commons.wikimedia.org/wiki/File:Centre_Block_-_Parliament_Hill.jpg#mediaviewer/File:Centre_Block_-_Parliament_Hill.jpg

Unit 16 p. 265 – Legislative Building in Ontario

"Pink Palace Toronto 2010" by Benson Kua from Toronto, Canada - The Pink PalaceUploaded by Skeezix1000. Licensed under Creative Commons Attribution-Share Alike 2.0 via Wikimedia Commons - http://commons.wikimedia.org/wiki/File:Pink_Palace_Toronto_2010.jpg#mediaviewer/File:Pink_Palace_Toronto_2010.jpg

Unit 16 p. 265 – City Hall in Toronto

"City Hall, Toronto, Ontario" by Jerome Decq - originally posted to Flickr as Toronto City Hall. Licensed under Creative Commons Attribution 2.0 via Wikimedia Commons - http://commons.wikimedia.org/wiki/File:City_Hall,_Toronto,_Ontario.jpg#mediaviewer/File:City_Hall,_Toronto,_Ontario.jpg

24

SOCIAL STUDIES

S = SASKATCHEWAN S = SOUTH DAKOTA

O = ONTARIO T = TEXAS

U = UNITED STATES

C = CANADA D = DELAWARE

I = INUIT I = INDIANA

A = ALBERTA E = ENCOURAGE

L = LABRADOR S = SOUTH CAROLINA

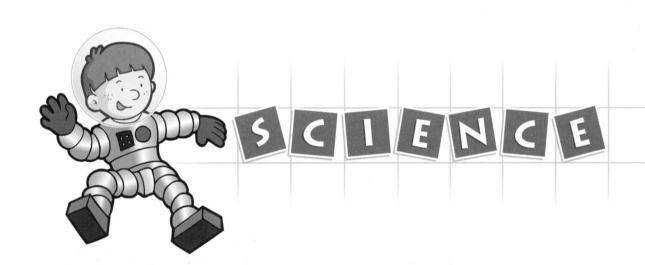

Matter

Hm...this must be gas.

- Matter is anything that takes up space.
- Matter exists in three states – solid, liquid, and gas.

solid   liquid   gas

A.   Look at the picture. Check the things that are matter.

✓ a cloud

✓ sunlight

a ball

a game   ✓ a daydream   a beach umbrella

✓ a sandcastle   ✓ a shell   a chat

✓ water   front crawl

B. Write "solid", "liquid", or "gas" for each description.

1.

   My shape stays the same.

   solid

2.

   My shape may change, and I can take up more space or less space, depending on the container I am in.

   gas

3.

   My shape may change, but I will take up the same amount of space.

   liquid

C. What state of matter does each group of pictures show? Label the group. Then draw one more thing that belongs to each group.

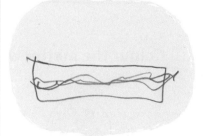

1. _gas_   2. _solid_   3. _liquid_

Science Fact

While most matter can exist in all three states, the only thing we commonly see in its three forms is water.

Water

Measures of Matter

- Mass measures the amount of matter in a substance.
- Density measures the amount of matter in a given space.
- Volume measures the amount of space matter takes up.

You are bigger than I, but we have the same weight.

A. Read what Misha says. Circle the correct words to complete the sentences.

> Weight is the measure of the effect gravity has on mass. So if a force acts against gravity, or the amount of gravity changes, weight changes but mass does not.

1. Misha feels heavier / (lighter) in the water than he does on land even though his (mass) / weight has not changed.

2. Clark has the same (weight) / mass on the moon as he does on Earth even though he is (heavier) / lighter on Earth.

B. Colour the matter with the greatest density.

1.

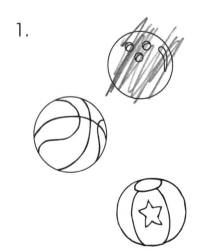

2.

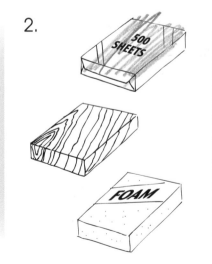

3.

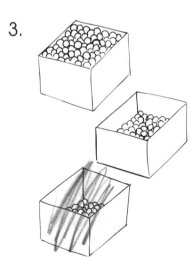

C. Put the matter in order from the one with the least volume to the one with the greatest. Write 1 to 4 in the circles.

D. Play "I spy". Find the answers.

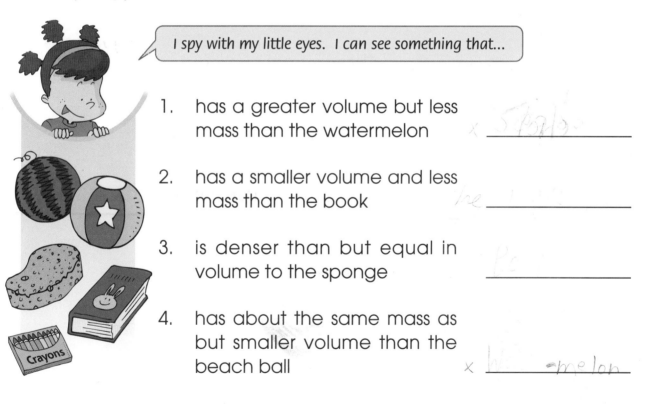

I spy with my little eyes. I can see something that...

1. has a greater volume but less mass than the watermelon _____

2. has a smaller volume and less mass than the book _____

3. is denser than but equal in volume to the sponge _____

4. has about the same mass as but smaller volume than the beach ball _____

Science Fact

Because of all the salt in it, sea water has a higher density than fresh water. It is so dense that you actually float better in an ocean than in a lake.

Changing States of Matter

Abracadabra – liquid to gas!

- Matter can change from one state to another.
- Changes in matter can be reversible or irreversible.

A. **Look at the pictures. Tell the states of the matter before and after the changes. Then fill in the blanks with the given words.**

condensed   melted   solidified   vapourized

1.

Change: from _solid versi_ to _liquid_

The snowman has _melted_ .

✗ 2.

Change: from _liquid into_ to _solid side_

The cake batter has _solidified_ .

✗ 3.

Change: from _gas_ to _liquid_

The water ~~vapour~~ _condense_ has _condensed_ .

✗ 4.

Change: from _liquid_ to _gas side_

The puddle has _vapour_ _vapourized_ .

B. Tell what must be done to the matter on the left to get the matter on the right. Fill in the blanks with "take away" or "give".

1. ice → water <u>give</u> heat

2. ice cream → melted ice cream <u>take away</u> heat

3. raw egg → cooked egg <u>give</u> heat

4. molten lava → solid rock <u>take away</u> heat

5. melted butter → butter <u>give</u> heat

6. wax candle → melted wax <u>take away</u> heat

C. Tell whether the changes in matter are reversible or irreversible. Write the letters.

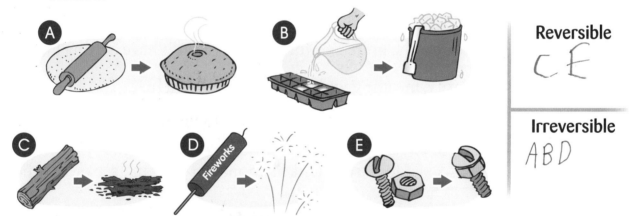

Reversible

C E

Irreversible

A B D

Experiment – Change the state of water!

- Pour cold water into a glass and let it sit in a warm room for a few minutes.

Why does water form on the outside of the glass? Where does it come from?

<u>Its a glass. The Sink</u>

Melting point
1500°C

steel

Science Fact

Ice melts at a temperature of 1°C; steel needs a temperature of about 1500°C to melt.

Properties of Matter

- We describe matter by its different properties.
- Properties of matter determine what we use the matter for.

A. Read the passage. Circle the eleven common properties of different materials.

Matter can be described by its properties. Colour, size, hardness, and taste are properties we think about every day. Matter can have other properties too. When we say a cinnamon bun's coating is sticky, we are describing its viscosity. The bun itself has a smooth texture. The knife and fork we use to eat it have a shiny lustre, and have an opaque clarity, meaning we can't see through them.

We may want something sweet and in a liquid state for a snack, like lemonade. We can't see or feel the sugar in our lemonade because it is dissolved; sugar has high solubility in water. The cook, making more cinnamon buns, is working with dough that has good malleability, changing from a round blob to a tasty, sticky, smooth spiral.

B. Look at the words you circled. Write the property that each word describes.

1. shiny   *lustre*
2. salty   *taste*
3. large   *size*
4. brittle   *hardness*
5. dissolves   *solubility*
6. gas   *state*

C. **Match each description with the correct picture. Then write another word that describes the matter.**

brittle

1 I am a soft and sweet solid. You can't see through me because my clarity is opaque.

2 I am soft and smooth but very malleable. I'm cold and opaque.

white

3 I am transparent, smooth, and hard. You cannot change my shape because I am not malleable.

brown

4 I taste good in soup, where I completely dissolve. Compared to most other things, I'm considered quite small.

salty

D. **Circle the properties you would want your blanket to have.**

Making a blanket

Hardness: soft as feathers / (hard as rock)

Colour: brown / (orange) / pink / yellow

Size: (large) / small / king-sized

Texture: (rough) / prickly / velvety

Science Fact

Plastics are useful to us because we can base on their properties to make different things. A bike may have hard plastic parts, but polar fleece clothing is an example of soft plastic.

Weather and Climate

I like summer.

- Weather is what is going on in the air – temperature, moisture, and movement – at a certain place and time.
- Climate is a pattern of weather in large areas over a long period of time.

A. **Read the sentences. Draw lines to tell whether they refer to weather or climate.**

1. Areas near the equator receive the sun's rays most directly.

2. Large, dark clouds usually bring rain or snow.

3. Higher areas of land are not as warm as lower areas.

4. Storms and heavy snowfall sometimes close roads and schools.

5. Canadians often holiday in warmer parts of the world.

6. A hailstorm might ruin a whole crop of wheat.

7.

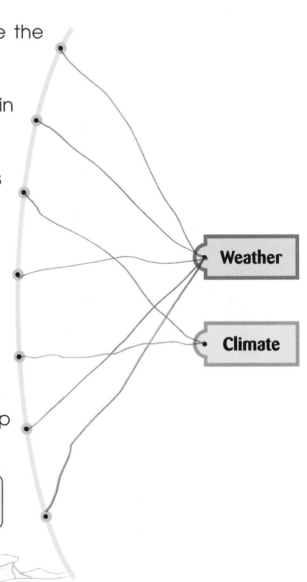

Weather

Climate

Polar bears require cold winters and cool summers.

B. Write "weather" or "climate". Then put the pictures in the circles in the correct groups. Write the letters.

Weather

B

Climate

A

A

Future site of the Summer Olympics

B

C. Match the descriptions with the correct climate words. Write the words on the lines.

desert　　mountain　　polar　　sub-polar
subtropical　　temperate　　tropical

1. always very hot, rain _Subtropical_

2. very cold, frozen ground _Polar_

3. mild climate throughout the year _tropical_

4. long winters, cool summers _SubPolar_

5. very little moisture, hot in daytime, cold at night _temperate_

6. hot summers, mild winters, rain _mountain_

7. higher ground makes it colder, fewer plants _desert_

 **Science Fact**

Climate change, caused in part by human activities, will change the weather patterns of different climates around the world.

Temperature

- Air temperature, the amount of heat in the air, is measured with a thermometer.
- Many things we do are based on what the temperature is outside.

A. Look at the record of the average monthly temperatures of Weatherton last year. Complete the broken-line graph and answer the questions.

Jan	-8°C
Feb	-2°C
Mar	1°C
Apr	8°C
May	12°C
Jun	18°C
Jul	25°C
Aug	26°C
Sep	19°C
Oct	8°C
Nov	3°C
Dec	-4°C

1.

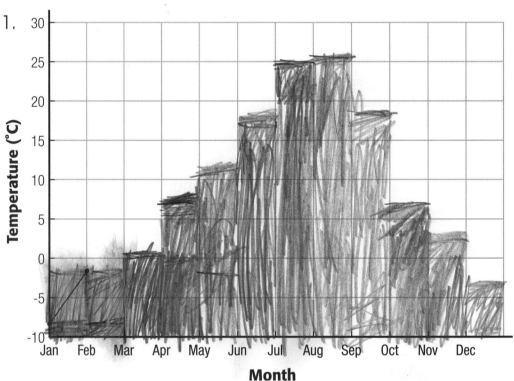

The Average Monthly Temperatures of Weatherton Last Year

2. Which month has the highest average temperature? _08_

3. Which month has the lowest average temperature? _01_

4.

If you want to go skating outside, the temperature must be below 0°C. During which month(s) would you go skating?

_____

B. Look at the graph on the previous page again and the outfits below. Answer the question.

> *These are the outfits I wore last year. In which months do you think I wore them?*

1.

05 07 08

2.

12 01 02

3.

04 05 10 11

C. Colour the thermometers to show the temperatures for the microclimates.

> Microclimates are where different conditions exist within a short distance from each other.

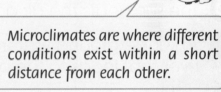

Science Fact

One of the hottest places on Earth is Libya, where temperatures can reach nearly 60°C. Antarctica is the coldest, with temperatures as low as -89°C.

Antarctica
-89°C

Water Cycle

- All the water that is on Earth is the same as it always was and always will be. It goes round and round in the water cycle.

A. Read the descriptions about the water cycle. Write the letters.

A Water in the ocean evaporates into the air, becoming water vapour.

B Clouds form when water vapour joins with dust particles in the air.

C Rainwater soaks into the soil, and below that into the underground.

D The sun heats the air around the earth and oceans.

E An underground water spring flows into a stream, which joins with a river that leads to the ocean.

F Water droplets in clouds join together, getting so heavy they come down from the clouds as precipitation, usually as snow or rain.

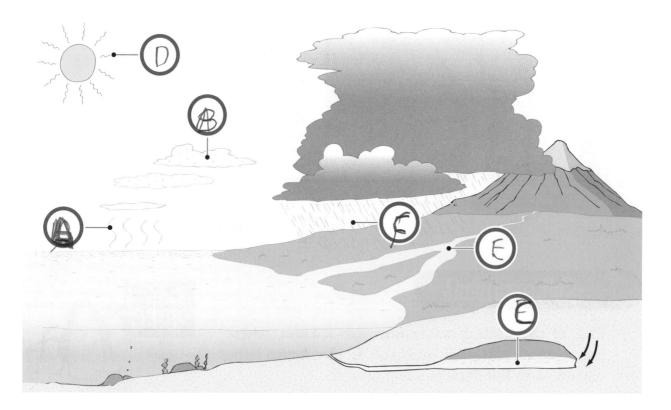

B.   Check the pictures of the water that may be the same as the water in your glass.

1. ✓

2. ✓

3. ✓

4. ✓

5. ✓

C.   Where is the Earth's water?   Read what Dr. Green says. Check the correct graph.

> Most of the water on Earth is in the oceans and is salt water. Only a small portion of it is fresh water. The majority of fresh water is locked up in glaciers and ice caps. The rest is underground and in lakes.

Earth's Water ✓

salt water

fresh water

Earth's Water ✗

fresh water

salt water

Earth's Water

salt water

fresh water

Science Fact

The atmosphere has a very important role in the water cycle although it holds less than one thousandth of the entire world's water.

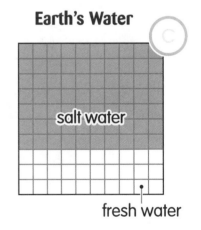

Clouds and Precipitation

- Clouds are named for their shapes and height in the sky.
- Not all clouds produce rain or snow, but all kinds of precipitation come from clouds.

A. Read the rules to see how to name a cloud. Then name the clouds.

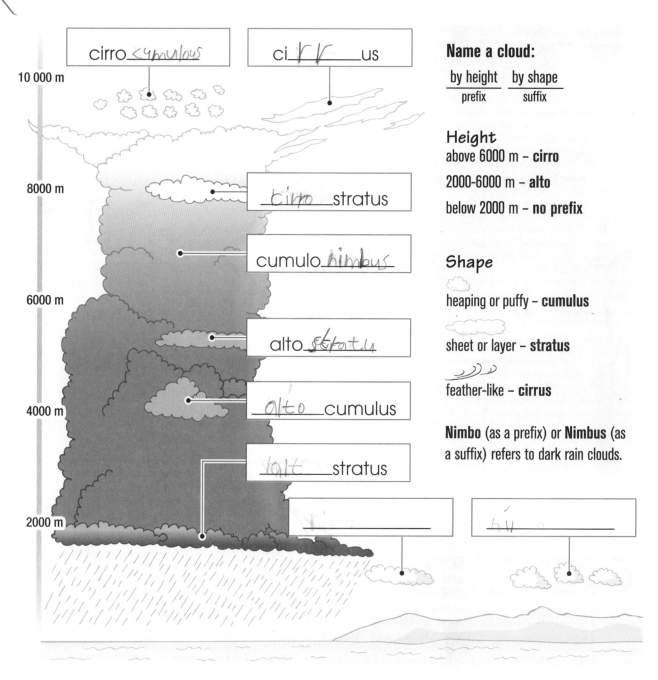

Name a cloud:

by height	by shape
prefix	suffix

Height

above 6000 m – **cirro**

2000-6000 m – **alto**

below 2000 m – **no prefix**

Shape

heaping or puffy – **cumulus**

sheet or layer – **stratus**

feather-like – **cirrus**

Nimbo (as a prefix) or **Nimbus** (as a suffix) refers to dark rain clouds.

10 000 m

cirro _cumulus_

ci _rr_ us

8000 m

cirro stratus

cumulo _nimbus_

6000 m

alto _stratu_

4000 m

alto cumulus

alt stratus

2000 m

B. Fill in the blanks with the names of the clouds.

1. Puffed up clouds 3 km above ground are _nimbystroths_

2. A low sheet of cloud is _cirronimbo_ .

3. A flat cloud at 8 km high is _nimbystratys_. _nimbystratys_

4. A cloud that spans all three layers of sky is _cirronimbo_ _cirrus_

C. Name the precipitation to complete the crossword puzzle.

Cold air near the ground changes rain to ice.

These raindrops are so tiny they are barely seen.

They are drops of water that fall to the ground.

The six-sided crystals give earth a white sheen.

The water is so heavy, an umbrella is nice.

Formed high in the sky, they are hard and round.

heavy rain   hail
sleet   snow
drizzle   rain

Science Fact

Clouds are usually not just water droplets. Water vapour in the air condenses around dust and other tiny particles in the sky.

Wind

- Wind speed is numbered from 0 to 12 on the Beaufort Scale.
- Wind is very useful in nature and to us.
- Winds are named for the directions they are coming from.

A. Look at the Beaufort Scale and each pair of pictures. Describe the wind in **A**. Then give the wind in **B** a scale and description.

1. **A** scale 4:
   Moderate breeze

   B scale ~~4~~ 0 :
   calm

2. **A** scale 2:
   Light breeze

   B scale ~~4~~ 0 :
   Calm

3. **A** scale 11:
   Storm

   B scale ~~11~~ 0 :
   calm

Beaufort Scale		
Rating	**Description**	(speed in km/h)
0	Calm	(<1.5)
1	Light air	(1.5 – 5)
2	Light breeze	(6 – 11)
3	Gentle breeze	(12 –19)
4	Moderate breeze	(20 – 30)
5	Fresh breeze	(31 – 40)
6	Strong breeze	(41 – 50)
7	Moderate gale	(51 – 60)
8	Fresh gale	(61 – 67)
9	Strong gale	(68 – 84)
10	Whole gale	(85 – 100)
11	Storm	(101 – 120)
12	Hurricane	(>120)

B. **See how the winds are at work. Match the descriptions with the pictures and fill in the missing letters.**

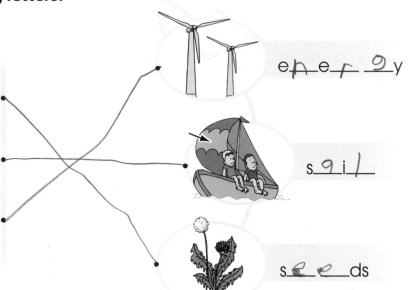

e n e r g y

Wind helps them travel to where they can grow.

s a i l

This part of the boat would not work without wind.

Wind moves the turbines to provide this for people.

s e e ds

C. **Read what Timothy says. Tell the directions of the winds.**

The arrow of a wind vane points in the direction the wind comes from. Winds are named for the direction they are coming from.

northerly wind

southerly   westerly   easterly   southeasterly   northwesterly

1.

easterly

2.

westerly

3.

westerly

 **Science Fact**

A jet stream, a narrow band of fast moving wind in the sky, can make a plane trip across Canada from the west half an hour faster.

Extreme Weather

- Storms, caused by turbulence in the atmosphere, come in different shapes and sizes.
- Sometimes when there is too much or too little precipitation, a number of disasters are possible.

A. Match the descriptions with the words.

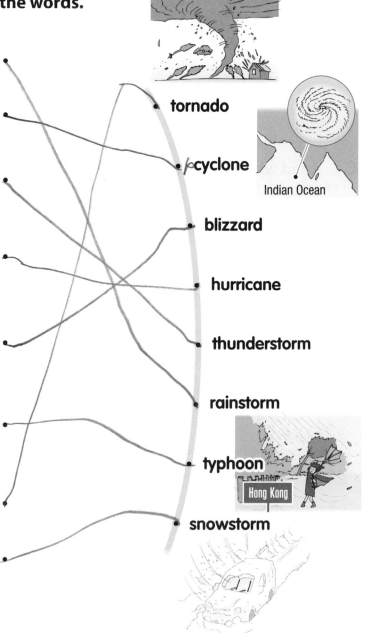

1. heavy rain

2. a hurricane formed in the Indian Ocean

3. snow and strong winds in cold temperatures

4. a churning, spiral cloud formed over tropical oceans

5. characterized by a funnel cloud with extremely strong winds

6. electrically charged, billowing clouds, lightning and hard-driving rain

7. a hurricane formed in the South China Sea

8. heavy snowfall

tornado

cyclone

Indian Ocean

blizzard

hurricane

thunderstorm

rainstorm

typhoon

Hong Kong

snowstorm

B. **Write whether the following happens due to "too much precipitation" or "too little precipitation".**

1.

too much Precipitation

2.

too much Precipitation

3.

No Water
too little Precipitation

4.

too little Precipitation

The snowflakes will hold their shapes longer than usual when they are on cold construction paper.

Experiment – Take a closer look at snowflakes!

Things needed:
- a magnifying glass
- black construction paper
- a snowy day

Steps:

1. Put the black construction paper in the freezer for at least an hour before use.
2. When snow falls, catch some flakes on the frozen construction paper.
3. Examine the snowflakes with the magnifying glass.

How many sides does each snowflake have?
_6_

Science Fact

Not all snowflakes are shaped like stars. There are columns, plates, columns with caps, and needles, too! Their only common feature is their six sides.

Weather Station

- Weather stations have special instruments for measuring and recording weather.
- Scientists who study the weather are meteorologists. They use information gathered at weather stations to predict future weather conditions.

A. **Look at the function of each weather instrument. Name the instrument. Write the letters.**

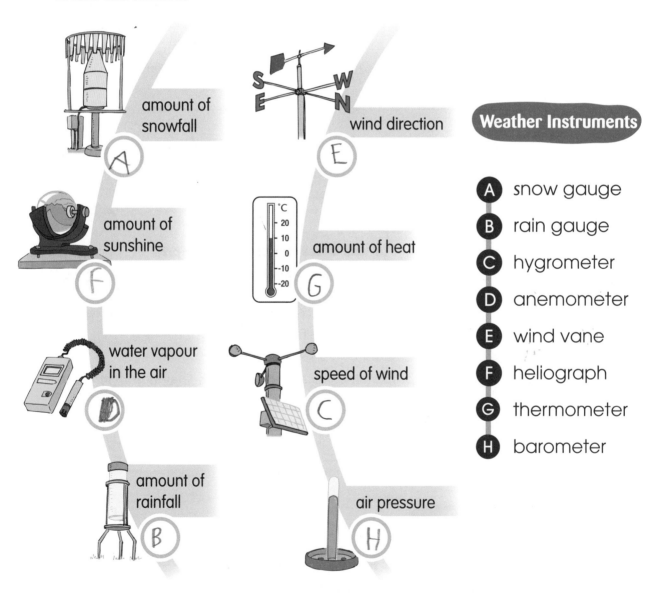

amount of snowfall — A

wind direction — E

amount of sunshine — F

amount of heat — G

water vapour in the air — D

speed of wind — C

amount of rainfall — B

air pressure — H

Weather Instruments

- A snow gauge
- B rain gauge
- C hygrometer
- D anemometer
- E wind vane
- F heliograph
- G thermometer
- H barometer

B. Read what the meteorologist says. Then tell who will be most affected by the information gathered at the weather station. Check the correct answers.

Dr. Smith, can you tell us what the weather will be like tomorrow?

1. Which sport teams will not practise tomorrow?

    (A) Golf Grannies

    (B) Serious Soccer Souls

    (C) Crazy Cross-Country Skiers

According to the information we collected, there will be a snowstorm tomorrow...

2. What does the store stock up on?

    (A) umbrellas   (B) snow shovels   (C) boots

3. Who will stay home from work tomorrow?

   (A) gardener   (B) veterinarian   (C) school bus driver

C. Answer the questions.

1. Give one reason why it is important to know what the weather conditions have been.

   If rainfalls has been low, there may be a high forest fire risk, or low waters level water level reserves, if precipitation has been high, there maybe a higher risk.

2. Give one reason why it is important to know what the weather conditions will be.

   _____

   _____

Science Fact

Weather stations keep their instruments far from the cover of buildings, trees, and hills. Shade and wind barriers will distort the results of some measurements.

Conservation of Energy

Heat energy

Electrical energy

- The energy that we use comes from various places and is either renewable or non-renewable.
- Energy cannot be created or destroyed. Rather, it takes on other forms.

A. Read what Nancy says. Match the pictures with the source of energy. Then tell whether each source of energy is renewable (R) or non-renewable (NR).

> Some sources of energy are good for future generations because they are renewable, which means they are always available for use. Other sources of energy, being non-renewable, take a very long time to accumulate, and cannot be replaced.

A

B

C

D

E

F

G

1. coal   (C) : NR

2. biomass   (E) : NR

3. oil   (A) : NR

4. wind   (D) : R

5. solar   (G) : R

6. hydro   (B) : R

7. natural gas (F) : NR

B. See how the device or structure shows the law of the conservation of energy. Write the change of energy in each situation.

chemical   electrical   gravitational   heat   mechanical

1.
Energy change:
from _electrical_ energy
to _heat_ energy

The Law of the Conservation of Energy
Not Created or Destroyed –
Just Changed

2.
Energy change:
from _electrical_ energy
to _chemical_ energy

3.
In a car, _electrical_ energy stored in the gasoline is changed into _mechanical_ energy that makes the wheels move. Thermal energy as heat is released as well.

C. Fill in the blanks with "kinetic" or "potential" to complete what Simon says.

The _kinetic_ energy in the stretched elastic is converted into _potential_ energy when it is "released".

Science Fact

Over half of the garbage that we throw away is organic, which means that it is stuff that came from living things. This ends up in our landfills and as it decays, it produces methane gas that, when collected, can be used to generate electricity.

The Wise Use of Energy

- We must use energy wisely, as our non-renewable sources, which we rely on so heavily, will not last forever.
- Everyone can do a little more to conserve energy.

A. Read what the people say. Tell whether each of them is a "wise energy user" or "unwise energy user".

1 I buy whatever is on sale. I don't even know what "watt" means; they are just light bulbs, after all.

unwise energy user

2 I don't know what I'd do without my bike. I get a workout on my way to work, and I don't have to pay for parking.

wise energy user

3 With this job, I found myself in a position of being able to choose my new vehicle, so I chose the most fuel efficient, environmentally friendly car that I could find.

wise energy user

4 I have the money, but why should I spend it on an energy efficient refrigerator? This old one has been my parents' for 25 years, and it still works!

wise energy user

5 We have tried to cut down on our meat consumption. We eat more vegetables, nuts, and fruit that we buy from local farmers.

unwise energy user

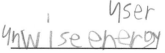

B. Circle the correct words to complete the sentences.

Things to Do to Conserve Energy

1. Turn the thermostat up /(down) when everyone goes to bed in winter.

2. (Use)/ Don't use blankets and socks to keep warm at night.

3. Find the cracks where the cold air is entering your house and (let)/ seal them.

4. Connect all stereo and TV equipment (to a power bar)/ separately so that all the parts of the systems will be easy to turn off.

5. If you must leave your computer on all the time, turn on /(off) the printer and the monitor.

6. Use (natural)/ artificial light whenever you can.

7. Turn lights on /(off) when they are not being used.

8. Don't take (long)/ short , hot showers.

C. Complete the chart to tell how to conserve energy.

Things I Do to Conserve Energy	Things I Could Do to Conserve Energy	Things I will Try to Do to Conserve Energy

Science Fact

Every spring, most Canadians set their clocks one hour ahead for daylight saving time. This extra daylight in the evening means less energy is used to light our homes.

Forces and Structures

This is compression!

- Many different types of forces act upon structures.
- Most structures must be able to withstand two common types of forces: compression and tension.

A. Dr. Shoes is doing a "boot test". Look at each picture. Name the force that acts upon the boot.

bending	sliding	squeezing	stretching	twisting

1. _squeezing_

2. _stretching_

3. _twisting_

4. _bending_

5. _sliding_

B. Name the words that mean the same.

1. sliding force   _shearing_

2. twisting force   _torsion_

3. stretching force   _tension_

4. squeezing force   _compression_

5. bending force   _bending_

compression
shearing
tension
torsion
bending

C. Label each arrow with the right kind of force: tension or compression.

1.

tension

When a force is acting on a structure, compression and tension are forces that can take place.

compression

2.

compression

3.

compression

4.

tension

5.

a. tension

b. compression

Experiment – Free-standing Structure

Using 50 straws and 2 metres of masking tape, make the tallest free-standing structure possible that will support a marble.

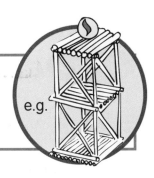
e.g.

Science Fact

The arch bridge is one of the oldest types of bridges. It is very strong because it can change the downward force of its own weight, and any other weight pressing down on it, into an outward force towards its very strong sides and bases.

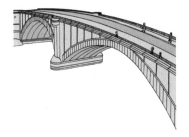

Forces and Mechanical Advantage

- Changing something in a simple machine can sometimes change the amount of force needed to move or lift an object.
- Mechanical advantage is a measurement of how this force is changed by using a simple machine or mechanism.

A. Look at the pictures in each pair. Check the one that requires less force to do the job.

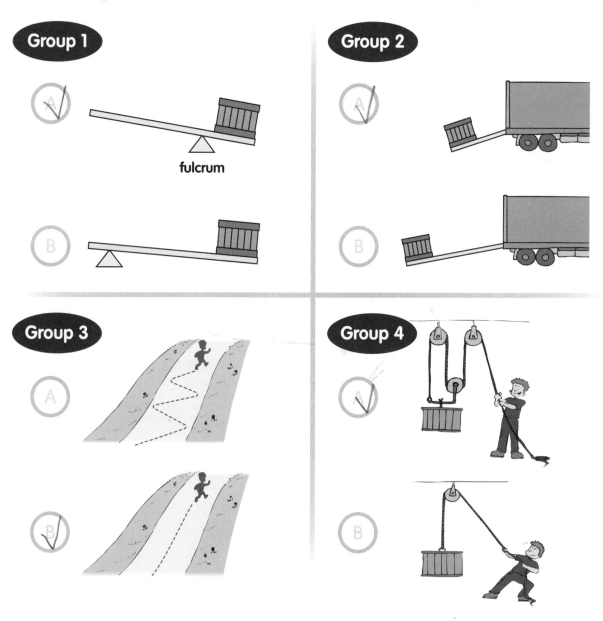

Group 1

A ✓

fulcrum

B

Group 2

A ✓

B

Group 3

A

B ✓

Group 4

A ✓

B

B. Look at each pair of pictures on the previous page again. Then fill in the blanks and answer the questions.

1. **Group 1**

   a. Which picture shows the greater mechanical advantage?

   _A_

   b. Moving the fulcrum closer to the load will _grain_ mechanical advantage.
   gain/lose

2. **Group 2** What would you do to the ramp length to make the job of getting the object into the truck even easier?

   _A_

3. **Group 3** Which hiker takes more steps?

   _B_

4. **Group 4** In B, there is no mechanical advantage in using a single fixed pulley. Why use it then?

   Because A has more pulleys.

C. Find and circle eight words that are related to force.

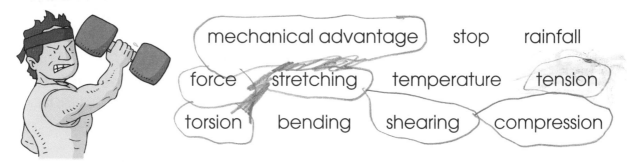

mechanical advantage   stop   rainfall

force   stretching   temperature   tension

torsion   bending   shearing   compression

Science Fact

a pulley system →

Archimedes of Syracuse (287 BCE - 212 BCE) was a great mathematician who invented the compound pulley. He once used a pulley system to pull ships onto a position that had previously required a lot of manpower.

Cells

Hi! I'm one of your cells.

- Cells are the building blocks of all living things.
- Cells can be in different shapes and sizes, but almost all of them have the same parts.
- Animal cells of the same shape and size work together to make up larger body tissue.

A. **Fill in the missing letters to name the different parts of a cell. Then draw lines to match the parts with the descriptions and answer the questions.**

cell membrane   cytoplasm   nucleus   organelles

1.

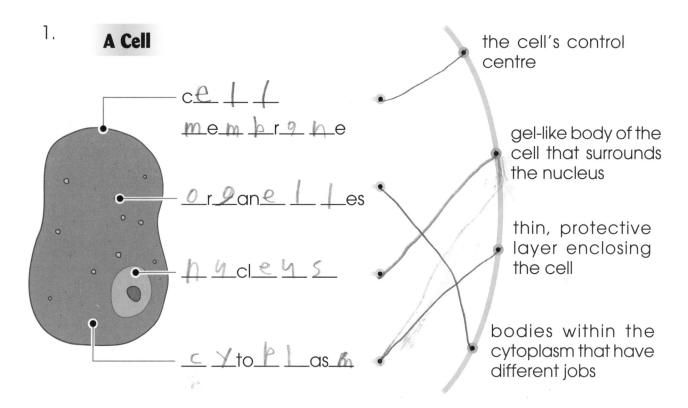

A Cell

c e l l
m e m b r a n e

o r g a n e l l es

n u cl e u s

c y to p l as m

the cell's control centre

gel-like body of the cell that surrounds the nucleus

thin, protective layer enclosing the cell

bodies within the cytoplasm that have different jobs

2. Which part of the cell controls

a. the cell's function?

cell membrane

b. the amount of water entering and leaving the cell?

cytoplasm

B. **Read what Dr. Stein says. Help him complete the drawing of the skin cells of an onion.**

Cells of onion skin can be seen under a microscope.

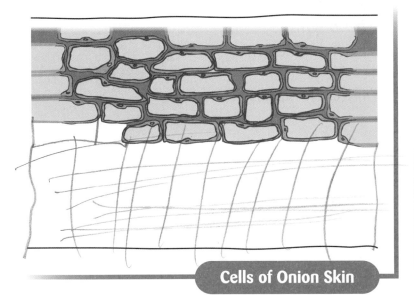

Cells of Onion Skin

C. **Read the following. Then tell what cell each picture shows. Fill in the blanks with the words in bold.**

Cells of the same shape and size make up a tissue. Tissues make up organs. **Skin** cells work together to form skin tissue. Longer **muscle** cells make up muscle tissue, and **nerve** cells build nervous tissue.

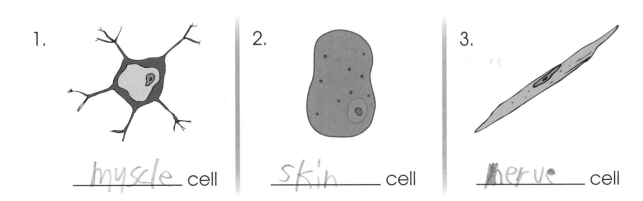

1. _muscle_ cell

2. _skin_ cell

3. _nerve_ cell

Science Fact

Humans and most other animals are made up of millions of cells, but some animals contain only one cell. Barely visible to the naked eye, one-celled protozoa are also the world's smallest animals.

Musculoskeletal System

My name's Skeleton.

- Bones hold our body up and protect our organs.
- Skeletal muscles work with the bones to let us move. This is our musculoskeletal system.
- Joints are where two bones connect. Different joints allow for different types of movement.

A. Name the bones in the skeleton. Then draw lines to match them with the descriptions.

humerus   femur   vertebra   tibia   rib   mandible   patella   frontal bone

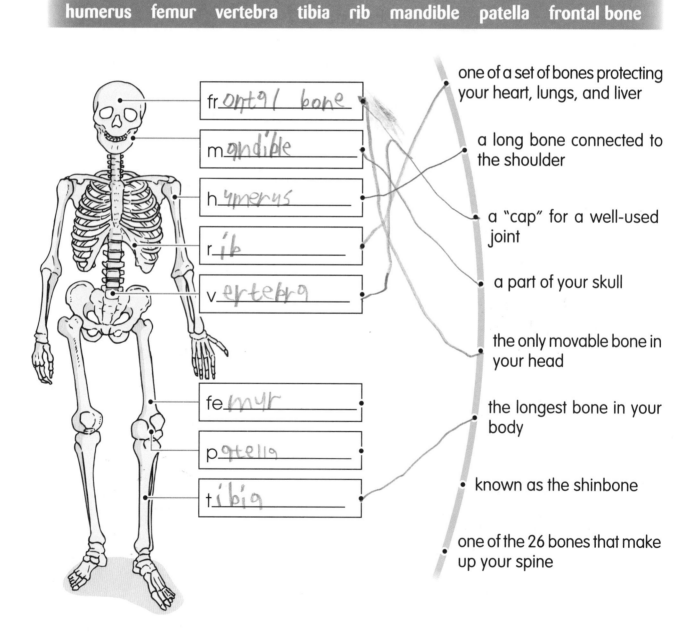

fr_ontal bone_

m_andible_

h_ymerys_

r_ib_

v_ertebra_

fe_myr_

p_atella_

t_ibia_

one of a set of bones protecting your heart, lungs, and liver

a long bone connected to the shoulder

a "cap" for a well-used joint

a part of your skull

the only movable bone in your head

the longest bone in your body

known as the shinbone

one of the 26 bones that make up your spine

B. Read what Susan says. Help her complete the puzzle by writing the names of the muscles.

deltoid
pectorals
quadriceps
biceps
frontalis

Skeletal muscles stretch over joints to connect two bones. Together, muscles and bones allow our bodies to move.

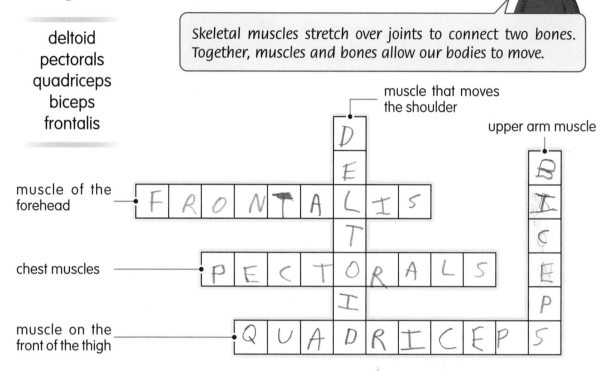

muscle that moves the shoulder

upper arm muscle

muscle of the forehead → F R O N T A L I S

chest muscles → P E C T O R A L S

muscle on the front of the thigh → Q U A D R I C E P S

Down: D E L T O I, B I C E P S

C. Identify these types of joints.

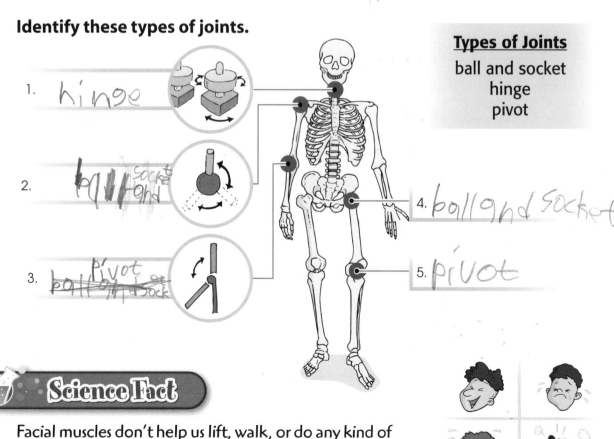

Types of Joints
ball and socket
hinge
pivot

1. hinge
2. ball and socket
3. pivot
4. ball and socket
5. pivot

Science Fact

Facial muscles don't help us lift, walk, or do any kind of work, but they do help us communicate our feelings.

Nervous System

You have nerves in your tail.

- The nervous system is made up of the brain, spinal cord, and many, many nerves placed all over the body.

A. Read the passage. Label the parts of the nervous system with the words in bold.

Protected by the skull and a liquid membrane called the meninges, the brain is our body's control centre. It is made up of three main parts: the **brain stem**, the **cerebellum**, and the **cerebrum**. The brain stem connects the brain to the **spinal cord**. It makes us breathe and swallow, and do other things we need to do to live. Behind the brain stem, the cerebellum controls our balance and our muscle coordination. The largest part of our brain, the cerebrum, is the thinking part of our brain. Giving a speech, counting change, and planning a science experiment are all activities that begin with the cerebrum.

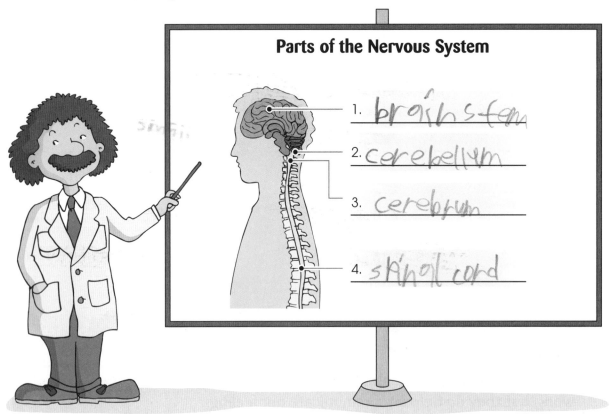

Parts of the Nervous System

1. brain stem
2. cerebellum
3. cerebrum
4. spinal cord

B. Read the passage on the previous page again. Answer the questions.

1. Which part of the brain is responsible for

   a. making your heart beat? _rib_

   b. a daydream? _frontal bone_

   c. helping you walk along a narrow log? _tibia_

2. Which two things protect our brain?

   brain stem frontal bone

3. What is our body's control centre?

   humerus

4.  What is connected to the brain by the brain stem?

   frontal bone

C. Find and colour the nervous system words.

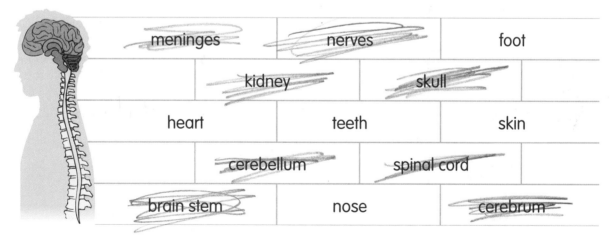

meninges	nerves	foot
kidney	skull	
heart	teeth	skin
cerebellum	spinal cord	
brain stem	nose	cerebrum

 **Science Fact**

In proportion to body size, the human brain is larger than the elephant's.

Respiratory System

- All we do is breathe in and out, and the respiratory system does the job of getting oxygen to our blood cells, and releasing as waste the carbon dioxide we do not need.
- The respiratory system needs clean air to stay healthy.

A. **Label the parts of the respiratory system.** **Then match the descriptions with the words in the diagram.**

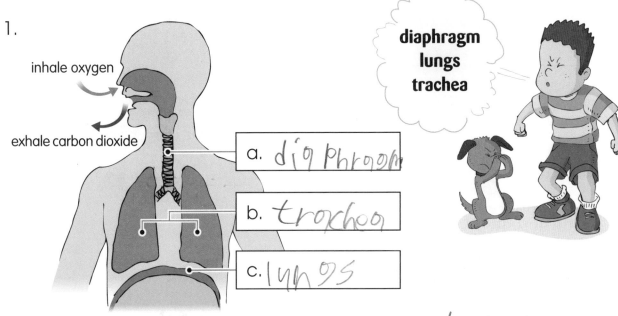

1.

inhale oxygen

exhale carbon dioxide

diaphragm
lungs
trachea

a. dia phragm

b. trachea

c. lungs

2. a gas that we breathe in

inhale oxygen

3. the tube that takes air from our mouth to our lungs

exhale carbon dioxide

4. what we do to release carbon dioxide

mouth

5. breathe in

inhale oxygen oxygen

6. the waste gas we exhale

carbon dioxide

7. the muscle beneath our lungs that allows them to expand

B. **Each picture shows something that affects our respiratory system. Unscramble the words to write what it is. Then put a check mark in the circle if it is good for us; otherwise, put a cross.**

1. smog
g m s o ⊗

2. croqetites
g a c r e t i t e s ⊗

3. Planting
a l p t n g i n ✓

4. Pollution
n o l l o p i t u ⊗

5. smoke
e m k s o ⊗

6. jogging
n g o j g i g ✓

Science Fact

The diaphragm plays an important role in every breath we take, but it is barely noticeable to us – unless we have hiccups! Hiccups are caused by a spasm of the diaphragm.

Circulatory System

- The heart has a left side and a right side that work together to pump and receive blood.
- The rate at which our heart pumps blood varies according to our activities.

A. Complete the labelling of the structure of a heart with the given words. Then fill in the blanks to complete the sequence of events in the circulatory system.

The Structure of a Heart

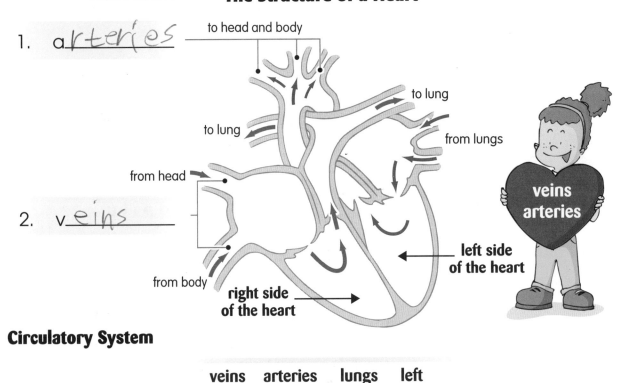

1. a*rteries*

2. v*eins*

Circulatory System

veins   arteries   lungs   left

- The left side of the heart pumps oxygen-rich blood through the arteries.

- The 3. *arteries* carry blood to vital organs, as well as every cell in our bodies.

- The 4. ~~lungs~~ *veins* take the oxygen-depleted blood back to the right side of the heart.

- The right side of the heart sends blood to the 5. ~~veins~~ *lungs* to receive oxygen.

- From the lungs, the blood goes back to the 6. *left* side of the heart.

B. **Match the heart rate with each activity.**

Heart rate (in beats per minute): 65   74   102   124

1.

Heart rate: 102

2.
Heart rate: 124

3.
Heart rate: 65

4.
Heart rate: 74

Experiment – Take your own pulse.

Things needed:
- *a clock with a second hand*

Steps:
1. Rest for a few minutes before you start.
2. Place two fingers on the inside of your wrist, as pictured. You can feel an artery beating here with every pump of your heart.
3. Wait until the second hand of the clock reaches the 12. When it does, count the beats until the second hand gets to the 6.
4. Multiply the number you got by 2. That is your resting heart rate.

Science Fact

Blood in the arteries is a brighter red than blood in the veins. The high oxygen level in arterial blood is responsible for its colour.

Digestive System

Hey! You have so much saliva.

- Food we eat travels through the body's digestive system, a group of organs that takes the nutrients and expels the waste.

A. Name each part of the digestive system. Then draw lines to match the events of digestion with the correct digestive organs.

mouth   rectum   stomach
colon   esophagus   small intestine

X **Digestive System**

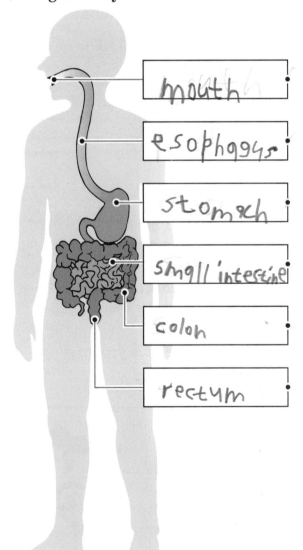

mouth

esophagus

stomach

Small intestine

colon

rectum

- Here, it is stored as waste before leaving the body.

- The body absorbs most nutrients when the food is here.

- This is where big pieces are broken down and saliva is added.

- This stretchy bag-like organ mixes the food up with gastric juices.

- Now called a bolus, the food enters the stomach through this tube.

- After the body has taken the nutrients, the food goes through this to have any extra water removed.

B. Read the clues. Complete the crossword puzzle with the names of the digestive organs.

mouth   esophagus
stomach   gall bladder
rectum   small intestine
pancreas   colon   liver

The pancreas, liver, and gall bladder contribute juices that aid in digestion.

absorbs nutrients into the bloodstream

a muscular tube pushing the food down into the stomach

E S O P H A G U S

removes water and pushes the rest out of our body as feces

C O L O N

stores the stool until evacuation happens

produces juices to digest oil

G A L L   B L A D D E R

uses enzymes and juices to break down the food into smaller bits

S T O M A C H

chews and uses saliva and enzymes to break down the food

M O U T H

secretes bile to help digest fat

secretes hormones that affect the level of sugar in the blood

P A N C R E A S

(Down words: SMALL INTESTINE, RECTUM, LIVER)

Science Fact

A flap of tissue, the epiglottis, stops food from going into the trachea when we swallow. This way, all food and liquid will go into the esophagus and stomach, instead of the lungs.

epiglottis

Excretory System

- The excretory system is a cleaning system. It cleans the blood and produces urine.

Jane, I can't hold it anymore!

A. Fill in the blanks to complete the paragraph with the words given in the diagram.

Excretory System

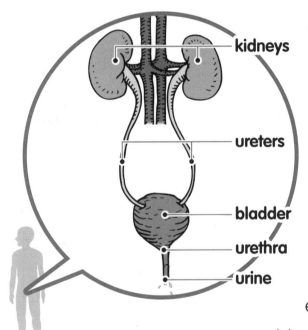

kidneys

ureters

bladder

urethra

urine

When cells in our bodies do work, they also make waste. The body has special organs that keep waste from building up. The 1. _kidneys_ do the most waste removal work. They filter blood as it passes through them, sending clean blood out while keeping the waste behind. With extra water, the waste is now called 2. _ureters_. Urine passes through the 3. _bladder_ and into the stretchy 4. _urethra_ where it is temporarily stored. When it is full, urine travels from the bladder, through the 5. _urine_, and out of the body.

B. Read the paragraph on the previous page again. Then match each part with its function.

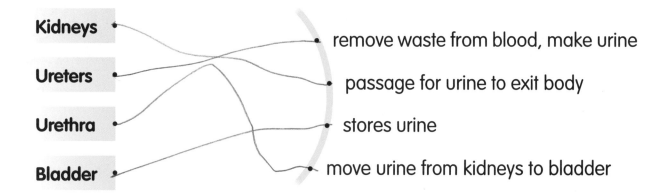

Kidneys • — remove waste from blood, make urine

Ureters • — passage for urine to exit body

Urethra • — stores urine

Bladder • — move urine from kidneys to bladder

C. Write "true" or "false" for each sentence.

1. The bladder is the last organ urine passes through before it leaves the body. _____

2. There are two ureters, one from each kidney. _____

3. The urethra is a passage that leads from one of the kidneys to the bladder. _____

4. Blood enters the kidneys to be cleaned, leaving behind waste that helps make urine. _____

5.  *Kidneys filter the blood and remove waste materials in the form of urine.* _____

Science Fact

Other organs excrete waste too. When we sweat, we get rid of excess salt and water, and we breathe out carbon dioxide from our lungs.

Nutrition

- *Our bodies get nutrients from the food we eat.*
- *A healthful diet contains a variety of healthful food.*
- *Nutrition labels provide us with information to make good eating choices.*

A. **Match the nutrients with the descriptions. Then tell which two food items are possible sources of each nutrient. Write the letters.**

fibre   vitamins   minerals   water
proteins   fats   carbohydrates

1. Water ___ ○
give energy ○

2. Fish ___ ○
helps digestive process ○

3. Fruits ___ ○
build tissues and muscles ○

4. Egg ___ ○
develop brain and nervous system ○ Ⓖ

5. Cresent ___
controls body temperature, moves nutrients and waste Ⓐ Ⓐ

6. ___ and 7. ___
help our bodies grow and stay healthy Ⓒ Ⓔ

(food items labelled A through G: A baguette, B watermelon, C Oatmeal, D fish, E Butter, F fruits and vegetables, G eggs)

B. Read the nutritional information labels. Then answer the questions.

Chocolate Chip Cookies

Nutrition Facts (serving size: 1 cookie)		
	Amount	% Daily Value
Calories	200	
Fat	9 g	14%
Saturated	0.4 g	2%
+ Trans	0.1 g	
Cholesterol	50 mg	17%
Sodium	140 mg	5%
Carbohydrate	26 g	9%
Fibre	2 g	4%
Sugars	14 g	
Protein	3 g	5%
Vitamin A 0%	Vitamin C 0%	
Calcium 0%	Iron 10%	

Banana Peach Muffins

Nutrition Facts (serving size: 1 muffin)		
	Amount	% Daily Value
Calories	260	
Fat	9 g	14%
Saturated	4.5 g	21%
+ Trans	0.5 g	
Cholesterol	90 mg	30%
Sodium	320 mg	11%
Carbohydrate	53 g	18%
Fibre	3 g	6%
Sugars	26 g	
Protein	8 g	14%
Vitamin A 0%	Vitamin C 3%	
Calcium 4%	Iron 20%	

1. Which bakery item has more calories per serving? _____

2. Which bakery item has no vitamins? _____

3. How many milligrams of sodium (salt) does the muffin have? _____

4. Which bakery item is richer in minerals? _____

C. Look at the menu. Add a food item to this meal to make it nutritionally balanced. Then explain your choice.

Tonight's Menu
- Roast Beef and Gravy
- Bread
- Potatoes

Food to add:

_____

_____

 Science Fact

While fat is an essential nutrient, too much is unhealthful. Animal fats and trans fats should be especially avoided or limited.

Defence System

Huh...huh... hut-chew!

- The body has different ways to defend itself against things that may make us ill.
- If the body's first defence fails, white blood cells can multiply and attack disease-causing microbes.

A. Read the paragraph. Complete the diagram with the words in bold.

Some organisms are so small they can only be seen under a microscope. They are called **microbes**. **Viruses** and **bacteria** are two microbes that can cause illness if they enter our bodies.

small organism

small organisms that cause illness

B. Match each body defence system with its description. Write the letter.

First Line of Defence

◯ Skin

◯ Mucus

◯ Cilia

◯ Earwax

◯ Stomach acid

A These are tiny hair-like projections that move dirt and mucus out of the trachea.

B It wraps around the whole body, acting as a barrier between the inside and the outside.

C Produced only in our ears, this sticky substance traps dust and germs that may enter the ear canal.

D This slimy substance, produced by the body, catches intruders of the body's air passages.

E This juice, also called hydrochloric acid, kills germs that enter through our digestive system.

C. Read what Dr. Howard says. Check the picture that shows the blood cells of a healthy person. Then colour the red blood cells red.

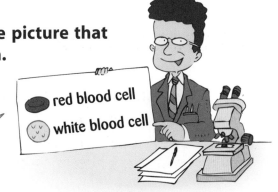

> Blood is made up of red blood cells and white blood cells, with the red far outnumbering the white.

red blood cell
white blood cell

Blood

A

Blood

B

D. Circle the correct word to complete what Jason says. Then trace the dotted lines and continue the pattern to complete the next group of cells.

> White / Red blood cells multiply themselves when dangerous microbes get past our first line of defence. They will start their job of attacking the intruders.

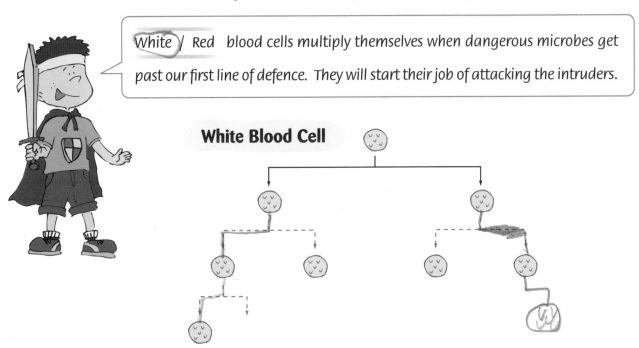

White Blood Cell

Science Fact

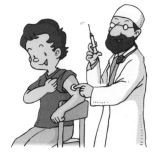

Another defence available to us is immunization. When we are immunized, our body makes antibodies to the disease we are immunized against.

SCIENCE COMPLETE

24

☑ SCIENCE

S = SOLAR

C = COLUMN

I = INTERBODY

E = EXPERIMENT

N = NUTRIENT

C = CARD

E = ENERGY